Automotive and Autonomous Vehicle Security Workshop 2021 (AutoSec 2021)

AA004923

Online
25 February 2021

ISBN: 978-1-7138-3764-0

Printed from e-media with permission by:

Curran Associates, Inc.
57 Morehouse Lane
Red Hook, NY 12571

CURRAN ASSOCIATES INC. proceedings.com

Some format issues inherent in the e-media version may also appear in this print version.

The Internet Society
11710 Plaza America Drive, Suite 400
Reston, VA 20190
U.S.A.

Phone: (703) 439-2120
Fax: (703) 326-9881

www.internetsociety.org

Additional copies of this publication are available from:

Curran Associates, Inc.
57 Morehouse Lane
Red Hook, NY 12571 USA
Phone: 845-758-0400
Fax: 845-758-2633
Email: curran@proceedings.com
Web: www.proceedings.com

Proceedings of AutoSec 2021 – Third International Workshop on Automotive and Autonomous Vehicle Security

Table of Contents

Proceedings

AutoSec 2021

Third International Workshop on Automotive and Autonomous Vehicle Security

February 25, 2021
Virtual

Hosted by the

Internet Society

Internet Society

Internet Society
11710 Plaza America Drive
Suite 400
Reston, VA 20190

Address your correspondence to: NDSS Program Manager, Internet Society, 11710 Plaza America Drive, Suite 400, Reston, VA 20190 USA, tel. +1 703 439 2120, fax +1 703 326 9881, ndss@elists.isoc.org.

The papers included here comprise the proceedings of the meeting mentioned on the cover and title page. They reflect the authors' opinions and, in the interest of timely dissemination, are published as presented and without change. Their inclusion in this publication does not necessarily constitute endorsement by the editors or the Internet Society.

Internet Society

Internet Society
11710 Plaza America Drive
Suite 400
Reston, VA 20190
tel +1 703.439.2120
fax +1 703.326.9881
http://www.internetsociety.org

Message from the Program Co-Chairs

It is our great pleasure to welcome you to the 3rd International Workshop on Automotive and Autonomous Vehicle Security (AutoSec) 2021. This workshop is organized to contribute to new theories, technologies, and systems related to security and privacy challenges in automotive and autonomous vehicles and their supporting infrastructures. Ground and aerial vehicles, such as cars, buses, trucks, airplanes, and drones make the whole world convenient and connected. Due to their wide usage and high safety criticality, any security and privacy problems in them pose direct threats to users and stakeholders in transportation. With the recent global interest in substantially increasing their autonomy and connectivity, including autonomous driving, drone delivery, vehicle-to-everything (V2X) communication, intelligent transportation, and drone swarm technologies, such problems become more critical than ever and thus require immediate attention and discussion in both academia and industry.

In addition to the regular session that presents regular papers and short position/work-in-progress research papers, AutoSec 2021 also features a demo session to allow academic researchers and industry companies to share demonstrations of their latest attacks, defenses, tools, or systems on automotive and autonomous vehicles. All accepted papers and demos are considered for Best Paper Award and Best Demo Award. The winner and runner-up win cash prizes, sponsored by UCI CS and UB CSE. In addition, a special Baidu Security AutoDriving Security Award is given to one of the accepted papers to recognize and reward research that makes substantial contributions to secure today's emerging autonomous driving technology.

In response to the call for papers of AutoSec 2021, 21 regular papers, five short/work-in-progress papers, and 10 demo papers were submitted. Each regular/short paper received at least three reviews, and each demo paper received at least one review. Consequently, the program committee selected 12 regular papers, and accepted all short and demo papers to broaden the community. These papers cover a variety of topics, ranging from various new contributions to in-vehicle network security (including new attacks, defenses, and also benchmarks), to new attack discovery and defense designs for emerging autonomous driving systems security, to connected vehicle infrastructure and protocol security, and to electric vehicle security and trusted software updates for embedded systems. Among them, the papers receiving the highest and second highest average review scores are the Best Paper Award winner and runner-up. In addition, among the short/work-in-progress papers, the ones receiving the highest and second highest average review scores are the Best Short Paper Award winner and runner-up. Among the papers studying autonomous driving security, the highest-scored regular one received the Baidu Security AutoDriving Security Award. Best Demo Award winner and runner-up are decided based on the voting results during the workshop.

The organization of a workshop requires the collaboration of many individuals. First, we would like to thank the authors for submitting to the workshop. Second, we thank the program committee members for their efforts in reviewing the papers and providing valuable feedback to authors. We hope that you will find this program interesting and that the workshop will provide you with a valuable opportunity to interact with other researchers and practitioners in automotive and autonomous vehicle security.

Qi Alfred Chen
UC Irvine, USA

Ziming Zhao
University at Buffalo, USA

Gail-Joon Ahn
Arizona State University, USA and Samsung Research, South Korea

Organizing Committee

Program Co-Chairs

Qi Alfred Chen, *University of California, Irvine*
Ziming Zhao, *University at Buffalo*
Gail-Joon Ahn, *ASU and Samsung Research*

Program Committee

Gedare Bloom, *University of Colorado Colorado Springs*
Alvaro Cardenas, *University of California Santa Cruz*
Stephen Checkoway, *Oberlin College*
Dongyao Chen, *Shanghai Jiao Tong University*
Jeremy Daily, *Colorado State University*
Sriharsha Etigowni, *Purdue University*
Thomas Forest, *General Motors*
Ryan Gerdes, *Virginia Tech*
Xiali Hei, *University of Louisiana at Lafayette*
Hongxin Hu, *Clemson University*
Zbigniew T. Kalbarczyk, *University of Illinois at Urbana-Champaign*
Taegyu Kim, *Purdue University*
Karl Koscher, *University of Washington*
Sekar Kulandaivel, *Carnegie Mellon University*
Kang Li, *Baidu, Inc.*
Chung-Wei Lin, *National Taiwan University*
Zhiqiang Lin, *The Ohio State University*
Peng Liu, *Pennsylvania State University*
Morley Mao, *University of Michigan*
Karthik Pattabiraman, *University of British Columbia*
Mert Pesé, *University of Michigan*
Jonathan Petit, *Qualcomm*
Hanif Rahbari, *Rochester Institute of Technology*
Indrakshi Ray, *Colorado State University*
David Starobinski, *Boston University*
Yuan Tian, *University of Virginia*
André Weimerskirch, *Lear Corporation*
Shengzhi Zhang, *Boston University*
Fengwei Zhang, *Southern University of Science and Technology*
Ning Zhang, *Washington University at St. Louis*

Car Hacking and Defense Competition on In-Vehicle Network

Hyunjae Kang, Byung Il Kwak, Young Hun Lee, Haneol Lee, Hwejae Lee and Huy Kang Kim
School of Cybersecurity, Korea University
{trifle19, kwacka12, dlddudfkr, roytravel, hwejae94, cenda}@korea.ac.kr

***Abstract*—Cybersecurity competitions can promote the importance of security and discover talented researchers. We hosted the Car Hacking: Attack & Defense Challenge from September 14, 2020 to November 27, 2020, and many security companies and researchers participated. To the best of our knowledge, it is the first competition to contest both attack and detection techniques on an in-vehicle network, specifically Controller Area Network (CAN). The participants developed various injection attacks and high-performance detection algorithms based on the real vehicle environment. Rule-based and ensemble tree-based models dominated the final round. Also, time interval and data byte patterns worked as major features to detect attacks.**

I. Introduction

The development of connected vehicles inevitably increases security threats to the vehicle. Modern vehicles contain three main components, in-vehicle systems, external communication interfaces such as Vehicle-to-Vehicle (V2V) or Vehicle-to-Infrastructure (V2I), and internet-based applications, to provide more innovative driving experiences like autonomous driving [3]. Unlike traditional vehicles, an in-vehicle network such as Controller Area Network (CAN) [14] is no longer isolated from an external attacker's threats. As one of the famous hacking cases, Miller and Valasek demonstrated that an attacker could control the 2014 Jeep Cherokee by obtaining access to the CAN network over a compromised radio [13].

In cybersecurity area, competitions to test hacking and defense skills are being held worldwide. Such competitions can promote the importance of security, discover professionals, and educate students in an efficient and attractive way [4]. However, there are only a few competitions held in car security area. Pwn2Own, a cybersecurity conference with hacking contests on popularly used software, included automotive category in 2019 and 2020 [5]. They used a Tesla Model 3 as a target and encouraged researchers to exploit the modem, infotainment, gateway, CAN bus of the vehicle. Also, SINCON 2020 conference opened a Capture The Flag (CTF) style competition on car security [8]. Each team could remotely access a virtual simulated vehicle environment or physical test bench and solved questions related to the CAN bus. Despite the positive effects of competitions, holding a car security competition has challenges due to difficulties of vehicle testbed set-up and lack of researchers in the related field.

Workshop on Automotive and Autonomous Vehicle Security (AutoSec) 2021
25 February 2021, Virtual

https://dx.doi.org/10.14722/autosec.2021.23035
www.ndss-symposium.org

The purpose of this paper is to share our experience of holding a car security competition. We hosted the Car Hacking: Attack & Defense Challenge from September 14, 2020 to November 27, 2020, in South Korea. The competition problem was to develop attacks and detection algorithms for CAN, a widely used standard of in-vehicle communication. The participants earned scores when they detect other team's attacks and inject critical or stealth attacks. The most significant difference from the events of Pwn2Own and SINCON is that we held attack and detection competitions simultaneously.

The contributions of our competition are listed below:

- We used a commercial car in the competition: Hyundai Avante CN7, a model released in 2020. The participants could inject attacks and see the following effects of a real vehicle.
- The competition aimed to challenge participant's attacks and detection algorithms concurrently. On the day of the main contest, we captured the CAN traffic while the red team injects attack messages into the car and transmitted the traffic to the rest of the teams' (i.e., blue teams) detection systems. It is the first attempt to contest both attack and detection skills in the same car security contest to the best of our knowledge.
- We ran a testbed with real vehicles before the finals, so even individual participants who do not have equipment could use the environment to inject and analyze CAN traffic. We believe this opportunity helped increasing interest in car security to researchers and students.
- We could test and compare attack and detect methods of many research teams, including companies and universities in car security field. They showed statistical rule-based approach is effective to detect attacks, and reducing frequency of attack messages helps to avoid detection systems.

II. Background

A. *In-vehicle network*

Most vehicles have standard protocols, i.e., LIN, CAN, MOST, and FlexRay, to communicate with in-vehicle nodes. In those protocols, the CAN protocol has high-integrity data communications for real-time applications, reliability, and excellent error detection. For such reasons, most common vehicles apply CAN to an in-vehicle network to transmit sensor data between the nodes: Electronic Control Unit (ECU), microcontrollers, and sensors [14]. It has characteristics such as multi-master bus access, bus topology, and message priority. An accessed CAN bus node can transmit CAN message without any configuration to communicate with other nodes. Accessed nodes broadcast CAN message because of its bus topology where all nodes share one line. When some nodes send messages into the CAN bus, messages identifier works as a priority of transmission.

B. *CAN message injection attacks*

The CAN bus' distinctive characteristics could be vulnerable due to no consideration of security. Many injection attacks, such as flooding, fuzzing, spoofing, replay, and bus-off attacks, exploits CAN bus vulnerabilities [7]. The CAN bus has no authentication for source and destination addresses, so the injected data can be processed in normal ECUs without verification. The flooding attack causes CAN message delaying of normal ECUs by sending bunch of messages that has the highest priority (CAN ID 0x000). The fuzzing attack injects random CAN IDs and data. The spoofing attack controls certain vehicle functions by setting specific CAN ID and data field. The replay attack is to inject normal CAN bus traffic, which was collected during driving. Lastly, the bus-off attack is to increase error counts via intentional message collision. When the target node's error count is large enough, the node is set to bus-off status [1].

C. *Intrusion detection techniques*

Various intrusion detection methodologies have been studied to increase the security of the CAN bus network. These researches could be categorized based on detection layers, i.e., physical layer, data link layer, and application layer. In the physical layer, voltage differences between a normal ECU and an abnormal ECU were used to detect intrusions [2], [9]. In the data link layer, the CAN traffic sequences were used to the deep learning algorithm to detect the in-vehicle intrusion [15]. Moreover, the status features, i.e., the survival analysis of CAN message's frequency [7] and CAN bus's self-similarity [10], were utilized for the anomaly detection algorithms. In the application layer, in-vehicle sensors' correlation was used to check the abnormality with an On-Board Diagnostic (OBD) data [6]. Various deep learning algorithms based on increased computing power have recently been studied to detect in-vehicle network anomalies and intrusions [11].

III. Competition Problems

This competition targeted the CAN bus of Avante vehicle. The CAN bus of the Avante is divided into several sections (e.g., D-CAN, C-CAN, B-CAN) according to its role. To focus on a specific goal, we tapped a DB9 cable directly to the C-CAN high/low wires, like Fig. 2a. C-CAN contains ECUs related to a cluster, motor-driven power steering, airbag control, rear camera, vehicle dynamic control, and several Advanced Driver Assistance Systems (ADAS).

We assumed the scenario that an attacker is already acquired access to the CAN bus. It can happen in practice by hacking the infotainment system or adding a physical node to the CAN bus. It is important to develop an intrusion detection system for the CAN layer because the attacker will eventually inject CAN messages to control the car in many cases. The participants were required to suggest a high-accuracy detection algorithm along with developing attacks (i.e., injecting CAN messages) by analyzing the CAN data. The scope was limited to C-CAN, considering the short period of the competition.

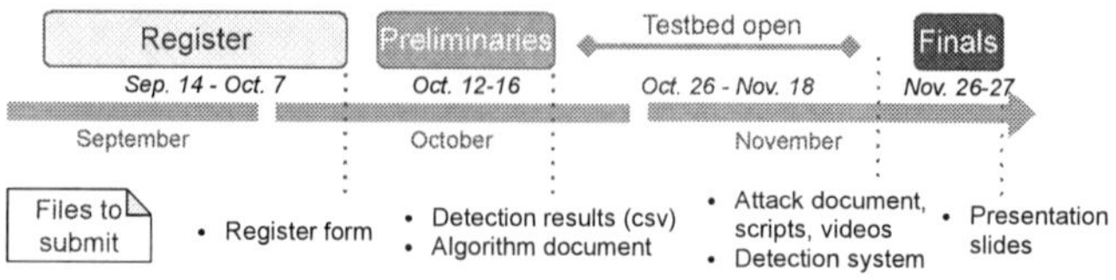

Fig. 1. Car Hacking: Attack & Defense Challenge 2020 timeline

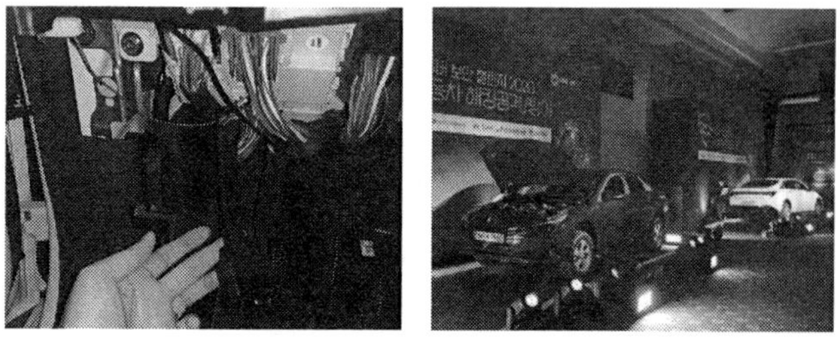

(a) Tapping C-CAN (b) Finals site

Fig. 2. Vehicle settings for the competition. (a) C-CAN wires were tapped to connect a CAN interface device. (b) Cars were lifted up in the finals.

A. *Preliminary round*

We gave CAN traffic files, including normal and attack messages, to the participants. Each team had to develop an attack detection method and submit the class ('Normal' or 'Attack') of each message. The teams, in order of high detection accuracy, could advance to the finals. For dataset description, see Section IV-A.

B. *Final round*

The teams were requested to develop five kinds of injection attacks. On the finals, the teams took turns to inject attack messages into the vehicle. Each team had one attack session for 10 minutes to inject their attacks into the vehicle; other teams should submit detection results. Each team's attacks were not shared with other teams; thus, all teams should prepare their detection algorithm to work on unknown attacks. There were some restrictions on the attacks. Teams could conduct only five injection attacks, and the attack effects should be visible in naked eyes to confirm the validity of attacks. Also, unlike preliminary round, attacks injecting random CAN messages such as fuzzing attacks were not allowed in order to prevent mixing no-effect messages.

IV. Running Competition

Overall competition schedule and submission files are briefly described in Fig. 1. Note that the competition was held during the period of the COVID-19 pandemic, so both preliminary and final rounds were held as virtual events. For preliminary, we opened a leaderboard website so the participants could see their scores. For finals, we provided a live broadcast along with the leaderboard.

A. *Preliminary round dataset*

In the preliminary round, we provided two datasets depending on the purpose: the training set and submission set. Table I shows the number of messages for normal and attack classes. Both datasets contained two status of the target vehicle.

TABLE I. SUMMARY OF PRELIMINARY ROUND DATASET

Purpose	Car Status	Normal	Flooding	Spoofing	Replay	Fuzzing
Training	Driving	1,724,630 (92.0%)	77,373 (4.1%)	3,879 (0.2%)	23,775 (1.3%)	45,474 (2.4%)
	Stationary	1,648,113 (91.7%)	76,807 (4.3%)	3,877 (0.2%)	23,818 (1.3%)	44,405 (2.5%)
Submission	Driving	1,799,046 (89.9%)	96,559 (4.8%)	22,489 (1.1%)	37,869 (1.9%)	44,770 (2.2%)
	Stationary	1,559,164 (89.0%)	95,120 (5.4%)	20,094 (1.1%)	25,012 (1.4%)	51,923 (3.0%)

TABLE II. EXAMPLES OF TRAINING DATA

Timestamp	Arbitration ID	DLC	Data	Class	SubClass
1597759747.427094	507	4	08 00 00 01	Normal	Normal
1597759747.427486	000	8	00 00 00 00 00 00 00 00	Attack	Flooding
1597759747.427742	356	8	00 00 00 80 1D 00 00 00	Normal	Normal

Driving. The data extracted when driving, including general driving motions (e.g., accelerate, braking, turning the steering wheel).
Stationary. The data extracted when the car engine is on but not moving (park gear), including subsidiary motions (e.g., pressing buttons of the center console).

In each state, there were four types of attacks:
Flooding. Flooding attack aims to consume the CAN bus bandwidth by sending a massive number of messages. We transmitted messages having the lowest value of CAN ID (0x000) to take advantage of the priority mechanism.
Spoofing. An attacker injects CAN messages to control the desired function after reversing the vehicle traffic. Several spoofing attacks were performed in the preliminaries; 1) factory mode activated warning, 2) printing higher RPM gauge, 3) engine off warning, 4) blind spot collision warning, 5) sudden turn-on of the rear camera screen. We included 1), 2) to the training set, and 3), 4), 5) to the test set; different CAN IDs were used in the test set to increase detection difficulty.
Replay. Replay attack is to extract normal traffic at a specific time and replay (inject) it into the CAN bus. It is relatively hard to make changes to a specific function, but much easier than spoofing attack because it does not require hard reversing. When we replayed the traffic, some warnings flashed on the cluster, and odd reactions appeared when driving the vehicle.
Fuzzing. If an attacker does not have sufficient information on the values of CAN IDs and the data field, he may inject random messages. When we transmitted randomly generated data of several arbitrary IDs, random warnings flashed on the cluster, and occasionally it caused sudden stop or flinching of the steering wheel.

As shown in Table II, the training dataset was CSV format files consisting of 6 fields: Timestamp, Arbitration ID (i.e., CAN ID), DLC, Data, Class, and SubClass. Timestamp indicates the Unix time when the CAN message was logged. CAN ID is a hex value of the identifier. DLC is an integer value of the data length code. Data is hex values of the data field, each byte separated by a space. Class and subclass are fields to indicate normal or attack, and type of attack of the CAN message.

In the submission dataset, we deleted Class and SubClass fields and added Number field indicating the row number in front of the Timestamp field. Participants submitted the predicted Class (Normal of Attack) of each CAN messages. Note that predicting SubClass (i.e., attack type classification) was not required in the competition to consider scalability, because participants may carry out any type of unknown attacks in the finals.

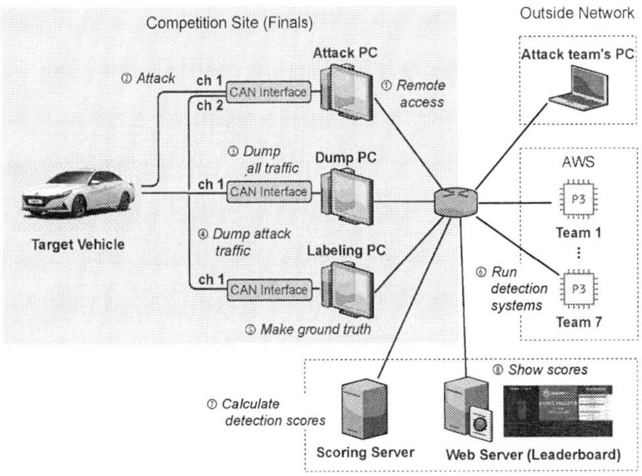

Fig. 3. Overview of final round systems and process

The preliminary round datasets are available for research purposes on our website.[1]

B. *Systems and process for final round*

In the finals, all teams had one attack session (10 minutes) in turn to inject five types of prepared attacks. In each attack session, all teams' attack detection systems, including the attack team's system, submitted the predicted Class of each CAN messages collected.

The overall systems and process is shown in Fig. 3. To hold attack and detection competition simultaneously, we considered the following conditions when building the finals environment:

- All C-CAN traffic of the vehicle and only attack traffic should be captured separately.
- Creating ground truth should be automated.
- Running each team's detection system and evaluation should be automated.

1) Performing attacks: For safety, the target vehicle was lifted up and kept stationary status. Participants may change the vehicle's settings except for drive or rear gear (e.g., park or neutral gear, turning the steering handle, opening/closing doors). Staffs changed the settings at the site if requested since the participants remotely accessed the attack PC because of the pandemic. Each team's pre-submitted attack scripts were downloaded on the PC, so the participants could run the scripts to send attack messages to the vehicle. The PC was connected to the vehicle through a CAN to USB interface product of Kvaser's. The interface supported a dual CAN channel, and the first channel was cabled with the vehicle's C-CAN.

2) Collecting CAN data: The CAN message frame does not contain sender information, so it is hard to distinguish attack messages only from the dumped traffic of the vehicle's CAN. We revised attack scripts after submission to make them re-send duplicate messages to the second channel to solve this problem. The second channel was connected to another CAN interface of other PC ("Labeling PC" in Fig. 3). Since it is a separate bus network from the vehicle's network, we could collect attack messages only. Also, another PC ("Dump PC") collected all traffic from the vehicle.

[1]https://ocslab.hksecurity.net/Datasets/carchallenge2020

TABLE III. COMPETITION PERFORMANCE EVALUATION INDICATORS

Category	Evaluation Indicators		Proportion		Remarks
Attack Score	Visibility of attack impact		Y/N		Qualitative
	Number of attack kinds		6%	30%	Quantitative
	Different attacks from preliminary round		6%		Quantitative
	Severity of attacks		6%		Qualitative
	Detection difficulty		12%		Quantitative
Detection Score	Attack detection accuracy (F1-score)	Host's session	10%	50%	Quantitative
		Participant's session	40%		
Presentation	Understanding of CAN data and validity of idea-making process		4%	20%	Qualitative
	Features, advantages, and differentiation of detection algorithm		8%		
	Features, advantages, and differentiation of attack techniques		8%		

3) Making ground truth: After each attack session was finished, the dump PC sends dumped traffic to the labeling PC. The labeling program flagged certain messages as "Attack" if the message could be found in attack traffic, dumped from the other channel. Timestamp, arbitration ID, DLC, and data fields were compared to determine the attack messages.

4) Running detection systems and scoring: Each team installed their attack detection system on an individual cloud server. We provided Amazon EC2 P3.2xlarge instance[2], and the teams were able to set up their system for two days before the finals. The system should be automated and the participants were inaccessible to the server on the day of the final. After each attack session was finished, we transmitted unlabeled CAN traffic and ran all detection servers in parallel. The servers submitted detection results and run times to a scoring server. The submission time limit was 20 minutes, twice the time of an attack session. The scoring server calculated detection scores by using the ground truth from the labeling PC, and finally, it uploads each team's detection score on a leaderboard. Considering the time required for data transmitting and processing, participants could check their scores in at most 25 minutes.

C. Scoring

We conducted quantitative and qualitative evaluations together for a comprehensive assessment. All evaluation indicators and distribution is on Table III.

1) Attack score: When making the indicators, we deliberated on how to tempt teams to make stealth and critical attacks; 'detection difficulty' and 'severity of attacks' are the related indicators. Since there are temporal constraints to hold a competition, we limited the attack ranges to the cases where we can visually identify the attack impact.

Visibility of attack impact. The impact of every attack should be visible; therefore, the staff could recognize that the team is injecting valid attack messages. If the staff cannot confirm the impact, the corresponding attempt is not counted as an attack.

Number of attack kinds. The teams could prepare at most 5 different attacks. The 'kind' of attack is distinguished as if an attack affects different functions of the vehicle, regardless of attack types such as flooding, spoofing, replay, and fuzzing. For example, if a first attack changes an RPM gauge value and a second attack turns a steering wheel, both attacks are counted as different.

Different attacks from preliminary round. This indicator is included to encourage participants to make different kinds of attacks from preliminary round datasets. If a team reuses the attack that is already performed in the preliminary round, this score will be deducted.

Severity of attacks. If an attack arises malfunctioning of essential driving functions such as controlling a brake or direction of wheels, the team gets a higher score.

Detection difficulty. If a team performs attacks that are difficult to detect from other teams' detection systems, the team gets points. From an attacker's point of view, it is important to carry out silent attacks that an IDS may miss. Note that this score is calculated on a session basis, unlike the above indicators, which are scored on each attack. If n is the total number of teams and F_i is the F1-score of team i, the red team gets an inverse proportion of all teams' F1-score average:

$$1 - \frac{\sum_{i=1}^{n} F_i}{n}$$

2) Detection score: We used F1-score indicator to assess an accuracy of detection algorithms. F1-score is a harmonic mean of precision and recall, where precision (recall) is the number of correctly identified attack messages divided by the number of all messages predicted as attack (divided by the number of all real attack messages). It can measure detection performance objectively even when normal and attack data distribution is unbalanced:

$$\text{F1-score} = 2 \cdot \frac{\text{precision} \cdot \text{recall}}{\text{precision} + \text{recall}}$$

For the preliminaries, only the detection score of the submission dataset was used. For the finals, the detection scores of all attack sessions were aggregated. There was a host's session; we injected attacks similar to the preliminaries to assess teams' basic detection performances. Also, each team submitted results for all team's sessions, including their own, and the weighted sum of F1-scores were the final score.

3) Presentation: Each team made a presentation for 25 minutes (15 min presentation, 10 min Q&A) on the 2nd day of finals, explaining the detection algorithm and prepared attacks. The evaluation committee composed of 6 experts estimated qualitative factors such as background knowledge level of CAN or in-vehicle IDS, the effectiveness of the proposed detection algorithm, and efforts to develop attack techniques.

D. Running testbed

A testbed, a real vehicle environment, was provided before the finals to test their skills and collect real data. We operated it from October 26, 2020 to November 18, 2020. Two cars were placed so that two teams could visit at the same time. Kvaser CAN interface, the same device used in finals, was equipped, and sample codes of reading and transmitting CAN messages were provided. For safety reasons, participants were only allowed to inject or collect data when the car was stationary.

[2]The instance's specifications are one NVIDIA Tesla V100 GPU, 16GB GPU memory, 8 virtual CPUs, and 61GB memory.

TABLE IV. COMPETITION RESULTS: DETECTION SCORES, ATTACK SCORES, AND DETECTION ALGORITHMS

Team	Fin. avg. F1-score	Fin. avg. detection time (s)	Fin. attack score	Detection algorithm
A	**0.869**	**33**	71.0	Rule-based
B	0.864	155	57.2	XGBoost, Light GBM, rule-based
C	0.816	355	**79.6**	Random Forest, white & black list
D	0.812	257	66.7	Light GBM
E	0.675	295	63.4	Rule-based, Random Forest
F	0.445	147	38.8	Random Forest, Light GBM
G	0	114	51.7	DBSCAN

Instead, they could request us to dump and share data while driving normal roadway with videos filmed driver actions and front views. Occasionally, wrong alarms were often turned on in the cluster when unusual CAN messages were injected, and they did not disappear by turning the car off and on. Every day after the testbed closed and anytime users requested, our staff drove the car for a moment to refresh sensors.

V. COMPETITION RESULTS

A. *Summary*

We had 25 registrations on the preliminary round, and 19 teams submitted results. Top 7 teams entered finals; two security companies, one university (professor and graduate students), one research institute, and three individual teams composed of undergraduate students or office workers. Table IV shows the final teams' overall scores and detection algorithms. We listed the teams in order of finals detection score. As shown in Table IV, Participant's detection scores decreased significantly compared to the preliminary round; -0.13 points based on the highest score. We surmised that there were two main reasons; 1) any information of attacks prepared by participants were not shared with other teams– unlike training sets provided in preliminaries, 2) the requests of the team varied vehicle settings during the attack session, so it increased diversity of normal traffic.

1) Detection algorithms: Interestingly, all teams except Team G used rule-based or tree-based ensemble classifiers (e.g., Random Forest, XGBoost, Light GBM) in finals. While many teams also used tree-based models in the preliminary round, five teams out of 19 submitted teams used deep learning models, such as BERT, CNN, autoencoder, and LSTM. However, even the teams that used deep learning models changed their algorithms to rule-based or tree-based models in finals. Final round teams preferred such models because of fast inference speed to submit results within the time limit (20 min). Also, the models did not lack detection performance compared to deep learning models in our competition environment.

2) Features: There were two major features that the final teams focused on–time interval and data field patterns.
Time interval. Most of the CAN IDs have regular transmitting cycle in normal status. When attack messages targeted on certain CAN ID are injected, time interval values becomes much shorter than the normal cycle, as shown in Fig. 4a.
Data field patterns. Several CAN IDs have constant, counter, or CRC (Cyclic Redundancy Check) bytes in the data field [12]. When an attack message is injected between normal messages, it breaks the pattern of such data bytes. For example, Fig. 4b shows abnormal counter bytes when an attack message

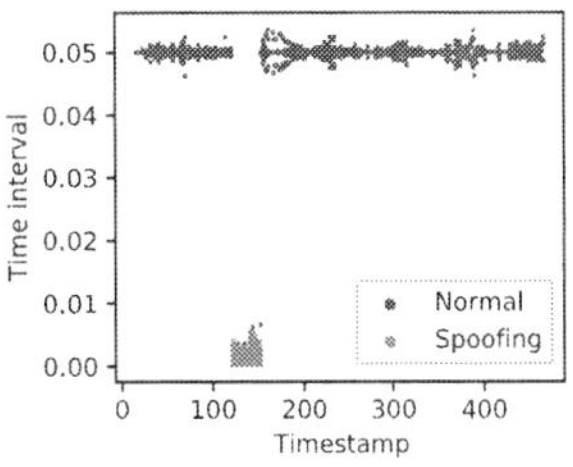

(a) Time interval example

Timestamp	ID	Data							
120.78377	490	00	00	08	21	00	00	3C	7C
120.83318	490	00	00	08	21	00	10	3C	C8
120.88338	490	00	00	08	21	00	20	3C	09
120.90583	490	03	00	08	21	00	00	3C	7C
120.93318	490	00	00	08	21	00	30	3C	BD
120.98348	490	00	00	08	21	00	40	3C	96
120.03387	490	00	00	08	21	00	50	3C	22

(b) Counter example

Fig. 4. Feature values observed in CAN ID 0x490. (a) shows a scatter plot of time interval values. Normal messages have regular intervals around 0.05 sec, while spoofing messages have intervals smaller than 0.005 sec. (b) shows sample data bytes of counter pattern. The red row is a spoofing message. It shows a wrong counter value while the data byte of normal messages increases 0x10 each time.

is injected. Rule-based models used certain condition of CAN ID, data byte, and type of pattern (e.g., constant, counter) while developing the rules. Tree-based models used data byte difference from last same CAN ID message as a feature, so they could train the pattern of change in data bytes.

3) Proposed attacks: To achieve high attack scores in the competition, severity of attacks and detection difficulty are major indicators.
Severity of attacks. The attacks were divided into two main categories: controlling powertrain and false alert. Attacks that could make changes on powertrain modules, such as steering wheel and brake, got high severity scores. These attacks may cause critical accidents by controlling the car's movement. False alerts are the attacks that spoof signs on the dashboard. Various scenarios were proposed, e.g., hiding door open sign, showing wrong gear sign, turning on the ADAS signs or warnings. The purpose of these attacks was to confuse the driver and interfere with driving. They got relatively low severity scores than powertrain related attacks.
Detection difficulty. To avoid detection, the process of reducing the frequency of attack messages and making them similar to normal messages was important. Regardless of the severity, the low frequency decreased time interval violation and the probability of detected by other teams' algorithms. Also, avoiding unused IDs and data bytes also helped.

B. *Team A's detection algorithm (detection score rank 1)*

Team A used only rule-based algorithm. Their algorithm mainly worked as following steps; 1) detect unused CAN ID and DLC, 2) check each data byte whether specific byte has wrong constant, counter, or CRC value, 3) check if time interval of packets is outside of normal range. These features were commonly used by other teams, though their strength was thorough analysis of each CAN ID and data bytes; they tried to discover each byte's pattern type (e.g., constant, counter, CRC, or reflecting sensor input) for all CAN IDs. Interestingly, it was the fastest algorithm among all teams; it took only 33 seconds in average to submit detection results of 10 min traffic, while other teams took 1-6 minutes generally.

C. *Team C's attacks (attack score rank 1)*

Team C endeavored to find attacks that could succeed with the minimum number of messages. They repeated fuzzing on

CAN ID and data fields to find messages that effects functions such as steering wheel, brake, autohold, and cruise control. Also, they tried ID elimination test–checking the car's reaction after eliminating certain ID from the collected traffic and replaying it. These process made them available to find the exact message that could control the car with small amount of messages. They injected only 2,000 messages while other team's injected at least 6,000 to at most 160,000 messages. As result, they got remarkable score on the detection difficulty.

VI. Discussion: Limitations and Potential Improvements

As we held data-driven hacking and defense style competition in the car security field for the first time, we would like to mention the limitations and factors that could be improved in the future.

1) Limited vehicle status: Using a commercial vehicle enables developing attacks and detection algorithms that work in practice; however, it inevitably causes cost and safety problems. The non-driving status was only allowed at the finals and the testbed because of safety issues such as driver injury due to unexpected movement while testing attacks. Therefore, some attacks, like changing the vehicle's speed by malfunctioning ADAS systems, were hard to develop in this competition. A proven testing place with a chassis dynamometer or a track should be reserved to provide a driving status. Otherwise, we may consider building a simulator similar to the real car environment. Also, the contest hall for the finals was an indoor place, so there were difficulties in resetting the wrong alarms on the car by driving. We removed the remaining error codes via the OBD-II scanner and disconnected the battery for more than 10 min to solve this problem; this process was repeated between all attack sessions.

2) Accessibility to a real vehicle: A real car is a costly device, especially for individuals. Although few teams owned or rented the same vehicle model, the other teams had to test their skills within a limited period at the testbed (at most two days per team). For a future competition, it is recommended to increase the testbed providing period more sufficiently by considering the schedule from the planning stage.

3) Extending the scope of challenge: As we mentioned in chapter III, only C-CAN was the competition's scope. We may consider extending the scope by adding other sections: P-CAN (connected to engine/transmission/powertrain, fuel injection pump, vehicle dynamic control modules, etc.) and B-CAN (connected to a seat position control module, etc.). Also, considering other important layers of a vehicle, such as Bluetooth/USB modules, infotainment, and gateway devices, would be challenging but valuable competition items.

VII. Conclusion

The Car Hacking: Attack & Defense Challenge 2020 is the first car security competition that held both attack track and detection track concurrently. Several security companies, researchers, and students participated and tested their detection system performance in the real-car environment. Surprisingly, the top-ranked detection algorithm was a rule-based model. The model scored 0.87 F1-score on binary classification per message ('Normal' or 'Attack'). It used precise rules of time intervals and data byte patterns of each CAN ID. The team with the highest attack score earned both great scores on severity and detection difficulty. They tried to find out the exact CAN message that could control the car with a small amount of injection.

There is a lot of room to expand the competition, such as targeting multiple vehicle models or preparing more various vehicle status. Continuing to hold competitions will help discover talented researchers and activate automotive security research.

Acknowledgment

This work was supported by Institute for Information & Communications Technology Planning & Evaluation (IITP) grant funded by the Korea government (MSIT) (No. 2020-0-00866, Challenges for next generation security R&D).

References

[1] K.-T. Cho and K. G. Shin, "Error handling of in-vehicle networks makes them vulnerable," in *Proceedings of the 2016 ACM SIGSAC Conference on Computer and Communications Security*, 2016, pp. 1044–1055.

[2] W. Choi, K. Joo, H. J. Jo, M. C. Park, and D. H. Lee, "Voltageids: Low-level communication characteristics for automotive intrusion detection system," *IEEE Transactions on Information Forensics and Security*, vol. 13, no. 8, pp. 2114–2129, 2018.

[3] J. den Hartog, N. Zannone *et al.*, "Security and privacy for innovative automotive applications: A survey," *Computer Communications*, vol. 132, pp. 17–41, 2018.

[4] E. Gavas, N. Memon, and D. Britton, "Winning cybersecurity one challenge at a time," *IEEE Security & Privacy*, vol. 10, no. 4, pp. 75–79, 2012.

[5] B. Gorenc, "Pwn2Own returns to vancouver for 2020," https://www.zerodayinitiative.com/blog/2020/1/8/pwn2own-returns-to-vancouver-for-2020, accessed on: Jan. 11, 2021.

[6] F. Guo, Z. Wang, S. Du, H. Li, H. Zhu, Q. Pei, Z. Cao, and J. Zhao, "Detecting vehicle anomaly in the edge via sensor consistency and frequency characteristic," *IEEE Transactions on Vehicular Technology*, vol. 68, no. 6, pp. 5618–5628, 2019.

[7] M. L. Han, B. I. Kwak, and H. K. Kim, "Anomaly intrusion detection method for vehicular networks based on survival analysis," *Vehicular communications*, vol. 14, pp. 52–63, 2018.

[8] Infosec In the City, "Overview of SINCON car security kampung," https://www.infosec-city.com/post/sin20-ctf-car-security, accessed on: Jan. 11, 2021.

[9] M. Kneib and C. Huth, "Scission: Signal characteristic-based sender identification and intrusion detection in automotive networks," in *Proceedings of the 2018 ACM SIGSAC Conference on Computer and Communications Security*, 2018, pp. 787–800.

[10] B. I. Kwak, M. L. Han, and H. K. Kim, "Cosine similarity based anomaly detection methodology for the can bus," *Expert Systems with Applications*, vol. 166, p. 114066, 2021.

[11] Y. Lin, C. Chen, F. Xiao, O. Avatefipour, K. Alsubhi, and A. Yunianta, "An evolutionary deep learning anomaly detection framework for in-vehicle networks-can bus," *IEEE Transactions on Industry Applications*, 2020.

[12] M. Markovitz and A. Wool, "Field classification, modeling and anomaly detection in unknown can bus networks," *Vehicular Communications*, vol. 9, pp. 43–52, 2017.

[13] C. Miller and C. Valasek, "Remote exploitation of an unaltered passenger vehicle," *Black Hat USA*, vol. 2015, p. 91, 2015.

[14] Robert Bosch GmbH, "CAN specification 2.0," http://esd.cs.ucr.edu/webres/can20.pdf, 1991, accessed on: Jan. 11, 2021.

[15] H. M. Song, J. Woo, and H. K. Kim, "In-vehicle network intrusion detection using deep convolutional neural network," *Vehicular Communications*, vol. 21, p. 100198, 2020.

MUVIDS: False MAVLink Injection Attack Detection in Communication for Unmanned Vehicles

Seonghoon Jeong, Eunji Park, Kang Uk Seo, Jeong Do Yoo, and Huy Kang Kim
School of Cybersecurity, Korea University
{seonghoon, epark911, tjrkddnr, opteryx25104, cenda}@korea.ac.kr

Abstract—**MAVLink protocol is a *de facto* standard protocol used to communicate between unmanned vehicle and ground control system (GCS). Given the nature of the system, unmanned vehicles use MAVLink to communicate with a GCS to be monitored and controlled. Such communication continues to grow on the Internet due to its rapidly grown nature. In the past few years, the unmanned vehicle security has been one of the key research topics in the security field. However, existing research has mainly focused on the sensor- and GPS-based attack detection methods. To this end, we propose MUVIDS, a network-level intrusion detection system to protect MAVLink-enabled unmanned vehicles managed by GCS over the Internet. MUVIDS includes two Long short-term memory models that leverage a sequential MAVLink stream from a victim vehicle. The two models are designed to solve a binary classification problem (in case of labels are available) and a next MAVLink message prediction problem (in case of no label is available), respectively. The experiment was performed on a software-in-the-loop unmanned aerial vehicle (UAV) simulator and a hardware-in-the-loop UAV simulator. The experiment result confirms that MUVIDS detects false MAVLink injection attacks effectively.**

I. Introduction

Unmanned vehicles, specifically known as unmanned aerial vehicles (UAVs) and unmanned ground vehicles (UGVs), are getting special attention because of shifting paradigms in commercial delivery, military operations, social protection such as rescue, disaster monitoring [4], and even keeping our health in the middle of COVID-19 pandemic [3]. Among unmanned vehicles, commercial drones are the most promising systems so far in which the drones are easy to be deployed due to their low dependence on ground infrastructure during flight. Given the nature of the system, UAVs communicate with a ground control system (GCS) using satellite links, radio frequency, Wi-Fi, LTE, 5G, and so on, to be monitored and controlled. Today, UAV-GCS communication continues to grow on the Internet due to its rapidly grown nature. Thus, the importance of ensuring secure UAV-GCS communications is highlighted.

While unmanned vehicles provide many positive effects on our lives, attacks against the vehicles lead to malfunction and fatal consequences for operators (lost vehicles) and the physical world (casualties). Some studies already showed the possibility of attacks targeting unmanned vehicles [8], [12]. Therefore, it is important to research methods for detecting abnormalities or intrusions on unmanned vehicles. Each unmanned vehicle has various external I/O interfaces, which could open up attack surfaces, notably inertial measurement units, global positioning system, and network interfaces (e.g., Wi-Fi card). However, existing research has mainly focused on the sensor- and GPS-based attack detection methods. Such research detects abnormal signs and intrusions by predicting the next sensor value and location information based on a given mission and the current driving context [11]. A drawback of proposed techniques is that sensor and GPS data highly rely on the operation environment and some parameters need to be tuned dependent on a specific vehicle. On the other hand, in the context of network security studies, the majority is in vehicular ad-hoc networks (VANETs). The main goal of such a study is to keep availability and reliability of wireless communication, as well as providing secure "wireless" communication channels.

Despite considerable efforts to detect intrusions for UAVs, however, no study has been conducted on intrusion detection methods in the field of UAV-GCS communication. Although sensor- or GPS-based anomaly detection methods could identify network-level intrusions because the UAV will not operate as expected, such previous methods will alert only after being compromised. While a communication protocol for unmanned systems and ground stations is getting used to major autopilot systems [7], some vulnerabilities were discussed by previous work. Kwon *et al.* [8] discover a vulnerability of MAVLink used for UAV-GCS communication. By exploiting the vulnerability (injecting a false command packet), they succeeded in hovering the drone against the pre-uploaded mission. In addition, through the fuzz test of the protocol, several vulnerabilities were discovered that could cause the autopilot system to crash. [5]. In summary, the studies imply that the target UAV can be exploited by the attacker if an attacker can inject false packets.

In this paper, we propose MUVIDS, a network-level intrusion detection system (IDS) to protect MAVLink-enabled unmanned vehicles managed by GCS over the Internet. We follow the previous literature [5], [8] that assumes an attacker injects false MAVLink messages to a target UAV without recognition of the connected GCS. Our goal is to let the GCS identify whether a connected unmanned vehicle is under attack or not based on a pattern of network traffic. For the experiment, we set up a network testbed. A GCS is connected to a software-in-the-loop (SITL) UAV simulator and a hardware-in-the-loop (HITL) UAV simulator. For the connection, MAVLink[1] is used, which is the *de facto* standard protocol designed to exchange

Workshop on Automotive and Autonomous Vehicle Security (AutoSec) 2021
25 February 2021, Virtual
https://dx.doi.org/10.14722/autosec.2021.23036
www.ndss-symposium.org

[1] https://github.com/mavlink/mavlink, https://mavlink.io/en/

STX (0xFE)	LEN	INC FLAGS	CMP FLAGS	SEQ	SYS ID	COMP ID	MSG ID 3 bytes	PAYLOAD 0–255 bytes	CHECKSUM 2 bytes	SIGNATURE 13 bytes, *optional*

Fig. 1. MAVLink 2.0 frame header. Each field contains a single byte unless noted otherwise.

messages between vehicle and GCS over various network media. At the GCS, MUVIDS captures inbound MAVLink packets from the vehicle and detects injection attacks using LSTM-based recurrent neural networks. Though we have labels for training our models, we also provide another use case of MUVIDS in a case of lack of the label information.

Our contributions can be summarized as follows:

- We propose MUVIDS to identify attacks on unmanned vehicles using MAVLink communication between unmanned vehicle and GCS.
- We extend false MAVLink injection attacks from previous works [8], [12] to evaluate MUVIDS.
- By using deep learning-based detection models, MUVIDS successfully detects three types of false MAVLink injection attacks in both a SITL and a HITL environment regardless of availability of label. That is a huge benefit for unmanned vehicle operators because they do not have to throw vehicles in the wild to collect train set.
- MUVIDS works for monitoring various MAVLink-enabled vehicles easily since it does not require any parameters regarding vehicles.

II. Background

A. MAVLink

MAVLink stands for Micro Air Vehicle Link. The goal of MAVLink is to provide efficient and reliable communication and covers various common functionality used at most GCSs, autopilot systems of unmanned vehicles. Unlike its name, MAVLink supports not only *air* vehicles but also *ground/underwater* vehicles. Thanks to the open-source policy and hard-working team Dronecode underneath the Linux Foundation to support many programming languages, MAVLink is now one of the most commonly adopted protocols in personal and commercial vehicles (especially drones). Currently, MAVLink 2.0 is the up-to-date protocol.

Fig. 1 shows the MAVLink 2.0 protocol header. We here introduce packet fields briefly. Since MAVLink can be used on various channels, the *STX* field implies that the next buffer is a MAVLink 2.0 message. The *LEN* field means the length of the *PAYLOAD* field. The *SEQ* field contains a number whose value increases at each transmission. The *SYS/COMP ID* points to a target vehicle and an in-vehicle component, respectively. The *MSG ID*, which we use in this paper, indicates how the *PAYLOAD* field should be parsed and consumed. Two flag fields and the *SIGNATURE* field are designed for message signing. However, message signing is not always available in all implementations, unlike essential communication features. Note that there is no security mechanisms like encryption and authentication. To this end, some security solutions are discussed in the literature. For the technical details and following state-of-the-art security solutions about the MAVLink protocol, the reader is kindly referred to [7].

B. Communication between UAV-GCS

The MAVLink connection is established through the following brief explanations of the steps: A vehicle starts to transmit a HEARTBEAT message in the broadcast domain or to a designated address of GCS. At the same time, the GCS listens to the HEARTBEAT message on the ground. When the GCS discovers the vehicle, then both systems continuously send a HEARTBEAT message to each other every second to keep it alive. Then, the connection ends with some silence of HEARTBEAT messages.

After a connection is established, the vehicle continually reports the current status toward the connection so that the GCS can follow the vehicle's status. The frequency of reports may vary depending on vehicle types, autopilot systems, link bandwidth, etc. On the other hand, the GCS sends MAVLink messages to the connected vehicle when triggered by humans (e.g., uploading mission, sending a new command), instead of a periodic transmission. The MAVLink message parser does not refer to any value in other protocol headers, such as source IP address. Thus, MAVLink communication is vulnerable to a false message injection if the message has a valid payload.

C. False MAVLink injection attack

Here, we introduce false MAVLink injection attacks, which we want to detect using MUVIDS. The attacks are more critical than sensor- or GPS-level attacks in terms that the attacks can be performed by an far remote attacker even she/he does not have any specially designed hardware. We assume the ability of the attacker, the GCS, the UAV as follows: (1) The attacker can access the target UAV through the compromised network. (2) The GCS does not become aware of the attacker's existence or false packets generated by the attacker. (3) The UAV and the GCS use plain text (no encryption) by following a standard implementation. (4) The attacker interferes with an established session between UAV-GCS because the target UAV only listens to an established session.

The attacker's goal is to disguise an accident as occurring on UAVs. Here, we consider flooding attacks to occupy the drone's resources and reduce its capacity, such as limited action radius by battery drain, insufficient object perception. Based on the assumption, we present three types of attacks as follows:

- **Heartbeat flooding.** The message is consumed by the MAVLink receiver process and does not pass across the inside of the autopilot system.
- **Ping flooding.** The ping message is designed for networks that do not support ICMP. The receiver needs to send a ping response to the opposite system.
- **Request flooding.** The request message is used to query the value of a specific parameter. The receiver sends the opposite system the requested parameter. It consumes much more computing power because of additional kernel tasks.

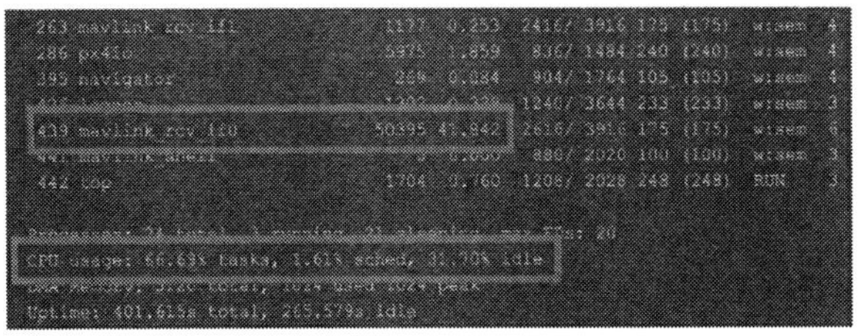

(a) Process list in NuttX OS. The MAVLink message receiver over-consumes the CPU in our Pixhawk 4 autopilot system.

(b) Simulated UAV crash due to the considered flooding attack

Fig. 2. False MAVLink injection attack realized in our HITL simulator

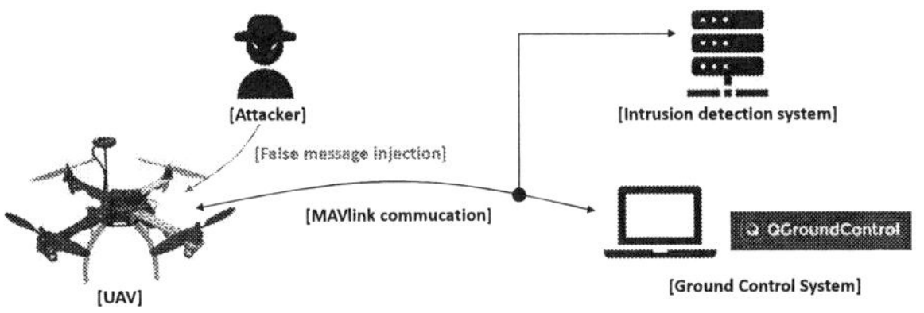

Fig. 3. Architectural overview of MUVIDS. The attacker inject false messages to the UAV whereas the IDS receives MAVLink communication from the UAV.

Fig. 2 shows the impact of the attack on our HITL simulator. The flooding attacks make the Arm processor of our Pixhawk 4 busy. The more messages an attacker sends per time, the busier the CPU becomes. As a result, the victim will consume much more battery power. Due to the bandwidth limitation in our Pixhawk 4 device, it seems the attacks does not overwhelm the system. However, the flooding may lead to blocking messages from GCS. Furthermore, when the target drone starts autonomous driving, the CPU utilization rises nearly 100%, and the drone falls in the simulation environment. In the meantime, the GCS receives usual status reporting messages and a large number of awkward ping/parameter responses.

III. MUVIDS: IDS FOR MAVLINK-ENABLED UNMANNED VEHICLES

We focus on the communication characteristics of UAVs that periodically report current driving situations. We assume that the periodic reports of a UAV will be ruined when the UAV is struggling with flooding attacks. In other words, we suppose the inherent sequence pattern of MAVLink messages will change. Consequently, we try to detect intrusion using *MSG ID* sequences from the MAVLink stream.

Our method is intended to recognize the network-level attacks toward UAVs effectively. The use case of the proposed methodology against the attacker is shown in Fig. 3. The IDS is installed along with the GCS. The IDS takes every packet that comes from the UAV. Then, the IDS parses the value of the *MSG ID* field in any MAVLink messages and enumerates the sequence of observed values in the order of arrival. The sequence is then sliced into fixed-size subsequences by the sliding window method. Finally, the subsequences are fed to an intrusion detection model. To build the intrusion detection model, we implement recurrent neural networks using long short-term memory (LSTM) cells. The LSTM cell is commonly adopted in intrusion detection model exploiting sequential data where the output correlates a sequence of inputs.

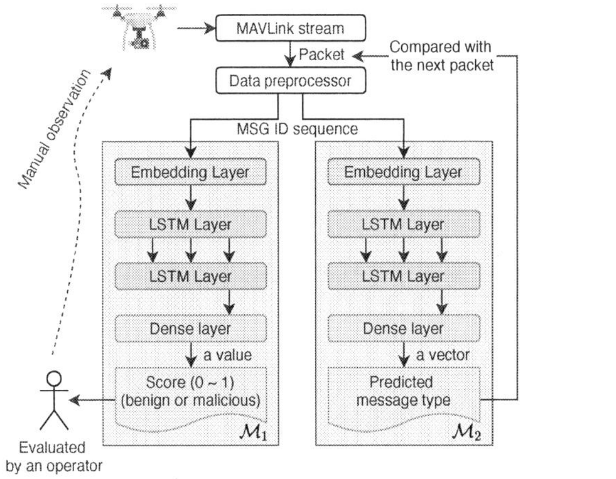

Fig. 4. MUVIDS scheme representing two models $\mathcal{M}_1$ and $\mathcal{M}_2$, and the model evaluation approaches

To respond to various situations, we design two types of detection models. The first model can be chosen when the IDS can use both an attack-free dataset and an intrusion dataset in a training phase. For training the model, we design the first model to solve the binary classification problem that judges whether the remote UAV is under attack at a specific time or not. Broadly speaking, the more intrusive cases the train set contains, the more accurate estimates the deep learning model can infer. On the contrary, if the IDS has not been faced an attack yet or is not aware of attack models, the first model should work for nothing. Such a case is a common problem in the area of intrusion detection studies. To this end, we design a second model that can be trained with only an attack-free dataset. Fig. 4 shows the proposed intrusion detection scheme, which is composed of the data preprocessing step and the classification/prediction step as follows:

Data preprocessing. The data preprocessor receives inbound MAVLink messages stream at the GCS and outputs a $w \times 4$ size of an array into the deep learning model, where w is the window size, and the value 4 means the size of the integer. At the beginning of the procedure, w-sized queue is initialized. On the arrival of every MAVLink message, the preprocessor cast the three bytes of value in the *MSG ID* field to the four bytes Int32 type, then puts the value in the queue. If the queue is not full after queueing, then wait for the next message. Otherwise, if the queue is full, the preprocessor yields the queue's entire values, then dequeues the oldest value. The procedure continues until the input stream is closed.

Intrusion detection model $\mathcal{M}_1$. The $\mathcal{M}_1$ is designed to solve a binary classification problem of whether a UAV generates the given subsequence under attack-free or under attack. To this end, a supervised intrusion detection model is built using a deep neural network. Specifically, the model is composed of an embedding layer, followed by two LSTM layers and a single dense layer. The embedding layer is used to convert an integer array (i.e., a subsequence of MAVLink *MSG IDs*) into a fixed-size vector for the LSTM layers. Two LSTM layers then extract features from given sequential data. As depicted in Fig. 4, the first LSTM layer returns a full sequence, whereas the second LSTM layer returns only the last output. The dense layer returns the detection result for each subsequence in a single floating point value of between 0 to 1 activated by a sigmoid function. To train the model, the operator should prepare benign and intrusive MAVLink stream and labels describing the situation (i.e., benign or under attack) of the given stream. The stochastic gradient descent algorithm is used to optimize the weights and biases of the model.

Message prediction model $\mathcal{M}_2$. In case of lack of label information, we further implement a predictive model that calculates the most promising value of the next *MSG ID*, instead of binary status, with a given subsequence of previous *MSG IDs*. Basically, the model shares the architecture of $\mathcal{M}_1$ that we discussed above, except the dense layer. The dense layer in $\mathcal{M}_2$ returns a vector representing possibilities of appearing MAVLink *MSG ID*. The Adam optimizer algorithm is used for the optimization of the model. In the training phase, only a "benign" MAVLink stream is required to allow the model to learn the next *MSG ID*. We expect that the trained $\mathcal{M}_2$ shows the poor prediction result when the input comes from an UAV under attack.

While incoming MAVLink messages contain operation information such as attitude and location of a vehicle, we design MUVIDS not to use them because using such data consumes much effort from a UAV operator for feature engineering, parameter tuning, by a specific vehicle model.

IV. Experiment Result

This section provides our packet generation environment, hyper-parameters for the proposed model, and the performance evaluation result. Our proposed method is tested by three common evaluation metrics: Precision, Recall, and F1-score.

Experiment environment. We deploy a network topology created with three virtual machine instances (i.e., GCS, SITL/HITL UAV simulator, an attacker) in a VMware ESXi hypervisor. Both SITL and HITL simulators are specially designed to replicates a real-world drone, including MAVLink 2.0 communication system. The only difference is that an autopilot system hardware (Pixhawk 4 in our experiment) operates actuators and executes MAVLink commands, whereas only a software-based autopilot system operates the SITL simulator. We use QGroundControl as the GCS to communicate with the UAV. Also, we implement three attack models (described in §II-C) using a Python library, pymavlink, that floods MAVLink messages to the UAV simulators. We implement $\mathcal{M}_1$ and $\mathcal{M}_2$ using Keras on a GeForce RTX 2080 installed PC. We set $w = 128$, the input/output dimension of embedding layer to 512/32, the units of each LSTM layer to 128, and the dropout ratio to 0.3. We set the learning rate to 10^{-3} and 10^{-4} for $\mathcal{M}_1$ and $\mathcal{M}_2$, respectively.

TABLE I. PERFORMANCE EVALUATION USING INTRUSION DATASET

Simulator	Attack type	Epochs	Precision	Recall	F1-score
SITL	Heartbeat flooding	93	0.98	0.97	0.98
	Ping flooding	1	1.00	1.00	1.00
	Request flooding	1	1.00	1.00	1.00
HITL	Heartbeat flooding	2	1.00	1.00	1.00
	Ping flooding	1	1.00	1.00	1.00
	Request flooding	1	1.00	1.00	1.00

Dataset. At the GCS, we collect four separated packet captures in the following situations: (1) attack-free, (2) heartbeat flooding, (3) ping flooding, and (4) request flooding. Consequently, we have eight datasets in total because we have two UAV simulators. The GCS and the UAV use UDP for MAVLink communication. We then generate a set of *MSG ID* subsequences using our data preprocessor. Note that each packet capture contains packets generated by an UAV and does not contain any packets generated by the attacker.

$\mathcal{M}_1$ evaluation. To train $\mathcal{M}_1$, we label the attack-free set to 0 and another set of each attack to 1, concatenate them, shuffle them, and split them into 80% of the train set and 20% of the validation set. The result of a performance evaluation using the validation set is given in Table I. The epochs column specifies when the model shows its best intrusion detection performance for the validation set. The experiment result shows that $\mathcal{M}_1$ provides satisfactory intrusion detection result. Interestingly, ping flooding and request flooding are completely identified by the proposed method. The subsequence is mostly dominated by response messages triggered as many as attacker requests, whereas such responses rarely appear in attack-free states. The heartbeat flooding is hard to be identified because it does not trigger any out-of-context messages from the target UAV to the GCS. Still, we confirm that $\mathcal{M}_1$ can accurately detect the heartbeat flooding after being trained with one more epoch. Note that the SITL is more robust to flooding with respect to computational power; a server CPU operates the autopilot firmware instead of a low-power embedded device. We find that some cases of heartbeat flooding are ambiguous to be identified in the SITL simulator, even after over 90 epochs of training. We achieve the best F1-score of 0.98 at 93 epochs.

$\mathcal{M}_2$ evaluation. We use the attack-free set to train $\mathcal{M}_2$. We randomly choose 20% of the attack-free dataset as the validation set to measure the prediction ability of trained $\mathcal{M}_2$. Table II provides the prediction evaluation of $\mathcal{M}_2$. For the reader's understanding, we use a descriptive name of the type instead of the *MSG ID* value. The empty count means no such message type found in the corresponding simulation environment. In summary, we achieve a F1-score of 0.96 in both simulators, which means that the $\mathcal{M}_2$ almost completely predicts which message will arrive at the GCS next time based on their given context MAVLink messages. However, it turns out that the $\mathcal{M}_2$ does not predict all message types well due to the nature of the packet generation strategy running on a UAV autopilot system. Specifically, we find that sporadic messages and event-driven messages were not correctly predicted by $\mathcal{M}_2$, while $\mathcal{M}_2$ predicts high-frequent low-jitter *MSG IDs*, e.g., attitude, location. Indeed this can be treated as a drawback of the proposed method since our model is not designed to

TABLE II. F1-SCORE FOR PREDICTION EVALUATION

MAVLink message type (MSG ID)	SITL		HITL	
	F1-score	Count	F1-score	Count
HEARTBEAT	0.96	126	0.76	111
SYS_STATUS	0.95	126	1.00	111
SYSTEM_TIME	–	–	0.96	110
PING	0.00	12	0.70	111
GPS_RAW_INT	0.97	126	0.90	2130
SCALED_IMU	–	–	0.97	2769
ATTITUDE	0.97	6302	1.00	5538
ATTITUDE_QUATERNION	0.99	6302	0.98	5538
LOCAL_POSITION_NED	0.98	6302	0.92	3323
GLOBAL_POSITION_INT	0.03	727	0.99	1108
SERVO_OUTPUT_RAW	0.99	6302	1.00	2215
MISSION_CURRENT	–	–	0.78	1047
VFR_HUD	0.93	504	0.94	2215
ATTITUDE_TARGET	0.98	6302	–	–
POSITION_TARGET_LOCAL_NED	0.99	6302	–	–
POSITION_TARGET_GLOBAL_INT	–	–	1.00	1108
HIGHRES_IMU	–	–	0.97	5538
TIMESYNC	–	–	1.00	1108
ACTUATOR_CONTROL_TARGET	–	–	0.99	3323
ALTITUDE	1.00	126	1.00	1107
BATTERY_STATUS	0.36	63	0.00	55
ESTIMATOR_STATUS	1.00	63	1.00	554
VIBRATION	1.00	12	1.00	554
HOME_POSITION	0.00	63	0.00	55
EXTENDED_SYS_STATE	0.75	126	0.78	221
UTM_GLOBAL_POSITION	0.06	63	–	–
F1-score, total sample count	0.96	39949	0.96	39949

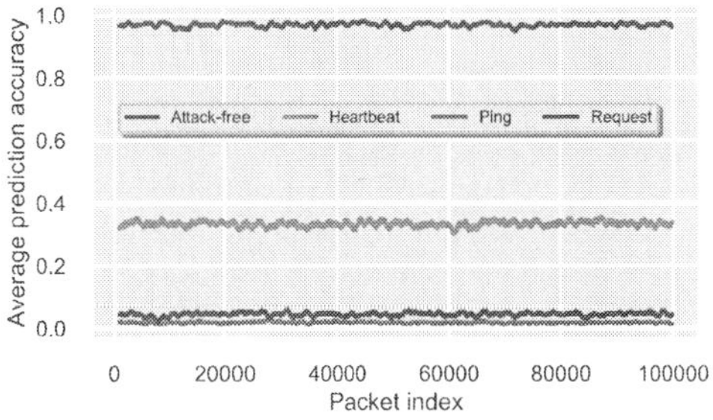

(a) Result from the SITL UAV simulator

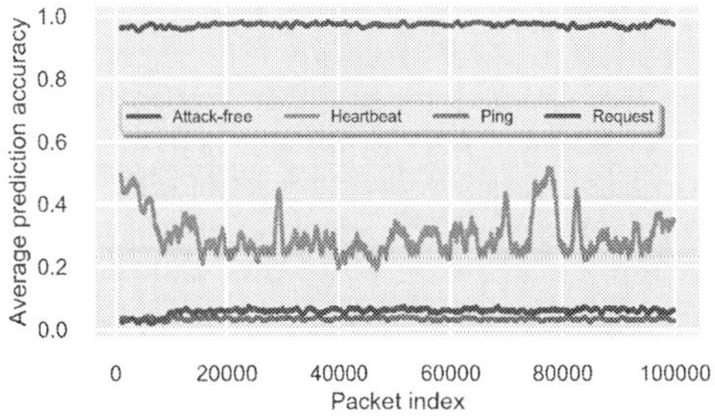

(b) Result from the HITL UAV simulator

Fig. 5. Average accuracy of MAVLink *MSG ID* prediction over a continuous series of MAVLink traffic

understand a complete operational context of UAV.

Next, we demonstrate detecting false MAVLink injection attacks using pre-trained $\mathcal{M}_2$ in SITL/HITL simulators. For the experiment, datasets are fed to the $\mathcal{M}_2$ in order of time. As discussed above, the prediction accuracy of the attack-free dataset is expected to be very high in an obvious manner. Meanwhile, the accuracy should be low when a victim UAV is under attack because the attack causes a concept drift of message sequences. We can identify the intrusion by applying a threshold to the average prediction accuracy.

In Fig. 5, we plot the 1000-messages moving average of accuracy over a series of MAVLink messages. We can see the significant differences between the attack-free dataset and the others. It proves the usefulness of $\mathcal{M}_2$ trained with only attack-free dataset. The gap between the heartbeat dataset and the attack-free dataset is interesting since the two datasets consist of a set of the same *MSG IDs*. The same applies to the heartbeat dataset of the HITL simulator; however, it fluctuates from time to time. It implies that our Pixhawk 4 hardware and the NuttX OS therein are lagging due to the attack. Notably, the fluctuation is not extreme. Thus, we can identify the three attacks by setting a detection threshold of 0.9 in a heuristic manner.

V. Related Work

In the past few years, UAV security has been one of the key research topics in the security field. The directions of research are heading two purposes: vulnerability analysis and intrusion detection.

Vulnerability analysis. The vulnerability analysis research analyzes the UAV security characteristics and designs potential possible attacks. Kwon *et al.* [8] investigated network vulnerabilities using the MAVLink protocol. As the MAVLink communication protocol uses no message encryption, the researchers insisted ICMP flooding attacks are possible. Besides, packet injection attacks are possible, considering the protocol as a Waypoint protocol. A study conducted by Rani *et al.* [12] examined the Wi-Fi protocol's vulnerabilities for analyzing UAV's security. Using one of the known WEP vulnerabilities, they demonstrated an attack that forces UAVs to be unauthenticated. Rodday *et al.* [13] offered a packet broadcasting attack adding to the research of Rani and others. The attack collected initial vector values by sending random packets to targets and exploited a WEP vulnerability using the vectors.

Rule-based approach. Another field of study focused on attack detection beyond vulnerability analysis. There are two approaches to detect attacks. First, we introduce researches that detect attacks by setting rules or in a heuristic manner. Sedjelmaci *et al.* [15] designed a rule-based IDS to detect network attacks, such as GPS spoofing, jamming, and false information injection. The researchers proposed algorithms to track network traffic and detect attacks by abnormal traffic changes. The research by Birbaum *et al.* [2] estimated parameters to detect attacks on UAV. Their proposed method predicted the parameters for UAV's operational conditions, such as system parameters and control parameters, and it identified attacks through differences from confidence intervals implying no attacks. They conducted the experiments in a simulated environment using the MAVLink protocol and extracted sensors and actuators data. Muniraj *et al.* [10] investigated which sensors were susceptible to damage by which attacks and defined the information as an attack signature. With safe sensors getting no damage from any attack, the detection system disclosed attacks based on other sensors' status.

Machine learning approach. Some other works proposed machine learning- or deep learning-based approaches to detect intrusion. Sedjelmaci [14] proposed an IDS containing a security game framework using the Bayesian game model. The framework monitored the network to catch abnormalities and ejected attackers in the case of attacks. Lukas *et al.* [9] researched on attack detection model using deep learning. Their research focused on network attacks such as a denial of service, command injection, and malicious code injection, and the proposed model combined multilayer perceptron (MLP) and LSTM. Arthur [1] designed a lightweight IDS that could be applied for UAVs using sensor data. With 27 kinds of sensor data collected in the simulated environment, the IDS was composed of self-taught learning and a multi-class support vector machine (SVM). Additional research that used the SVM model was a state estimation analysis done by Panice *et al.* [11]. The research was directed to estimate the UAVs' state, and it focused on GPS spoofing with other various attacks. Shoufan [16] studied to establish the operators' signature. The research used UAV's sensor data to build operators' behavior patterns and classify pre-defined operators based on their signatures. The classification experiment utilized a random forest classifier, and it demonstrated the significant performance of the identification. Kim *et al.* [6] used the MLP model to detect attacks and correlate them with a generative adversarial network to examine its effects. They composed a SITL simulator using MAVLink protocol and extracted sensor data for the experiment.

In other domains, several researchers decided to use sensor and actuator data from UAV for security purposes. The data gives us more intuitive views of the current state. Despite the advantage, sensors are too sensitive to the drone's operation environment, and actuators can be too many to consider in the lightweight system. For these reasons, we used the data extracted from the MAVLink protocol. It covers both sensor/actuator data and network communication. The protocol is specialized to the UAV and other vehicles to represent the UAV operation system.

VI. Conclusion

This paper proposes a novel IDS, MUVIDS, to detect false MAVLink injection attacks toward unmanned vehicles. To the best of our knowledge, this study is the first intrusion detection method analyzing MAVLink communication. Based on the experiment result, MUVIDS gives the following benefits to unmanned vehicle operators. First, the experiment result shows that MUVIDS can detect the three types of false MAVLink injection attacks effectively, even without label information. Second, MUVIDS works for various MAVLink-enabled vehicles. We confirm that by using both SITL and HITL UAV simulators. Third, MUVIDS does not require any vehicle- and environment-specific parameters. Fourth, the operator can implement MUVIDS at the GCS. Consequently, the operator does not have to risk failure while adding components to the vehicle directly.

The limitation of our work is that only a few flooding attacks are considered to validate MUVIDS. It is due to the lack of prior systematic study of attacks on MAVLink-enabled vehicles. At this moment, only three types of false MAVLink injection attacks in which the actual impact (e.g., resource consumption and vehicle crash) occurs in our simulators were used in the study. In future work, we will extend this work with various attacks. Also, we will use MAVLink payloads that contain sensor/actuator/GPS information to enhance intrusion detection performance on real driving/flying vehicles.

Acknowledgment

This work was supported by Institute for Information & Communications Technology Planning & Evaluation (IITP) grant funded by the Korea government (MSIT) (No. 2020-0-00374, Development of Security Primitives for Unmanned Vehicles).

References

[1] M. P. Arthur, "Detecting signal spoofing and jamming attacks in UAV networks using a lightweight IDS," in *Proceedings of Computer, Information and Telecommunication Systems (CITS)*, 2019.

[2] Z. Birnbaum, A. Dolgikh, V. Skormin, E. O'Brien, D. Muller, and C. Stracquodaine, "Unmanned aerial vehicle security using recursive parameter estimation," *Journal of Intelligent & Robotic Systems*, vol. 84, no. 1, pp. 107–120, 2016.

[3] V. Chamola, V. Hassija, V. Gupta, and M. Guizani, "A comprehensive review of the COVID-19 pandemic and the role of IoT, drones, AI, blockchain, and 5G in managing its impact," *IEEE Access*, vol. 8, pp. 90 225–90 265, 2020.

[4] G. Choudhary, V. Sharma, I. You, K. Yim, I.-R. Chen, and J.-H. Cho, "Intrusion detection systems for networked unmanned aerial vehicles: A survey," in *Proceedings of International Wireless Communications & Mobile Computing Conference (IWCMC)*. IEEE, 2018, pp. 560–565.

[5] K. Domin, "Security analysis of the drone communication protocol: Fuzzing the MAVLink protocol," Master's thesis, KU Leuven, 2016.

[6] K. H. Kim, S. Nalluri, A. Kashinath, Y. Wang, S. Mohan, M. Pajic, and B. Li, "Security analysis against spoofing attacks for distributed UAVs," in *Proceedings of Decentralized IoT Systems and Security (DISS)*, 2020.

[7] A. Koubaa, A. Allouch, M. Alajlan, Y. Javed, A. Belghith, and M. Khalgui, "Micro Air Vehicle Link (MAVlink) in a Nutshell: A Survey," *IEEE Access*, vol. 7, pp. 87 658–87 680, 2019.

[8] Y.-M. Kwon, J. Yu, B.-M. Cho, Y. Eun, and K.-J. Park, "Empirical analysis of MAVLink protocol vulnerability for attacking unmanned aerial vehicles," *IEEE Access*, vol. 6, pp. 43 203–43 212, 2018.

[9] G. Loukas, T. Vuong, R. Heartfield, G. Sakellari, Y. Yoon, and D. Gan, "Cloud-based cyber-physical intrusion detection for vehicles using deep learning," *IEEE Access*, vol. 6, pp. 3491–3508, 2017.

[10] D. Muniraj and M. Farhood, "A framework for detection of sensor attacks on small unmanned aircraft systems," in *Proceedings of International Conference on Unmanned Aircraft Systems (ICUAS)*, 2017.

[11] G. Panice, S. Luongo, G. Gigante, D. Pascarella, C. Di Benedetto, A. Vozella, and A. Pescapè, "A svm-based detection approach for GPS spoofing attacks to UAV," in *Proceedings of International Conference on Automation and Computing (ICAC)*, 2017.

[12] C. Rani, H. Modares, R. Sriram, D. Mikulski, and F. L. Lewis, "Security of unmanned aerial vehicle systems against cyber-physical attacks," *The Journal of Defense Modeling and Simulation*, vol. 13, no. 3, pp. 331–342, 2016.

[13] N. M. Rodday, R. d. O. Schmidt, and A. Pras, "Exploring security vulnerabilities of unmanned aerial vehicles," in *Proceedings of Network Operations and Management Symposium*, 2016, pp. 993–994.

[14] H. Sedjelmaci, S. M. Senouci, and N. Ansari, "Intrusion detection and ejection framework against lethal attacks in UAV-aided networks: A bayesian game-theoretic methodology," *IEEE Transactions on Intelligent Transportation Systems*, vol. 18, no. 5, pp. 1143–1153, 2016.

[15] ——, "A hierarchical detection and response system to enhance security against lethal cyber-attacks in UAV networks," *IEEE Transactions on Systems, Man, and Cybernetics: Systems*, vol. 48, no. 9, pp. 1594–1606, 2017.

[16] A. Shoufan, "Continuous authentication of UAV flight command data using behaviometrics," in *Proceedings of Very Large Scale Integration (VLSI-SoC)*, 2017, pp. 1–6.

Object Removal Attacks on LiDAR-based 3D Object Detectors

Zhongyuan Hau§, Kenneth T. Co§, Soteris Demetriou, Emil C. Lupu
Imperial College London
{zy.hau17, k.co, s.demetriou, e.c.lupu}@imperial.ac.uk

Abstract—**LiDARs play a critical role in Autonomous Vehicles' (AVs) perception and their safe operations. Recent works have demonstrated that it is possible to spoof LiDAR return signals to elicit fake objects. In this work we demonstrate how the same physical capabilities can be used to mount a new, even more dangerous class of attacks, namely *Object Removal Attacks* (ORAs). ORAs aim to force 3D object detectors to fail. We leverage the default setting of LiDARs that record a single return signal per direction to perturb point clouds in the region of interest (RoI) of 3D objects. By injecting illegitimate points behind the target object, we effectively shift points away from the target objects' RoIs. Our initial results using a simple random point selection strategy show that the attack is effective in degrading the performance of commonly used 3D object detection models.**

I. Introduction

We are currently undergoing a revolution in transportation and mobility. New generations of vehicles are increasingly equipped with high-precision depth sensors to better perceive their environment and offer unprecedented levels of driver assistance and driving autonomy. Such vehicles commonly rely on LiDAR sensors, which collect high definition depth measurements stored in 3D point clouds. Reliably detecting objects from such point clouds is vital to the safety of the autonomous vehicle, its users and passengers.

LiDAR spoofing attacks. Recent studies have shown that it is possible to attack LiDAR-based perception systems by spoofing LiDAR return signals [6], [1], [10], [5]. Petit *et al.* first demonstrated this with physical attacks that can inject up to 10 fake 3D points in a point cloud. Cao *et al.* and Sun *et al.* progressively improved on the physical capabilities of the LiDAR spoofing adversary showing that one could reliably inject up to 60 and 200 fake points respectively. More importantly, Cao *et al.* developed a white-box model-level digitally simulated LiDAR spoofing attack that can introduce front-near fake measurements in a scene, which are then detected as objects by an end-to-end autonomous vehicle (AV) system. Sun *et al.* then demonstrated both white-box and black-box attacks that spoof vehicles in front-near locations by exploiting patterns of occluded and distant vehicles. Xiang *et al.* [13] examined the vulnerability of point-cloud based object detectors and proposed white-box approaches for point shifting and point injection to craft adversarial point-clouds. Zhao *et al.* [14] proposed a class of point cloud perturbation attacks that minimizes the number of points perturbed to flip the results of point-cloud based object detectors. They use gradient-based and genetic algorithm approaches to generate adversarial point clouds with perturbations of up to 150 points to subvert object detection with a 95% success rate.

Object hiding. Tu *et al.* [12] proposed both white-box and black-box methods to generate adversarial objects that when placed above a target vehicle, would evade point-cloud based object detectors with a success rate of 80%. For the white-box attack, the adversarial object is generated using a gradient-based approach to minimize the confidence score of the target object (vehicle). A black-box attack was also demonstrated, where the adversarial objects are chosen using a genetic algorithm approach to iterate and improve adversarial object meshes. Object-hiding attacks are considered more dangerous than spoofing objects. Whilst detecting a spoofed object can bring the ego-vehicle to a full stop, failing to detect an object has a higher chance of leading to a fatal collision.

Our work. We leverage the demonstrated state of the art capabilities of the physical LiDAR spoofing adversary [6], [10], [1] to design a new model-level *object removal attack* (ORA) that aims to hide objects from 3D object detectors. Compared to prior work with spoofed objects [6], [10], [1] ORAs have a different goal: the adversary aims not to introduce a ghost object but force mis-detection of a genuine object which can have more severe consequences. Moreover, in contrast with related work on 3D object hiding [12], we introduce a new technique that does not aim to introduce patterns on top of genuine objects, but rather to spoof points within a genuine object's bounding box such that they appear away from their original position and cause object mis-detection. ORAs are stealthier since they do not require placing adversarial objects on the target, are easier to mount and have high success rates. We conduct digital ORA attacks, emulating the physics of LiDAR operation. Their effectiveness is evaluated against popular 3D object detectors (PointRCNN [8] and Point-GNN [9]).

We found that an adversary with the ability to inject $\leq$ 200 points can reduce their *recall* to less than 25% for *Pedestrian* and *Cyclist* object classes on both models with a *random* point selection strategy. Our work demonstrates the feasibility of ORAs and we hope to inspire future work on more sophisticated ORA strategies that can lead to a better understanding of the LiDAR spoofing adversary model.

§Equal contribution

Workshop on Automotive and Autonomous Vehicle Security (AutoSec) 2021
25 February 2021, Virtual

https://dx.doi.org/10.14722/autosec.2021.23016
www.ndss-symposium.org

TABLE I. AVERAGE PRECISION (AP) OF 3D OBJECT DETECTION FOR DIFFERENT CLASSES UNDER THE ORA RANDOM ATTACK.

Model	Attack Budget	Car AP (IoU = 0.7)			Pedestrian AP (IoU = 0.5)			Cyclist AP (IoU = 0.5)		
		Easy	Moderate	Hard	Easy	Moderate	Hard	Easy	Moderate	Hard
PointRCNN [8]	0 (Clean)	88.86	78.61	77.75	62.87	54.88	48.95	73.08	56.33	52.36
	10	79.30	65.09	58.11	50.69	42.96	38.15	61.03	39.04	35.58
	20	78.85	59.57	51.00	48.06	40.38	35.42	54.66	31.67	30.12
	40	77.02	54.36	46.13	43.66	35.84	31.96	41.81	24.36	22.96
	60	72.97	48.01	40.42	38.70	31.97	27.82	33.54	19.14	18.64
	100	64.69	40.97	33.47	35.99	28.46	23.20	24.48	15.75	15.77
	150	55.74	34.05	28.33	29.04	22.79	19.93	17.01	11.95	11.33
	200	47.32	31.05	25.00	25.62	19.02	16.92	13.07	9.43	9.42
Point-GNN [9]	0 (Clean)	89.89	88.82	87.75	73.74	70.34	63.57	85.69	64.44	62.25
	10	89.62	78.33	69.31	73.74	70.25	63.49	85.69	64.17	62.01
	20	89.34	71.38	62.06	71.89	64.01	61.19	76.79	52.78	48.32
	40	86.40	62.50	53.08	63.18	55.57	48.28	57.00	36.70	34.85
	60	80.26	53.71	44.60	56.27	48.10	44.42	43.45	26.98	26.04
	100	70.47	43.89	35.36	47.15	39.24	32.50	25.63	16.06	15.86
	150	57.15	34.61	29.17	39.23	31.65	27.72	10.86	8.14	7.40
	200	45.58	28.01	22.01	31.99	26.64	23.81	4.76	3.66	3.85

II. OBJECT REMOVAL ATTACK

We introduce a new class of attacks, namely object removal attacks (ORAs). ORAs are black-box, model-level attacks that can be launched by a physical LiDAR spoofing adversary. The goal of ORAs is to displace the original depth measurements within a genuine object's bounding box to appear outside that bounding box such that the target object is not detected by 3D object detectors. Below we elaborate on our threat model and a preliminary strategy to demonstrate the feasibility of ORAs.

A. Threat Model

Physical Capabilities. We assume an adversary $\mathcal{A}$, who can spoof the LiDAR return signals of a target AV [1], [6], [10], [11]. The adversary can achieve this by deploying a device within the line of sight of a victim vehicle's LiDAR sensor. The adversarial device can capture LiDAR signals, alter them and emit them toward the victim sensor with a controlled delay. By controlling the return signal, $\mathcal{A}$ can manipulate the resulting 3D measurements reported in a 3D point cloud by the victim sensor. We assume $\mathcal{A}$ has state of the art sensor spoofing capabilities and can inject ≤ 200 points in a 3D scene within a horizontal angle of $10°$ [11]. We also assume that $\mathcal{A}$ can spoof resulting measurements to appear further away from the target vehicle than they actually are [10].

Digital Capabilities. Since $\mathcal{A}$ is in physical proximity, we assume it can also sense the environment and detect objects within the vicinity of the target vehicle. Using basic transformations, $\mathcal{A}$ can change the coordinate system of a 3D scene from the reference point of $\mathcal{A}$ to that of the target vehicle.

B. Object Removal Attack (ORA) Rationale

LiDAR spoofing has been previously demonstrated [1], [10], [11]. These attacks exploit the fact that LiDARs deployed in AVs operate under the Strongest Return Mode setting, where only a single measurement can be recorded per ray direction. Therefore, the injection of a spoofed point results in the original corresponding point in the direction of the ray (from the LiDAR to the spoofed point) to be displaced. We also leverage this phenomenon, but to achieve a different goal. Instead of aiming to introducing objects, we highlight a new class of attacks, namely *Object Removal Attacks (ORAs)* that aim to remove objects. Our proof of concept hides an object from AV perception by displacing points from a target object's point cloud with LiDAR point injection behind that object.

Algorithm 1 Obtaining Attack Trace (ORA-Random)

Input: list(obj_pts_coords) ▷ Target Object's Point Cloud
$candidate\_pts\_coords$ =[]
$attack\_trace\_pts\_coords$ = []
for each `pt` **in** obj_pts_coords **do**
  if `pt` **within** `spoofing_horizontal_angle` **then**
    $candidate\_pts\_coords \leftarrow$ `pt`
  end if
end for
$attack\_pts \leftarrow$ random($candidate\_pts\_coords$, $\mathcal{A}_{budget}$)
$attack\_trace\_pts\_coords \leftarrow$ (pts in obj_pts_coords $\wedge$ not in $attack\_pts$)
for each `pt` **in** $attack\_pt$ **do**
  $attack\_pt\_coords \leftarrow$ dist_increment_along_ray(`pt`)
  $attack\_trace\_pts\_coords$.append($attack\_pt\_coords$)
end for
return $attack\_trace\_pts\_coords$

C. ORA Operating Mechanism

An ORA exploits the LiDAR's default mode for recording the measurements of return signals–where a single return signal per ray direction is recorded. This enables an adversary to perform point injections that can remove points from a target object's original point-cloud by spoofing another signal at a different location in the same direction of the rays that are incident on an object. The resulting perturbed point-cloud would cause point-cloud based object detectors to miss detecting the target object, and thus evading object detection.

The process of ORA first starts with the adversary identifying the target object's location and the region of interest (RoI) where points are to be selected from and removed. Here, we assume that the adversary has knowledge of the 3D scene and is able to obtain bounding boxes of target objects and the coordinates of the points in the bounding boxes (i.e. object points). This can be achieved by finding a translation matrix that changes the coordinates system from the reference point of the attacker to the ego-vehicle [3]. Next the adversary obtains a set of points from the object points that are within its spoofing horizontal angle (i.e. candidate points); one way of achieving

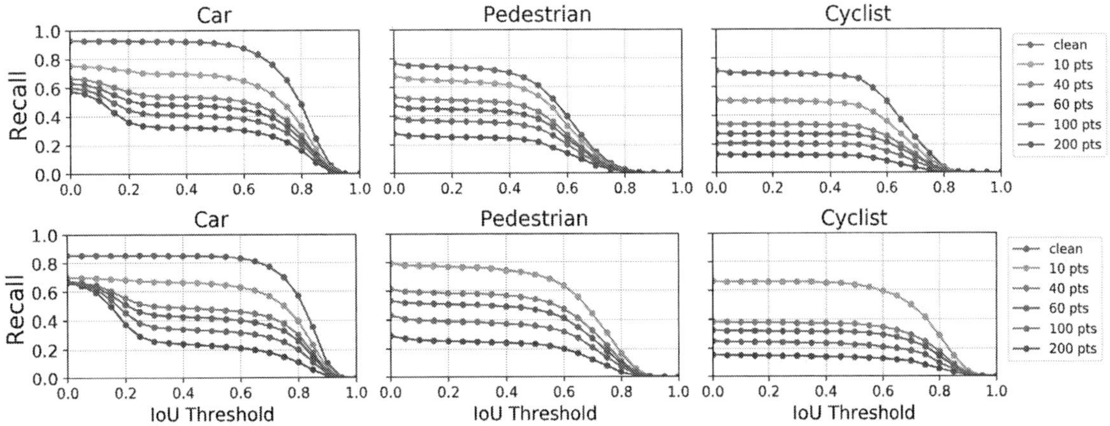

Fig. 1. Recall-IoU curves for (top) PointRCNN and (bottom) Point-GNN under the ORA random attack with different IoU thresholds.

this is to segment the object bounding box by the spoofing angle and only use the points within the segment. In our case, we used the left-most coordinates of the bounding box as an anchor point to calculate the points that are within the horizontal spoofing angle. Lastly from the subset of candidate points within the spoofing angle, the adversary picks points within its budget to perform point injection, spoofing points at a random distance behind the original points' location (in the direction of the ray). ORA is modular and can be used with various point selection strategies. We demonstrate ORA with a random point selection (*ORA-Random*) from the candidate points. *ORA-Random* is detailed in Algo. 1.

III. Experiments & Results

Models & Datasets. The proposed attack was conducted on the validation set (3769 out of 7481 scenes) of the KITTI dataset [4]. Objects in these scenes are subjected to *ORA-Random* and the resulting perturbed point clouds of the scenes are subsequently passed to popular 3D object detectors to evaluate the performance of the attack. We perform the attacks on three object types, *Cars*, *Pedestrians* and *Cyclists* as these objects are commonly encountered in AV scenarios. We perform our attack evaluations on widely-used models for 3D point cloud object detection that rely solely on LiDAR data, Point-GNN [9] and PointRCNN [8]. The two models differ in how feature extraction is performed for the object detection task. Point-GNN uses a graph neural network that encodes the point-cloud directly as a graph representation for object detection. Whereas, PointRCNN uses a multi-layer perceptron learning approach on point sets to obtain point feature vectors of the point cloud(PointNet++ [7]), which are then further processed for object detection.

Performance Metrics. For all models and scenarios, we measure the 3D AP and Recall-IOU curves of the models under attack. The 3D AP (average precision) captures the ratio of true positive predictions over all positive predictions and is the primary measure for overall performance of 3D object detectors. The Recall-IOU curve measures the recall of the detector for various IOU thresholds. The goal of the attacker would be to hide real objects from the model, so the measurement of recall is relevant in our case since it captures the ability of the detector to **not miss** objects. Therefore, $\mathcal{A}$'s goal would be to lower recall scores for target detectors.

Evaluation Scenarios. We consider two scenarios for evaluating the models' performance when under attack. The first is on the performance of the attack applied on the entire KITTI validation dataset. The second evaluation focuses on the impact of ORAs on the detection of *front-near* objects. For both scenarios, we use *ORA-Random* to perturb the point cloud of each individual type of target object found in the scenes with various point-perturbation budgets (10, 20, 40, 60, 100, 150, 200 points) that are within $\mathcal{A}$'s capabilities.

A. Attack Performance Evaluation

Table I shows the AP of the 2 models for clean (no point perturbation) and for the various attack budgets used to perturb the 3 object types. The evaluation criteria follows that of the KITTI 3D object detection benchmark (where the detection difficulty levels are determined by the size and occlusion of object). We observed that the AP decreases for increasing $\mathcal{A}_{budget}$. The effect of *ORA-Random* is most significant for *Cyclist* objects and then followed by *Pedestrian* and then *Car* objects. One reason could be that Cyclists are not as common in the dataset compared to the other two classes, resulting in poorer performance. *Pedestrian* and *Cyclist* objects are smaller objects and have significantly fewer points in their point clouds.

From Fig. 1, we observed that when increasing the point budget, the recall falls. For Cars at IoU $\geq$ 0.7 and for *Pedestrians* and *Cyclists* at IoU $\geq$ 0.5, we observe a significant decline in recall for both clean and attack, with recall falling below 0.5 for most of the attacks, with the exception of the 10-point attack on Point-GNN for pedestrian and cyclist. Our analysis on the KITTI validation set shows that the *ORA-Random attack is very effective in degrading the object detector's performance and hiding a target object.*

B. Attacking Front-Near Objects

We further investigate whether ORAs can mask front-near objects (objects in close proximity to the ego-vehicle), where accurate detection is critical to the safe operation of the autonomous vehicle. Our results are summarized in Fig. 2. We observe a general trend where objects further away from the

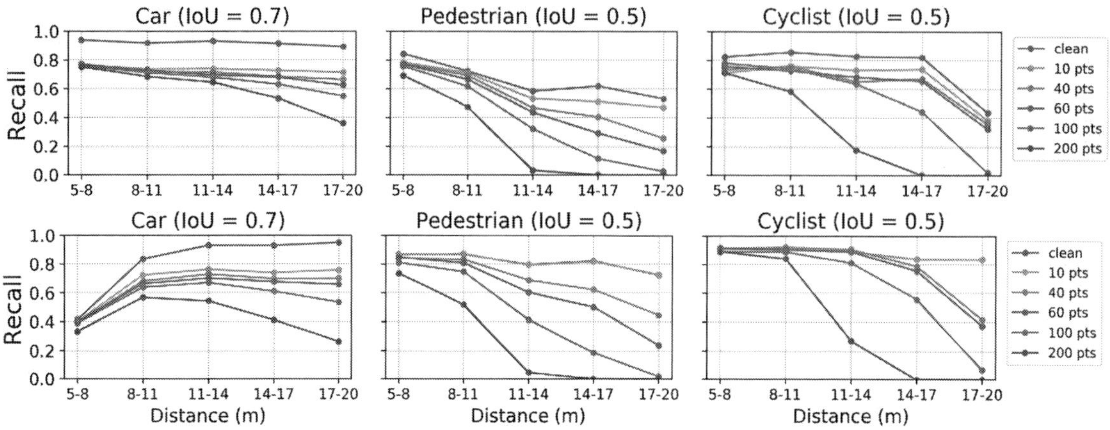

Fig. 2. Recall metrics by distance (in metres away from the LiDAR) for different IoU configurations of (top) PointRCNN and (bottom) Point-GNN.

LiDAR have lower recall but with the effects being visible even for objects $\leq 11m$. The extent of the drop in recall (w.r.t clean) is also correlated to the increase in $\mathcal{A}$'s budget. Noticeably for smaller objects such as *Pedestrian* and *Cyclist*, we observe a higher decrease in recall when increasing $\mathcal{A}_{budget}$ and distance. This is due to the smaller objects' inherent low number of points and its decreasing point density as distance increases. This provides an opportunity for the adversary to use its limited $\mathcal{A}_{budget}$ to perturb a larger proportion of points in the object's point cloud–increasing its success rate of evading detection.

C. Discussion & Implications

Although *ORA-Random* does not drastically damage the recall for front-near objects, it is still able to significantly lower recall and AP when considering the more general validation dataset. The detection of further away objects remains a critical function especially during the high-speed operation of vehicles. Thus being able to damage model recall in the general case with a random point selection strategy raises grave security concerns. Additionally, the random point selection can be improved upon with more optimized strategies that use methods such as genetic, evolutionary, or Bayesian algorithms [2], [12], [14] to create effective adversarial attacks within a point budget. Overall *ORA-Random* demonstrates that object removal attacks are a real concern which we plan to investigate in depth in future work.

IV. Conclusion

In this paper, we provide preliminary evidence that with a simple approach of shifting 3D points from a RoI, a LiDAR spoofing adversary is able to effectively perturb the point cloud of a target object to render it undetectable. We performed a sensitivity analysis and found that for smaller objects, the attacks are highly effective at a distance beyond 11m. This poses a safety concern as failure to detect such objects could have life-threatening consequences. In future work, we plan to implement optimization-based point selection ORA strategies, verify the feasibility of ORAs in the physical domain and study the effect of ORA at various distances and driving speeds on AV driving decisions with an AV simulator. As this new class of attack targets a single sensor modality, we are exploring defenses using multi-sensor fusion with RGB cameras.

References

[1] Yulong Cao, Chaowei Xiao, Benjamin Cyr, Yimeng Zhou, Won Park, Sara Rampazzi, Qi Alfred Chen, Kevin Fu, and Z Morley Mao. Adversarial sensor attack on lidar-based perception in autonomous driving. In *Proceedings of the 2019 ACM SIGSAC Conference on Computer and Communications Security*, pages 2267–2281, 2019.

[2] Kenneth T. Co, Luis Muñoz González, Sixte de Maupeou, and Emil C. Lupu. Procedural noise adversarial examples for black-box attacks on deep convolutional networks. In *ACM Conference on Computer and Communications Security*, CCS '19, pages 275–289, 2019.

[3] Sundaram Ganapathy. Decomposition of transformation matrices for robot vision. *Pattern Recognition Letters*, 2(6):401–412, 1984.

[4] Andreas Geiger, Philip Lenz, Christoph Stiller, and Raquel Urtasun. Vision meets robotics: The kitti dataset. *International Journal of Robotics Research (IJRR)*, 2013.

[5] Zhongyuan Hau, Soteris Demetriou, Luis Muñoz-González, and Emil C. Lupu. Shadow-catcher: Looking into shadows to detect ghost objects in autonomous vehicle 3d sensing. *arXiv preprint arXiv:2008.12008*, 2021.

[6] Jonathan Petit, Bas Stottelaar, Michael Feiri, and Frank Kargl. Remote attacks on automated vehicles sensors: Experiments on camera and lidar. *Black Hat Europe*, 11:2015, 2015.

[7] Charles Ruizhongtai Qi, Li Yi, Hao Su, and Leonidas J Guibas. Pointnet++: Deep hierarchical feature learning on point sets in a metric space. In *Advances in Neural Information Processing Systems*, pages 5099–5108, 2017.

[8] Shaoshuai Shi, Xiaogang Wang, and Hongsheng Li. Pointrcnn: 3d object proposal generation and detection from point cloud. In *IEEE Conference on Computer Vision and Pattern Recognition*, pages 770–779, 2019.

[9] Weijing Shi and Raj Rajkumar. Point-gnn: Graph neural network for 3d object detection in a point cloud. In *IEEE Conference on Computer Vision and Pattern Recognition*, pages 1711–1719, 2020.

[10] Hocheol Shin, Dohyun Kim, Yujin Kwon, and Yongdae Kim. Illusion and dazzle: Adversarial optical channel exploits against lidars for automotive applications. In *International Conference on Cryptographic Hardware and Embedded Systems*, pages 445–467. Springer, 2017.

[11] Jiachen Sun, Yulong Cao, Qi Alfred Chen, and Z. Morley Mao. Towards robust lidar-based perception in autonomous driving: General black-box adversarial sensor attack and countermeasures. In *29th USENIX Security Symposium (USENIX Security 20)*, pages 877–894. USENIX Association, August 2020.

[12] James Tu, Mengye Ren, Siva Manivasagam, Ming Liang, Bin Yang, Richard Du, Frank Cheng, and Raquel Urtasun. Physically realizable adversarial examples for lidar object detection. *arXiv preprint arXiv:2004.00543*, 2020.

[13] Chong Xiang, Charles R Qi, and Bo Li. Generating 3d adversarial point clouds. In *IEEE Conference on Computer Vision and Pattern Recognition*, pages 9136–9144, 2019.

[14] Yiren Zhao, Ilia Shumailov, Robert Mullins, and Ross Anderson. Nudge attacks on point-cloud dnns. *arXiv preprint arXiv:2011.11637*, 2020.

CANCloak: Deceiving Two ECUs with One Frame

Li Yue
Tsinghua University
yuel18@mails.tsinghua.edu.cn

Zheming Li
Tsinghua University
lizm20@mails.tsinghua.edu.cn

Tingting Yin
Tsinghua University
ytt18@mails.tsinghua.edu.cn

Chao Zhang✉
Tsinghua University
chaoz@tsinghua.edu.cn

Abstract— **Modern vehicles have many electronic control units (ECUs) connected to the Controller Area Network (CAN) bus, which have few security features in design and are vulnerable to cyber attacks. Researchers have proposed solutions like intrusion detection systems (IDS) to mitigate such threats. We presented a novel attack, CANCloak, which can deceive two ECUs with one CAN data frame, and therefore can bypass IDS detection or cause vehicle malfunction. In this attack, assuming a malicious transmitter is controlled by the adversary, one crafted CAN data frame can be transmitted to a target receiver, while other ECUs shall not receive that frame nor raise any error. We have setup a physical test environment and evaluated the effectiveness of this attack. Evaluation results showed that success rate of CANCloak reaches up to 99.7%, while the performance depends on the attack payload and sample point settings of victim receivers, independent from bus bit rate.**

I. Introduction

The number of electronic devices in vehicles keeps increasing over the past decade. A modern vehicle could have tens of ECUs as well as hundreds of sensors connected to the CAN bus, which are used by engine units, braking system, transmission system, and infotainment module etc. to improve both safety and comfort of driving. However, due to the lack of security features in design, vehicles are prone to cyber attacks. Several research groups have demonstrated successful attacks against modern vehicles [1]. For instance, attackers could exploit vulnerabilities in WiFi or Bluetooth modules to access vehicles remotely, and then exploit vulnerabilities in infotainment modules to compromise reachable ECUs that are connected to the CAN bus, and finally issue malicious commands through the compromised ECU to control other ECUs and therefore vehicles.

CAN bus is the de-facto standard used by all vehicle manufacturers to provide reliable communication between different in-vehicle ECUs. However, CAN protocol in design lacks modern security features, e.g., end-to-end encryption, message authentication or node authorization. It therefore opens the door to attackers, i.e., a malicious or compromised ECU that connects to the CAN bus could compromise the whole network and take control of a vehicle.

Researchers have proposed several mitigations to address such threats. The first type of solutions is message authentication, which relies on either symmetric keys shared among legitimate ECU nodes [2], or key establishment schemes derived from pre-shared keys [3], or cryptography support with special hardware [4]. These solutions are hard to deploy in practice, since they have to extend the standard CAN protocol and require collaboration from all ECU devices. Another type of solutions provided by researchers are intrusion detection systems (IDS), e.g., [5, 6], which in general attach a detector ECU to the CAN bus and listen all CAN messages to perform anomaly detection, signature or pattern matching. This type of solutions is attractive and easy to deploy in practice.

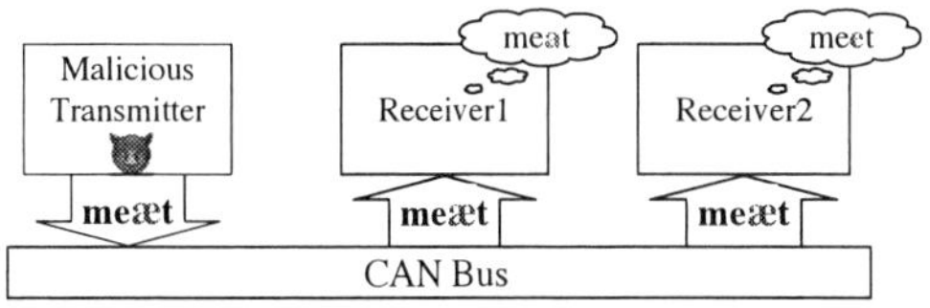

Fig. 1: CANCloak Attack: A malicious transmitter sends an ambitious waveform, different receivers read it differently.

In this paper, we point out a new attack, CANCloak, which can deceive IDS to make wrong decisions, or confuse ECUs to work collaboratively. More specifically, attackers can transmit specially-crafted ambiguous waveform on CAN bus (via a compromised ECU, or a maliciously ECU attached to the On-Board Diagnostics (OBD) port), and lead two receivers to interpret it as two different data frames, as illustrated in Figure 1. In this way, if one of the receivers is an IDS, it may fail to detect command received by the other victim ECU. Besides, if none of the deceived ECUs is an IDS, then attackers may issue two instructions at the same time. The vehicle may have abnormal behavior if these instructions are mutually exclusive(e.g., full-throttle while full-braking).

We studied the data link layer CAN standard [7], and pointed out the root cause is the ambiguous settings of ECU nodes connected to the CAN bus. Specifically, each ECU has a sample-point setting in physical layer, which controls when this ECU reads state of CAN bus and then determines the logic bit value. ECUs with different sample-point settings can communicate on a same CAN bus, which is a common case in practice. Attackers could exploit this inconsistent setting to launch the CANCloak attack.

We make the following contributions in this paper:

- We found a security issue in the physical layer of CAN, which could cause inconsistency to ECU nodes.
- We proposed a CANCloak attack to exploit this issue, which is able to deceive two ECUs with one CAN frame.
- We developed a test environment consisted of 3 ECUs, including a transmitter capable of launch CANCloak attack.

Workshop on Automotive and Autonomous Vehicle Security (AutoSec) 2021
25 February 2021, Virtual

https://dx.doi.org/10.14722/autosec.2021.23024
www.ndss-symposium.org

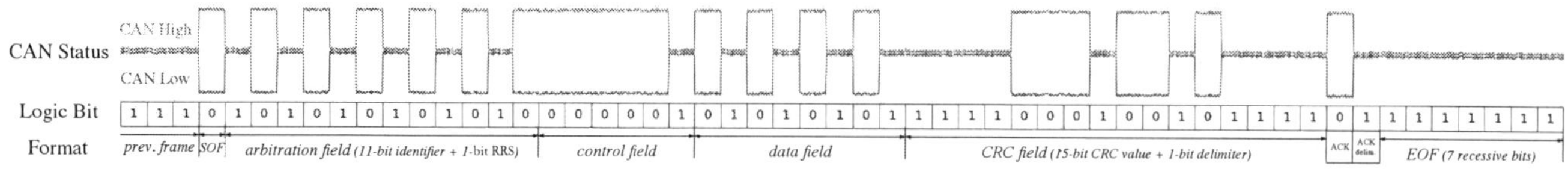

Fig. 2: A Sample CAN Data Frame Signal

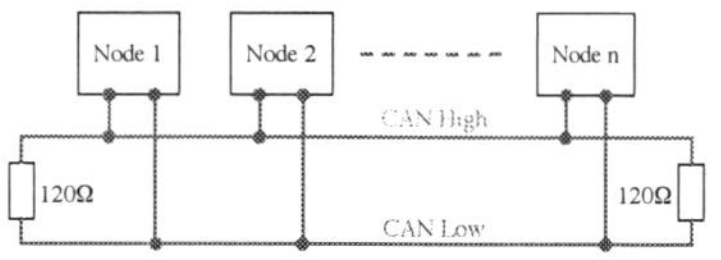

Fig. 3: CAN Bus Topology

- We evaluated the performance of CANCloak, showing an attack success rate up to 99.7% under certain experiment parameter.

II. Background

Over the past few decades, automobile manufacturers equip their new cars with more and more high-tech features, like lane departure warning (LDW) system, blind-spot warning (BSW) systems, and automatic emergency braking (AEB) systems to improve both safety and convenience of driving. Autonomous driving is coming to reality with the help of those devices. The structure of modern cars has transformed from machinery to complex in-vehicle electronics networks. For example, modern vehicles are running with up to 2500 signals exchanged by 70 electronic control units (ECUs) [8].

A. Controller Area Network (CAN)

The controller area network (CAN) is widely used to provide a communication channel for different ECUs within a car. Bosch released the CAN protocol specification [9] in 1986 and then updated it to CAN 2.0 [10] in 1991. After that, the CAN specification became an ISO standard [7] and was widely used by all automobile manufacturers.

Figure 3 shows a typical CAN bus topology. Any node could act as a master (*multi-master*) to send a message over the bus, while other nodes will receive and act on the message (*multi-cast*). Modern vehicles may have multiple CAN buses.

CAN uses a two-wire twisted cable as bus to connect all embedded control units (ECUs). These 2 cables, i.e., CAN High (CANH) and CAN Low (CANL), hold differential signal to achieve high reliability and noise tolerance. As shown in Figure 2, the voltage difference between these two signals turns the bus to one of two states, i.e., the *dominant* state (logic "0") when $V_{CANH} > V_{CANL}$, and the *recessive* state (logic "1") when $V_{CANH} \leq V_{CANL}$. For convenience, we use **negative edge** to represent logic "1" to "0" transition, and use **positive edge** to represent logic "0" to "1" transition.

B. CAN Frame

CAN frame, or "message", is the basic data unit sent through CAN bus. Though there are other type of frames, in this paper, we will only focus on data frames.

As Figure 2 shows, a CAN data frame consists of several fields, including the start of frame (SoF), arbitration field, control field, data field, cyclical redundancy check (CRC) field, acknowledge (ACK) field, and the end of frame (EoF).

SoF and EoF mark the beginning and the end of a data frame, consisting of 1 dominant bit and 7 recessive bits respectively. The arbitration field consists of an 11-bit unique identifier (which represents the message priority) and one Remote Transmission Request (RTR) bit. The control field has several control flags, including IDentifier Extension bit (IDE) and Data Length Code (DLC). The data field contains data to be transmitted with a maximum length of 8 bytes. CRC is applied to detect any transmission error in the whole data frame, followed by acknowledge bits.

C. Arbitration

CAN uses Carrier Sense Multiple Access/Collision Detection (CSMA/CD) as an arbitration scheme. Following this scheme, every ECU must check whether there are no activities for a while on the bus before sending messages, and then monitor collisions during transmission. If an ECU sends a recessive bit and then reads back a dominant bit, it learns that another ECU is sending a message with a higher priority, and thus will stop transmitting immediately.

D. ERROR Handling

To keep robust and functional even under high electrical disturbances, the CAN protocol adopts several error detections.

a) Bit Monitoring: ECU keeps tracking the actual bus status while sending a message. If any inconsistency happens (e.g., sending a recessive bit but reading back a dominant bit), a transmit error shall be raised.

b) CRC Check: Every frame includes a 15-bit CRC. All receiver nodes will re-calculate the CRC and compare it with the one in the received message. If two CRC values mismatch, a receive error shall be raised.

c) Stuff Bit Check: The CAN bus does not have an independent clock wire, and ECU nodes rely on monitoring *negative edges* to synchronize. However, the CAN protocol uses the Non-Return-to-Zero (NRZ) bit encoding scheme, in which consecutive bits of the same polarity exhibit no voltage level changes on the bus. Therefore, if many consecutive bits of the same polarity are being transmitted, then there will be no negative or positive edges on the CAN bus for a period of several bits, therefore receiver nodes may get out-of-synchronization.

To address this issue, a CAN transmitter must actively insert one bit of opposite polarity (called stuff bit) after five consecutive bits of the same polarity have been transmitted in the stream. On the receiver side, if a node detects any violation against this stuffing rule, i.e., six consecutive bits of same polarity (except EoF bits) are found in a stream, then a stuff error will be raised.

d) Acknowledge Check: Each receiver node should send a dominant bit to the bus during the ACK slot. The transmitter will signal an ACK error if no dominant bit was detected during the ACK slot.

E. CAN Sub-Bit Structure

TABLE I: Segments of CAN bit

Segment	Length	Explanation
Synchronization Segment	1 tq	To synchronize the various CAN nodes on the bus
Propagation Segment	1~8 tqs	Compensate for physical delay times within the network
phase-1 Segment	1~8 tqs	Compensate for edge phase errors, may be lengthened during re-synchronization
phase-2 Segment	2~8 tqs	Similar to phase-1, may be shortened during re-synchronization

tq: time quanta

The minimum time unit used in a CAN controller is **time quanta**, derived from the ECU's system clock. For each ECU, the time period of receiving a bit is split into four segments, i.e., synchronization segment, propagation segment, phase-1 segment, and phase-2 segment, whose time duration are all multiples of the ECU's time quanta. Table I lists the structure of a bit transmission time period, the length limit of each segment and the explanation of each segment.

The separation point between phase-1 and 2 segment is called the **sample-point**. ECU will read voltage of CAN bus at sample-point to get bus state. Note that, segments' length (in number of time quanta) are up to the ECU's settings, so does the position of the sample-point. It is not necessary, and could be physically infeasible, to synchronize all ECUs' sample-points. To make multiple ECUs work on the same CAN bus simultaneously, the only hard requirement is the bus rate, i.e., the length of a bit time of every ECU, must be the same. It is common to find ECUs with different sample-point settings working on a same CAN bus[1].

F. Synchronization Mechanisms

CAN is a message-based protocol and does not have a specific timing wire for synchronization. Thus, CAN receivers rely on extracting timing information from signals on the bus. To receive every bits in a frame correctly, the CAN standard provides two synchronization mechanisms in different layers.

Hard synchronization is the main mechanism used in frame level synchronization. It happens when receiver detects the first negative edge occurs after the last frame and inter-frame interval on bus. This negative edge indicates the bus idle status is over, and the first bit (SoF) of a new frame is incoming. Once detected, the bit timing logic unit of the ECU will be reset to the initial state.

[1]We have confirmed it in multiple real world ECUs.

Bit re-synchronization is a bit level synchronization mechanism. Ideally, all ECUs' bit length are identical, then they will keep synchronized, receivers should observe bus state flips only in its synchronization segment. However, due to the accuracy limitation of physical and environmental factors such as unequal temperature over the bus, different ECUs may have different bit lengths. The CAN bus protocol has to be tolerate and thus allows reasonable minor clock shift among ECUs.

While receiving a frame, a receiver may observe bus state flip outside the synchronization segment, since the transmitter may have an inconsistent bit length. Specifically, the bus status flip (a negative or positive edge) may arrive slightly later than expected, i.e., in the receiver ECU's propagation or phase-1 segment. Or, the bit flip may arrive slightly earlier than expected, i.e., in the phase-2 segment of the previous bit.

The bit re-synchronization mechanism is proposed to compensate for this phenomenon. In every CAN controller, there is a variable named re-Synchronization Jump Width (SJW). If the receiver ECU finds a negative edge outside its synchronization segment, it will adjust its bit length with SJW number of time quanta, in order to keep pace with the transmitter in the following bits. Specifically, if the receiver ECU finds a negative edge in the propagation or phase-1 segment, it learns that its last bit length is shorter than the transmitter's, and thus will lengthen its bit length, by expanding the phase-1 segment with SJW time quanta. Otherwise, if receiver ECU finds a negative edge in the phase-2 segment, it learns that its bit length is longer than the transmitter's, and thus will shorten its bit length, by reducing the phase-2 segment with SJW time quanta.

III. The CANCloak Attack

In this section, we will present a security issue of CAN protocol, and present the CANCloak attack which could exploit this issue to deceive ECUs.

A. Threat model

We assume the target CAN bus follows the latest CAN data link layer and physical signalling standard [7], and at least two ECUs connected to the CAN bus have different sample-point settings. Regarding the defense, we assume no authentication mechanisms have been deployed, but an IDS may or may not be attached to the CAN. This is a common scenario in practice.

On the other hand, we assume the adversary knows sample-points of two victim CAN receivers (which may or may not include an IDS). It is feasible for attackers to get such information, e.g., by disassemble another adversary-owned vehicle of the same model, extract target ECU, then take experiments on it. Moreover, we assume the adversary could attach a malicious ECU which can send crafted waveform to the CAN bus, e.g., via the OBD-II diagnose port. In practice, this is also feasible for attackers.

Given a designated CAN frame ($Frame_A$), goal of CAN-Cloak attack is to let a target victim receiver, $Receiver_A$, accepts $Frame_A$ as intended, and the other receiver, $Receiver_B$, cannot notice $Frame_A$ from the same bus. It is important to make sure that $Receiver_B$ would not raise any receive error during this attack, otherwise it will send an active error frame immediately to interrupt $Receiver_A$.

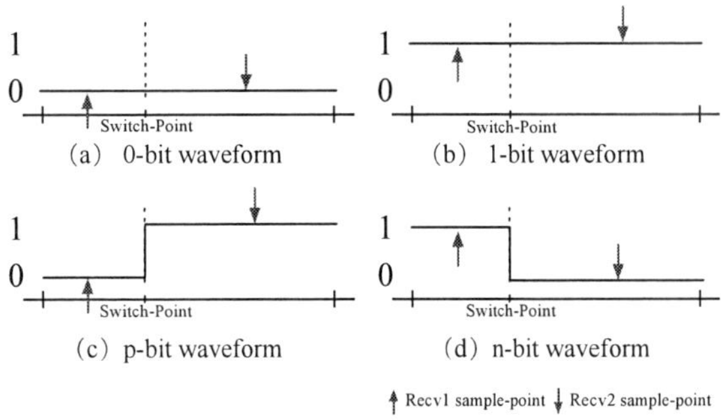

Fig. 4: The adversary transmitter could send a waveform of 0-bit, 1-bit, p-bit and n-bit, by switching bus state between sample-points of two receiver ECUs, to trick them getting different combination of bit values.

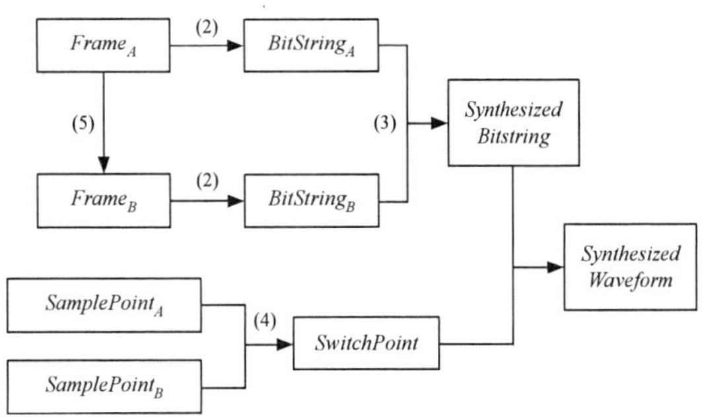

Fig. 5: Design of CANCloak

B. Intuition: One Bit Deceiving

Given that ECUs read CAN bus state only at sample-point, it is possible to craft an ambiguous signal letting receivers decoding it differently, if these receivers have different sample-points.

In a 3-ECU transmission scenario, while one ECU act as transmitter and other two as receivers, without loss of generality, assuming $Receiver_A$ has a sample-point earlier than $Receiver_B$. While these two ECUs are about to receive next bit from bus simultaneously, they would extract same polarity of result from bus, as illustrated by 4 (a) and (b) for 0-bit and 1-bit respectively.

However, if the transmitter of current waveform is malicious, intending to trick two receivers to read different bit values, Adversary could switch the bus state around a specially chosen **switch-point**, which sits in between sample-points of receivers. As shown in Figure 4 (c), the adversary maintain bus state to logic '0' before switch-point of bit, and manipulate it to logic '1' after it. Thus $Receiver_A$ would recognize this bit as '0', while $Receiver_B$ mark it as '1'. Figure 4 (d) shows the opposite scenario. For simplicity, since these abnormal bit introduces positive (logic '0' to '1') or negative (logic '1' to '0') edge to waveform, we denote them as **'p'-bit** and **'n'-bit**

C. Design of the CANCloak Attack

Since a frame is transmitted as a bit string and an adversary is able to deceive ECUs with one bit as discussed in previous sections, she/he could then synthesize an attack waveform bit by bit. Figure 5 shows the overview of the workflow.

Though, there are several issues to address in this attack.

1) Introduce $Frame_B$: As described in III-A, $Receiver_B$ should neither detects $Frame_A$ nor raises any error. Thus, we shall let $Receiver_B$ receives another frame, $Frame_B$, which meets the following basic requirements.

- Has a legitimate CAN data frame structure.
- Is different from $Frame_A$.

2) Construct Bit-Strings: After choosing both frame in application layer, we need to craft their counterpart in data link layer, bit-string of '0's and '1's. Usually, this step is automatically complete by transmitter part of CAN controller hardware. However, those bit-strings would be blind to application layer, which is needed in further phase of our attack. So, we manually finish this step (fill control field and CRC field, etc.) of both frame, resulting in $BitString_A$ and $BitString_B$ respectively.

3) Synthesize Bit-String: Given two bit-strings expected by the victim receivers, the adversary needs to synthesize a special bit string consisting of 0-bit, 1-bit, p-bit, and n-bit, in order to deceive victim ECUs bit by bit.

Table II shows an example of synthesized bit string.

TABLE II: Example Synthesized Bit-String

$BitString_A$	1	0	0	1	1	0	0	0	1	1	0	1	0
$BitString_B$	1	0	1	1	0	1	0	1	0	0	0	1	1
Synthesized BitString	1	0	p	1	n	p	0	p	n	n	0	1	p

4) Determine Switch-Point: Theoretically, the switch-point could be placed anywhere between sample-points of the two ECUs, and would not affect the attack performance. In practice, considering the electromagnetic interference, we set the switch-point around the center of sample-points' gap. We will discuss the success rate of different switch-point settings in Section IV-B.

5) Optimize $Frame_B$: In this section, we will demonstrate how content of $Frame_B$ influence attack performance, and show a practical method of generating an acceptable $Frame_B$.

The synthesized bit-string may introduce some 'n'-bits, which introduce negative edge inside bits. These edges could easily trigger receivers' re-synchronization mechanism. For the receiver having earlier sample-point, it will consider this negative edge come later then sample-point and lay in phase-2 segment of bit, then shorten this bit for SJW. For the other receiver, this negative edge is in propagation or phase-1 segment, thus the bit time would be longer. As a result, there will be a time gap between 2 receivers while stepping into next bit. The cumulative effect of such time gap will confuse receivers and possibly result in receive errors.

To avoid this chaos, we add another requirement:

- By manipulate $Frame_B$, synthesized Bit-string should have minimum number of 'n'-bits, (i.e., 1->0).

It is easy to eliminate 'n'-bits in most part of frame, because we can arbitrarily manipulate $Frame_B$. In contrast, CRC field of frame is not directly controllable, it is calculated from other fields of the frame. Thus, we forge a large amount of $Frame_B$

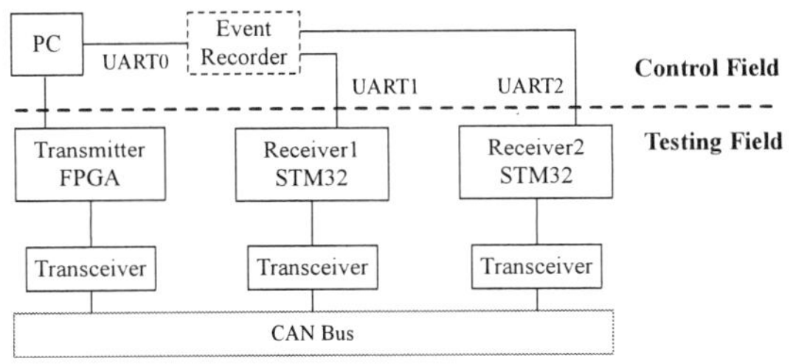

Fig. 6: Illustration of a CANCloak attack scenario. Components in the analyzing field are not needed in real world attacks.

candidates which does not create any 'n'-bit outside CRC field, and elect the one create least number of 'n'-bit in CRC field to be the actual $Frame_B$. Though there are 15 bit in CRC field, in most circumstance, we can find a solution having equal or less than 1 'n'-bit in 10 second, on a modern PC.

D. Implementation of CANCloak Test Bench

To demonstrate this attack, we setup a basic CAN bus environment connected with the malicious transmitter and two victim receiver ECUs. The structure is shown in the testing field in Figure 6.

1) Malicious Transmitter: As the core of this attack, the malicious transmitter is responsible for generating malformed waveform to deceive two receivers. An off-the-shelf CAN transceiver cannot generate crafted waveform directly, because the synthesize CAN frames do not conform the normal CAN bus data frame structure. We implemented a proof-of-concept (POC) malicious transmitter based on an ALTERA EP4CE6 FPGA. FPGA can handle complex low-level logic of CAN transmitter, while concurrently sending precise synthesized waveform.

2) Victim Receivers: To make our testing platform closer to a real-world scenario, the receivers are set up in the most common way. Core of receivers are STM32F429 micro-controllers, integrated with CAN controller peripheral module. In our implementation, a CAN time quanta is 200ns. To meet the most common bit rate of CAN bus, 500 kHz, each bit time should be exactly 2ms, so each bit takes 10 time quantas in our demonstration configuration.

3) Transceivers: Note that, since the I/O ports of the FPGA and the STM32 micro-controllers are not able to handle differential voltage signals on the CAN bus, we use three extra NCV7342 CAN transceivers to connect the FPGA and micro-controllers to the actual cable of the CAN bus.

4) Attack Verification: To verify whether the attack succeeds, we collect the messages received by victim ECUs and compare them with the intention of the adversary. Note that, this part is only for verification purpose, **not** required for real world attacks. The structure is shown in the analyzing field in Figure 6.

The work flow of event recorder is described as follow. Every time a synthesized waveform is sent to CAN bus, event recorder will wait for 50ms to let receivers process it, then ask receivers if they accepted any frame recently. An success attack is count only if $Receiver_A$ accepted designated $Frame_A$, and both receiver did not raise any error. Finally, event recorder uploads all result to PC for further process.

IV. Evaluation

We conducted several groups of experiments on our test environment to evaluate the performance of CANCloak attack. The performance might be affected by the following parameters:

- The *Switch-Point* used to synthesize the attack payload.
- The *Bit Rate* of CAN bus.
- The *Gap of Sample-Points* of victim receivers, determined by their timing configuration.
- The *Content of* $Frame_A$ expected to accept by receivers.

We only change one parameter in each experiment to reveal their influence.

A. Attack Payload Data Set

$Frame_A$ in CANCloak is designated, shall be determined by real attack purpose. In our experiment, $Frame_A$ is an eight bytes data frame whose ID and all data bytes are random. $Frame_B$ is determined by $Frame_A$. We spent 20 seconds finding the best (least 'n'-bit in synthesized frame) $Frame_B$, on a modern laptop with Intel Core i7-8550U CPU. This process was repeated 1000 times. Thus we have a data set consists of 1000 frame pairs after less than 6 hours.

B. Change the switch-point

We choose the switch-point as the variable for the first set of experiments, while all other parameters are controlled. The output port of the transmitter in CANCloak is working at a 50 MHz maximum flip rate. This rate is 100 times faster than the CAN bus bit rate (500 kbps, Bits Per Second). So we have 101 potential switch-point positions (from 0% to 100%). If the switch-point is 0%, the synthesized frame will be identical to $Frame_B$ since there is no space leaving for $Frame_A$. On the contrary, if the switch-point is set to 100%, both receivers will get $Frame_A$.

For more details, we take switch-point as the variable in this experiment and change it from 0% to 100%. The other parameters are configured as follow: bit rate is 500 kbps, sample-points of receives are 40% and 70%, i.e. their ratio of segments' length *Synchronization:Phase-1:Phase-2* are 1:3:6 and 1:6:3 respectively. We tested all 1000 frame pairs in our data set with every switch-point. So there are 101,000 tests in total.

Figure 7 shows the success rate of CANCloak attack, i.e., CANCloak alienate the $Receiver_A$ to get $Frame_A$ and $Receiver_B$ to get $Frame_B$. The valid attack window is from 30% to 70%. The highest success rate is 99.7%, appears when switch-point is 45%. And the success rate is near 100% when switch-point lies in 40% and 60%.

C. Change the Bus Rate

Although CAN standard [7] allows the rate vary from 10 kbps to 1 Mbps, there are two major CAN bus rates usually used, *High-Speed CAN Bus* at 500 kbps and *Low-Speed*

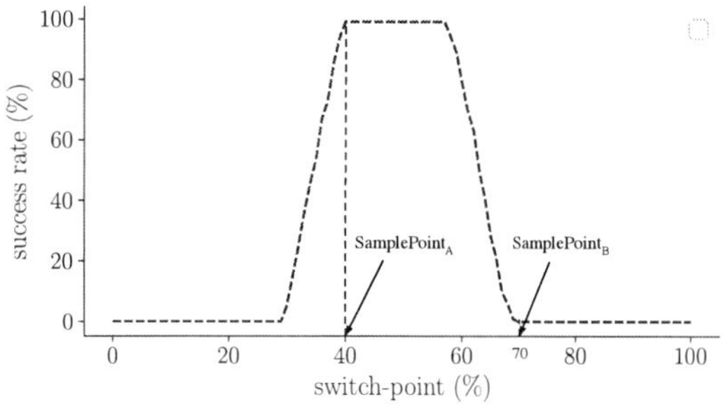

Fig. 7: Attack Success Rate Over Different Switch Point

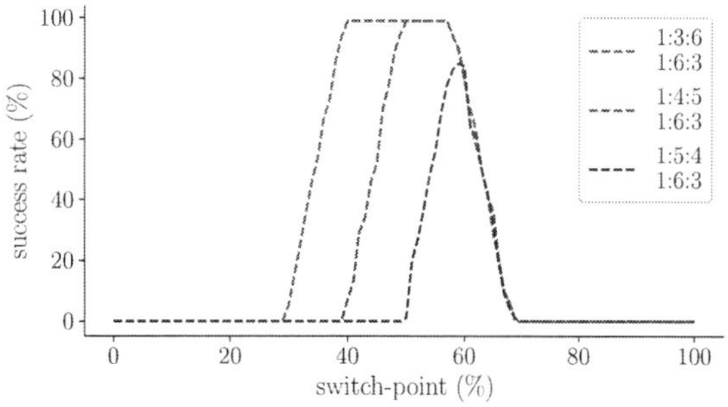

Fig. 8: Attack success rate in different receiver timing settings

CAN Bus at 250 kbps. We select four representative rates for evaluation, the maximum rate (1 Mbps) and the minimum rate (10 kbps), and two commonly used rates (250 kbps, 500 kbps).

Other parameters are the same as the previous experiment. While switch-point varies from 0% to 100% for each bit rate. sample-points of receivers is 40% and 70%, All frame pairs in our data set are tested on every switch-point, every bus rate. Thus 404,000 tests in total were performed.

The result is omitted because the success rate curve remains the same at different bus rates, indicating that CANCloak's performance stable over different bus rate settings.

D. Change the Gap Between Receivers' Sample-Points

Timing parameters of different ECUs, like the length of time quanta or segments, may different, though they are connected to the same bus. For $Receiver_A$, 3 sets of timing parameters are used, which are 1:3:6, 1:4:5 and 1:5:4, i.e., sample-point are 40%, 50% and 60% respectively. For $Receiver_B$, the sample-point is fixed at 70% with the timing parameters of 1:6:3. Other parameters are still the same as the previous experiment. The bus rate is 500 kHz, The payloads are all frame pair from our data set, The switch-point varies from 0% to 100% for each sample-point setting. So there are 303,000 tests in total.

Figure 8 shows how attack success rate varies with 3 different sample-point settings. In general, the more deviation these two receivers have in the sample-point settings, the wider attack window adversary could have. In the first configuration, there are 30% time interval between two receivers' sample-points. In this case, we have a 20% width perfect attack window, which starts at 40% (i.e., identical to sample-point of $Receiver_A$) and ends at 60% (i.e., a time quanta (10%) ahead of $Receiver_B$'s sample-point). The perfect attack window drops to 10% and 0 for the second and third settings, respectively.

In summary, the length of the perfect attack window of switch-point is one time quanta less than the gap between the sample-points. The ideal attack window starts at the sample-point of $Receiver_A$, and ends at one time quanta before sample-point of $Receiver_B$.

V. Conclusion

In this paper, we propose a new type of attack, CANCloak, which takes advantage of the deviation between two CAN ECUs. We then design and implement CANCloak attack. As far as we know, CANCloak is the first attack against CAN physical layer. Furthermore, we evaluate the overall performance of CANCloak attack by changing sample-point of CAN receivers, bit rate of bus, switch-point settings, and attack payload. The results show that CANCloak attack has up to 99.7% of success rate in certain conditions.

References

[1] C. Miller and C. Valasek, "Remote exploitation of an unaltered passenger vehicle," *Black Hat USA*, vol. 2015, p. 91, 2015.

[2] Q. Wang and S. Sawhney, "Vecure: A practical security framework to protect the can bus of vehicles," in *2014 International Conference on the Internet of Things (IOT)*. IEEE, 2014, pp. 13–18.

[3] A. Van Herrewege, D. Singelee, and I. Verbauwhede, "Canauth-a simple, backward compatible broadcast authentication protocol for can bus," in *ECRYPT Workshop on Lightweight Cryptography*, vol. 2011, 2011, p. 20.

[4] E. Wang, W. Xu, S. Sastry, S. Liu, and K. Zeng, "Hardware module-based message authentication in intra-vehicle networks," in *2017 ACM/IEEE 8th International Conference on Cyber-Physical Systems (ICCPS)*. IEEE, 2017, pp. 207–216.

[5] M. Marchetti and D. Stabili, "Anomaly detection of can bus messages through analysis of id sequences," in *2017 IEEE Intelligent Vehicles Symposium (IV)*. IEEE, 2017, pp. 1577–1583.

[6] H. M. Song, H. R. Kim, and H. K. Kim, "Intrusion detection system based on the analysis of time intervals of can messages for in-vehicle network," in *2016 international conference on information networking (ICOIN)*. IEEE, 2016, pp. 63–68.

[7] "Road vehicles - Controller area network (CAN) - Part 1: Data link layer and physical signalling," International Organization for Standardization, Standard, Dec. 2015.

[8] E. C. De Oliveira, "Electrical architectures and in-vehicles networks," SAE Technical Paper, Tech. Rep., 2007.

[9] U. Kiencke, S. Dais, and M. Litschel, "Automotive serial controller area network," *SAE transactions*, pp. 823–828, 1986.

[10] R. Bosch *et al.*, "Can specification version 2.0," *Rober Bousch GmbH, Postfach*, vol. 300240, p. 72, 1991.

Demo: Curricular Reinforcement Learning for Robust Policy in Unmanned CarRacing Game

Yunzhe Tian*, Yike Li*, Yingxiao Xiang*, Wenjia Niu*, Endong Tong*, and Jiqiang Liu*

*Beijing Key Laboratory of Security and Privacy in Intelligent Transportation,
Beijing Jiaotong University, China.

Email: {tianyunzhe,yikeli,yxxiang,niuwj,edtong,jqliu}@bjtu.edu.cn

Wenjia Niu and Endong Tong are corresponding authors

Abstract—**Robust reinforcement learning has been a challenging problem due to always unknown differences between real and training environment. Existing efforts approached the problem through performing random environmental perturbations in learning process. However, one can not guarantee perturbation is positive. Bad ones might bring failures to reinforcement learning. Therefore, in this paper, we propose to utilize GAN to dynamically generate progressive perturbations at each epoch and realize curricular policy learning. Demo we implemented in unmanned CarRacing game validates the effectiveness.**

I. Design and Implementation

In this work, at each training epoch of average 400 episodes, we firstly use an improved Least-Sqaures GAN (LSGAN) [1] to generate a set of progressive perturbations. We then evaluate and label the generated perturbations, according to whether those are at the intermediate level of difficulty for current policy and update the policy under positive perturbations implemented on rllab [2]. This process and formula are presented in Fig.1. As to control the training difficulty, we define perturbations of intermediate difficulty ($POID$), and require $POID_i := \{p : R_{min} \leq R^{\pi_i}(p) \leq R_{max}\}$, for perturbation value p on current policy π_i. The label y_{p_j} used in next iteration indicates whether $p_j \in POID_i$. We thus collect trajectories under positive environment perturbations and use RL algorithm as policy optimizer to update our policy.

II. Results and Conclusion

Fig. 2 shows the experimental training process in Unmanned CarRacing Game of OpenAI gym environment [3]. The friction coefficient (FC) of current environment is 0.6. Through curricularly updating at appropriate difficulty, the car is increasingly robust and finally makes a successful turn. Our approach even achieves 11 times score (869.37 over 77.58) higher than baseline reinforcement learning and 2 times score (869.37 over 397.29) higher than robust reinforcement learning with domain randomization [4]. This demo has good potential to apply into non-game reinforcement learning of unmanned driving.

Workshop on Automotive and Autonomous Vehicle Security (AutoSec) 2021
25 February 2021, Virtual

https://dx.doi.org/10.14722/autosec.2021.23011
www.ndss-symposium.org

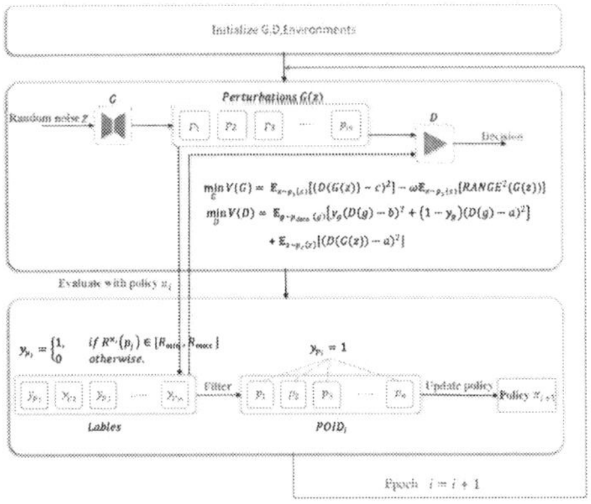

Fig. 1. The framework of curricular reinforcement learning.

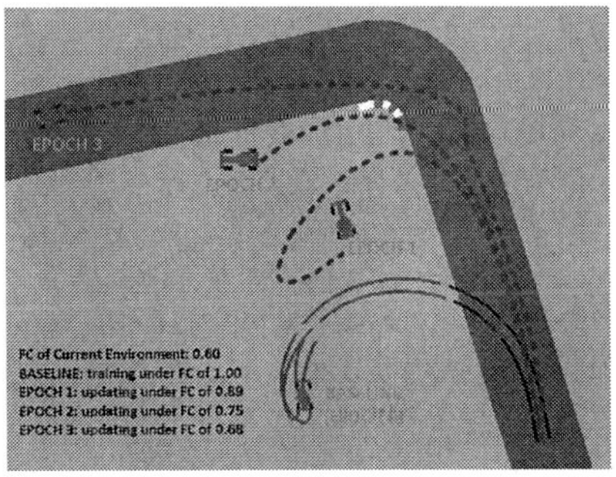

Fig. 2. Training process in Unmanned CarRacing Game.

Acknowledgment

This research is supported by the National Natural Science Foundation of China (61972025), Fundamental Research Funds for the Central Universities of China (2019RC008).

References

[1] Florensa, C., Held, D., Geng, X., and Abbeel, P. Automaticgoal generation for reinforcement learning agents. *ICML*, 2018.

[2] Duan Y, Chen X, Houthooft R, et al. Benchmarking Deep Reinforcement Learning for Continuous Control. *International Conference on Machine Learning (ICML). JMLR.org*, 2016.

[3] G. Brockman, V. Cheung, L. Pettersson, J. Schneider, J. Schulman, J. Tang, and W. Zaremba. Openai gym, 2016.

[4] X. B. Peng, M. Andrychowicz, W. Zaremba and P. Abbeel. Sim-to-Real Transfer of Robotic Control with Dynamics Randomization. *ICRA*, 2018.

Demo: Sequential Attacks on Kalman Filter-based Forward Collision Warning Systems

Yuzhe Ma, Jon Sharp, Ruizhe Wang, Earlence Fernandes, Xiaojin Zhu
University of Wisconsin–Madison

Abstract—**Kalman Filter (KF) is widely used in various domains to perform sequential learning or variable estimation. In the context of autonomous vehicles, KF constitutes the core component of many Advanced Driver Assistance Systems (ADAS), such as Forward Collision Warning (FCW). It tracks the states (distance, velocity etc.) of relevant traffic objects based on sensor measurements. The tracking output of KF is often fed into downstream logic to produce alerts, which will then be used by human drivers to make driving decisions in near-collision scenarios. In this work, we demonstrate planning-based attacks on Forward Collision Warning — a machine-human hybrid system that uses KF. Based on our work published at the AAAI-2021 conference, we use an MPC-based algorithm and show how an attacker can sequentially perturb vision measurements to change the FCW alert signals at desired points in time. We simulate our attack on CARLA using standard test protocols from the National Highway Traffic Safety Administration.**

I. Demo Description

Advanced Driver Assistance Systems (ADAS) are hybrid human-machine systems that are widely deployed on production passenger vehicles. They use sensing, traditional signal processing and machine learning to detect and raise alerts about unsafe road situations and rely on the human driver to take corrective actions. Popular ADAS examples include Forward Collision Warning (FCW), Adaptive Cruise Control and Autonomous Emergency Braking.

Although ADAS hybrid systems are designed to increase road safety when drivers are distracted, attackers can negate their benefits by strategically tampering with their behavior. For example, an attacker could convince an FCW or AEB system that there is no imminent collision until it is too late for a human driver to avoid the crash.

This demo is based on recent work (appearing at AAAI-2021) that studies the robustness of ADAS to attacks. The core of ADAS typically involves tracking the states (e.g., distance and velocity) of road objects using Kalman filter (KF). Downstream logic uses this tracking output to detect unsafe situations before they happen. We focus our efforts on Forward Collision Warning (FCW), a popular ADAS deployed on production vehicles today. FCW uses KF state predictions to detect whether the ego vehicle (vehicle employing the ADAS system) is about to collide with the most important object in front of it and will alert the human driver in a timely manner. Thus, our concrete attack goal is to trick the KF that FCW uses and make it output incorrect state predictions that would induce false or delayed alerts depending on the specific physical situation.

Recent work has examined the robustness of road object state tracking for autonomous vehicles [2]. Their attacks create an instantaneous manipulation to the Kalman filter inputs without considering its sequential nature, the downstream logic that depends on filter output, or the physical dynamics of involved vehicles. This leads to temporarily hijacked Kalman filter state predictions that are incapable of ensuring that downstream logic is reliably tricked into producing false alerts. By contrast, we adopt an online planning view of attacking KFs that accounts for: (1) their sequential nature where current predictions depend on past measurements; and (2) the downstream logic that uses KF output to produce warnings. Our attack technique also considers a simplified model of human reaction to manipulated FCW warning lights.

Based on our model predictive control algorithm published at AAAI-2021, we demonstrate attacks that can hijack FCW behavior. Our attacks force FCW alerts that mask the true nature of the physical situation involving the vehicles until it is too late for a distracted human driver to take corrective actions. Our demon uses a high-fidelity driving simulation using CARLA, a popular tool for autonomous vehicle research and development. We create test scenarios based on real-world driving data [1] and demonstrate the practicality of the attack in causing crashes involving the victim vehicle.

Specifically, we show that attack planning in advance of the targeted point is beneficial compared to without planning. Given 25 steps of planning (or 1.25 seconds based on specific physical situations in our tests) before the targeted time point, the attacker can cause the desired effect, while the attack fails without planning.

Acknowledgements. This work was supported in part by the University of Wisconsin-Madison Office of the Vice Chancellor for Research and Graduate Education with funding from the Wisconsin Alumni Research Foundation. XZ acknowledges NSF grants 1545481, 1704117, 1836978, 2041428, 2023239 and MADLab AF CoE FA9550-18-1-0166.

References

[1] European New Car Assessment Programme, “Euro NCAP LSS Test Protocol. Version 2.0.1,” 2018. [Online]. Available: https://cdn.euroncap.com/media/26996/euro-ncap-aeb-c2c-test-protocol-v20.pdf

[2] Y. Jia, Y. Lu, J. Shen, Q. A. Chen, H. Chen, Z. Zhong, and T. Wei, “Fooling detection alone is not enough: Adversarial attack against multiple object tracking,” *2020 International Conference on Learning Representations (ICLR)*, 2020.

Workshop on Automotive and Autonomous Vehicle Security (AutoSec) 2021
25 February 2021, Virtual

https://dx.doi.org/10.14722/autosec.2021.23015
www.ndss-symposium.org

WeepingCAN: A Stealthy CAN Bus-off Attack

Gedare Bloom
University of Colorado Colorado Springs
gbloom@uccs.edu

Abstract—**The controller area network (CAN) is a high-value asset to defend and attack in automobiles. The bus-off attack exploits CAN's fault confinement to force a victim electronic control unit (ECU) into the bus-off state, which prevents it from using the bus. Although pernicious, the bus-off attack has two distinct phases that are observable on the bus and allow the attack to be detected and prevented. In this paper we present WeepingCAN, a refinement of the bus-off attack that is stealthy and can escape detection. We evaluate WeepingCAN experimentally using realistic CAN benchmarks and find it succeeds in over 75% of attempts without exhibiting the detectable features of the original attack. We demonstrate WeepingCAN on a real vehicle.**

I. Introduction

Motor vehicles are complex cyber-physical systems (CPS) with more software on more electronic control units (ECUs) coupled by expansive in-vehicle networks. Increasing complexity provides ubiquitous connectivity for autonomous driving and infotainment but comes with opportunities to exploit vulnerabilities in the networks and ECUs [1], [3], [4], [10], [16], [22], [25], [30]. These exploits motivate authentication and intrusion detection systems (IDSs) [17], [19], [21], [24], [26]–[28], [31], [38]–[40] especially in the controller area network (CAN) because it is used in the majority of vehicles.

A noteworthy attack on CAN is the *bus-off attack* discovered by Cho and Shin [4]. This attack leverages CAN's fault confinement mechanism to cause an ECU to enter the bus-off state, which removes its access to the bus. The attack, while interesting, exhibits features that make it easily detectable.

In this paper, we introduce a novel bus-off attack that is *stealthy*—it does not provide an obvious feature for detection. We call this attack WeepingCAN.[1] We make the following contributions with this paper:

1) exposition of WeepingCAN;
2) a skipping attack strategy to increase success;
3) and empirical evaluation of performance and stealthiness.

WeepingCAN is able to bus-off an ECU with success rates above 75% and low detectability.

Threat Model: Consistent with prior CAN attacks [3], [4], [10], [16], [30], we assume an adversary ($\mathcal{A}$) controls the software on a *compromised ECU*. $\mathcal{A}$ can execute arbitrary code and can send/receive arbitrary messages on the CAN bus. Arbitrary code execution implies that $\mathcal{A}$ can reprogram CAN controller registers and interrupt handlers. Although the exploit to compromise an ECU is out of scope, ECUs are known to be vulnerable via multiple surfaces [3], [16], [36].

$\mathcal{A}$'s goal is to cause a *victim ECU* ($\mathcal{V}$) to enter the bus-off state while $\mathcal{A}$ remains *stealthy* to escape detection. We assume $\mathcal{A}$ conducted an offline analysis and knows the CAN message parameters [9], [10], [18], [26], [28], [29], [37]. We expect $\mathcal{A}$ can determine the vehicles that satisfy the threat model.

Fault Model: To simplify the attack analysis, we assume the CAN bus does not incur faults. In reality, faults may increase or decrease the success of attacks and countermeasures.

II. Background and Related Work

We refer interested readers to Natale et al. [23] and Hu [13] for in-depth coverage of CAN and its error handling.

A. CAN Overview

CAN is a multi-leader broadcast bus with decentralized arbitration based on the sender's identifier (ID). Logic-0 bits are encoded as a *dominant* signal and logic-1 as a *recessive* signal. All nodes float recessive to transmit a 1 and drive a dominant signal to transmit 0.

A few of the basic CAN data frame's fields are relevant to the bus-off attack. The data field can be between 0 and 8 bytes, and senders encode its size in the 4-bit data length code (DLC) field. The ID field can be 11 or 29 bits. Other fields are not used explicitly by the attack.

CAN's error handling is central to the bus-off attack. Each node can be in one of three states—error-active, error-passive, and bus-off—depending on the values of its receive error counter (REC) and transmit error counter (TEC). A node increases its REC by 1 for each error observed while not transmitting, and its TEC by 8 for each error while transmitting. Each successful receive (transmit) decrements the REC (TEC) by 1. Each node that detects an error transmits an error-active (error-passive) flag of six dominant (recessive) bits in the error-active (error-passive) state. Fig. 1 shows the state machine that governs how the node states change based on the TEC/REC.

B. Original Bus-off Attack

$\mathcal{A}$ identifies some periodic message v that $\mathcal{V}$ transmits. $\mathcal{A}$ fabricates two messages: a *preceded* and an attack message.

[1] The attack name is a play on the TT emote for crying and TTCAN, which originally led to our discovery of the attack.

Workshop on Automotive and Autonomous Vehicle Security (AutoSec) 2021
25 February 2021, Virtual

https://dx.doi.org/10.14722/autosec.2021.23002
www.ndss-symposium.org

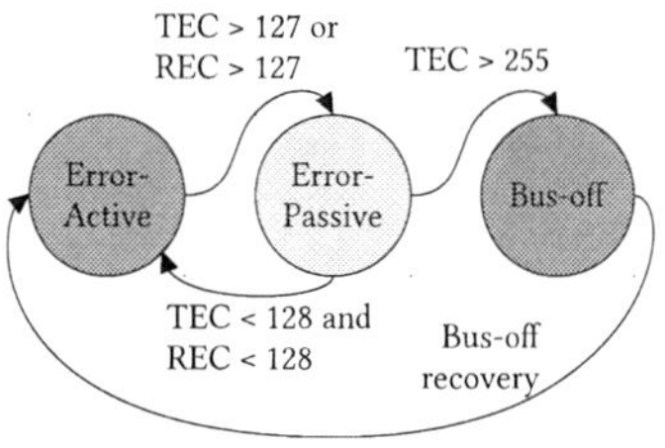

Fig. 1. CAN error state machine with initial state of error-active and transitions based on transmit/receive error counters (TEC/REC).

1) Preceded Messages (IDs): The preceded message of v is some message that transmits immediately before v. Sometimes $\mathcal{A}$ can use an authentic message as a *genuine preceded ID* of v. The attack success rate can go from below 1% to above 90% by using preceded messages [4].

2) Attack Message ($v_\mathcal{A}$): The attack message $v_\mathcal{A}$ has the same ID as v and an identical bit-wise prefix up to some bit at which v is recessive and $v_\mathcal{A}$ is dominant.

3) Attack Cycle: The attack proceeds in two phases:
Phase 1: $\mathcal{A}$ synchronizes with $\mathcal{V}$ by enqueueing the preceded message and the attack message isochronously with v but at a small negative offset. $v_\mathcal{A}$ and v transmit in tandem, which causes a bit error and both ECUs increment their TEC by 8. They also retransmit synchronously, thus repeating the error in a cascade of retransmissions. On the 15th retransmission (16th transmission), both ECUs reach TEC=128 and enter the error passive state before retransmitting again.
Transition: On the 17th transmission, $\mathcal{V}$'s TEC increases by 8 (to 136) and it transmits a passive error flag, which does not affect $\mathcal{A}$. Thus, $\mathcal{A}$ successfully transmits $v_\mathcal{A}$ and decrements its TEC by 1 to reach 127 and re-enter the error active (normal) state. Then the retransmission of v succeeds and $\mathcal{V}$ decreases its TEC by 1. $\mathcal{V}$ is now in the error passive state with a TEC of 135, and $\mathcal{A}$ in the error active state with a TEC of 127.
Phase 2: $\mathcal{A}$ continues to inject messages synchronized with v to increase $\mathcal{V}'s$ TEC by 7 and decrement its own TEC. This phase iterates with the period of v. Eventually $\mathcal{V}$'s TEC reaches 255 putting it in bus-off.

C. Bus-off Attack Countermeasures

Cho and Shin [4] identified two features that make detecting the bus-off attack possible: **feature F1** occurs in Phase 1 when a message encounters consecutive errors; **feature F2** happens in Phase 2 when the victim observes a successful message over its passive error flag. The authors described a two-pronged countermeasure in which a node that observes F1 followed by F2 determines a bus-off attack is in progress. Others have used the same approach [32], [33].

1) Detection: Physical-layer IDSs may detect the bus-off attack due to differences in the physical characteristics of $\mathcal{A}$'s and $\mathcal{V}$'s hardware [5]–[7], [11], [15], [41]. These IDSs generally require additions to a bus, and methods exist to confuse or circumvent them [10], [30].

2) Prevention: Secure hardware [8], [12], [20], may prevent the attack by detecting and blocking the local transmission of $v_\mathcal{A}$. However, an attacker with access to even one node that allows arbitrary message transmissions may still conduct the bus-off attack.

MAuth-CAN [14] is a CAN bus authentication mechanism that protects the authenticator by using two CAN interfaces and switching from one to the other in case the TEC exceeds 96. This approach is unlikely to be generalized because it would require every ECU to duplicate its CAN hardware.

III. Anatomy of the Attack

WeepingCAN is a variation of the original bus-off attack with a few critical differences, namely: (i) $\mathcal{A}$ disables retransmission of $v_\mathcal{A}$; (ii) $\mathcal{A}$ causes *recessive* bit errors; (iii) $\mathcal{A}$ does not fabricate preceded messages; (iv) $\mathcal{A}$ randomizes the injected bit error. These differences enable the attack without the detectable features of the original.

A. Attack Message: $v_\mathcal{A}$

The attack message has v's ID, bit-time, and prefix bits until a random position where v is dominant but $v_\mathcal{A}$ is *recessive*.

B. Attack Cycle

Unlike the original attack, WeepingCAN does not exhibit behavioral differences due to the error state transitions. Initially $\mathcal{A}$ and $\mathcal{V}$ have a TEC of 0 in the error-active mode. WeepingCAN proceeds as follows:

1) $\mathcal{A}$ synchronizes with $\mathcal{V}$ using the periodic approach of the original attack.
2) $\mathcal{A}$ disables retransmission of $v_\mathcal{A}$.
3) $\mathcal{A}$ injects the attack message $v_\mathcal{A}$.
4) $\mathcal{A}$'s CAN controller sends an error-active flag due to the bit error in $v_\mathcal{A}$ that increases $\mathcal{A}$'s and $\mathcal{V}$'s TEC by 8.
5) $\mathcal{V}$ retransmits v and decrements its TEC by 1.
6) $\mathcal{V}$ and $\mathcal{A}$ decrease their TECs by 1 for other transmissions.

C. Disable Retransmission of $v_\mathcal{A}$

Step 2 of the attack aims to avoid feature F1. The effect of disabling retransmission of $v_\mathcal{A}$ is that the attack is characterized by active error flags followed by successful transmissions. We have found two ways to disable $v_\mathcal{A}$'s retransmission: (i) Disable automatic retransmissions for all messages; (ii) Abort transmission on transmit error.

1) Disable Automatic Retransmissions for All Messages: Many commercial CAN controllers can disable automatic message retransmissions for use with time-triggered CAN (TTCAN) applications. Prior to injecting $v_\mathcal{A}$, $\mathcal{A}$ disables automatic retransmission by writing to a control register, which typically affects all messages handled by the CAN controller. Disabling automatic retransmissions also disables retransmissions due to losing arbitration, so the injection of $v_\mathcal{A}$ must occur exactly during the transmission of the message that precedes v so that v and $v_\mathcal{A}$ both win arbitration together.

2) Abort Transmission on Transmit Error: Most CAN controllers can raise an interrupt on transmit errors and allow $\mathcal{A}$ to abort retransmission in the interrupt handler.

D. Recessive Injection

$\mathcal{A}$ injects a *recessive* (1) bit when v contains a *dominant* (0), which causes $\mathcal{A}$'s CAN controller to send an error flag and increment its TEC by 8. $\mathcal{V}$ increments its TEC by 8 and attempts to retransmit. Since $\mathcal{A}$ disabled retransmissions, the retransmission by $\mathcal{V}$ will succeed, decrementing $\mathcal{V}$'s TEC by 1. Unfortunately, disabling retransmissions means that $v_{\mathcal{A}}$ never successfully transmits: the attack could actually put $\mathcal{A}$ into bus-off! Instead, $\mathcal{A}$ can identify additional messages it can transmit to keep its TEC less than $\mathcal{V}$'s. $\mathcal{A}$ needs to transmit at least 1 more message than $\mathcal{V}$ for each $v_{\mathcal{A}}$, and $\mathcal{V}$ has to transmit fewer than 7 other messages or its TEC will recover.

Let M be a set of messages, with $M_{\mathcal{V}}$, $M_{\mathcal{A}}$ the set of messages transmitted by $\mathcal{V}$ and $\mathcal{A}$, respectively. Let m_T denote the period of $m \in M$. Then $\mathcal{A}$ can keep its TEC beneath $\mathcal{V}$'s if the following holds:

$$\exists v \in M_{\mathcal{V}} \; s.t. \; 8 > \sum_{m' \in M_{\mathcal{V}}} \frac{v_T}{m'_T} < \sum_{m \in M_{\mathcal{A}}} \frac{v_T}{m_T}. \tag{1}$$

Example 1 (Basic Attack Strategy): Suppose $|M_{\mathcal{V}}| = |M_{\mathcal{A}}| = 1$, and $\mathcal{A}$'s authentic message is sent with one-fifth the period of $\mathcal{V}$'s. Eq. 1 holds as $8 > 1 < 5$. For every attack on $v \in M_{\mathcal{V}}$, $\mathcal{A}$ successfully transmits 5 messages and $\mathcal{V}$ transmits 1 message; their TECs will increase by 3 and 7, respectively. Thus, $\mathcal{V}$ can be forced to error passive with 19 attack messages, while $\mathcal{A}$'s TEC only reaches 57. When $\mathcal{V}$ reaches bus-off after 37 injections, $\mathcal{A}$'s TEC reaches 116 and it remains error-active.

Skipping Injections: Subject to Eq. 1, $\mathcal{A}$'s TEC grows slower than $\mathcal{V}$'s, but $\mathcal{A}$ can reach error-passive before $\mathcal{V}$ reaches bus-off. For example, if $\mathcal{V}$'s TEC grows by 7 and $\mathcal{A}$'s grows by 6, then $\mathcal{A}$'s TEC is 114 when $\mathcal{V}$ enters error-passive on the 19th injection. However, $\mathcal{A}$ becomes error-passive on the 22nd, and $\mathcal{A}$ eventually goes to bus-off while $\mathcal{V}$ recovers. $\mathcal{A}$ can avoid going to bus-off by skipping some injections of $v_{\mathcal{A}}$. Skipping every other injection will increase $\mathcal{V}$'s TEC by 6 and $\mathcal{A}$'s by 4, which still is not good enough. Injecting on every third message of v increases $\mathcal{V}$'s TEC by 5 and $\mathcal{A}$'s by 2, which puts $\mathcal{V}$ in bus-off on the 51st injection.

Example 2 (Skipping Attack Strategy): Consider the case when $|M_{\mathcal{V}}| = |M_{\mathcal{A}}| = 1$, and $\mathcal{A}$'s message is sent with one-fourth the period of $\mathcal{V}$'s. Eq. 1 holds as $8 > 1 < 4$. For every transmission of v by $\mathcal{V}$, $\mathcal{A}$ will successfully transmit 4 messages and their TECs will increase by 7 and 4, respectively. If $\mathcal{A}$ injects on every v, then $\mathcal{V}$ goes to error passive with 19 attack messages, while $\mathcal{A}$ would only reach a TEC of 76, but $\mathcal{A}$ gets stuck in the error-passive state on the 31st attack injection before $\mathcal{V}$ reaches bus-off, and the attack would fail. If instead $\mathcal{A}$ injects every other v, skipping one iteration, $\mathcal{V}$ would increase its TEC by 6 and $\mathcal{A}$'s TEC would increase by 0 (fully recover) between attack injections. Thus, $\mathcal{V}$ would reach error passive after 21 injections, and bus-off after 43.

E. Randomized Bit Positions

Creating a generalizeable non-deterministic attack strategy is challenging because it depends on $\mathcal{A}$'s ability to predict the bits of v. Despite this challenge, $\mathcal{A}$ can employ simple heuristics to increase the variability of the bit-error position within the DLC and data fields of $v_{\mathcal{A}}$. The DLC of most messages is a fixed constant that can be discovered by offline analysis of a CAN trace. The number of dominant bits in valid DLCs vary between 1 and 3, so the entropy for a random injection is low; a clever adversary will inject recessive errors in the data field.

The data field often encodes a number that does not change quickly because of physical constraints or an event identifier that comes from a limited set of events. Messages often repeat identically for long intervals. If $\mathcal{A}$ can identify a deterministic pattern, then the recessive error can be injected in the data. Variation within the data field—or lack thereof—is vehicle-specific. Taylor et al. [34] found that one vehicle (2012 Subaru Impreza) used 20 IDs for which "many bits were observed to always be zero" that could reliably be used by $\mathcal{A}$ to inject recessive errors.

IV. Evaluation

We use a benchtop CAN bus and real vehicle for experimental validation of WeepingCAN using off-the-shelf hardware and in-house software. We conducted several experiments to evaluate the ideas presented in this paper.

A. Experimental Setup

The benchtop platform includes five microcontrollers—two BeagleBone Black (BBB), and three TM4C129EXL (TM4C) boards—that integrate hardware CAN controllers with the processor chip. We connect them to SN65HVD23x CAN transceivers that connect via 3.3v CAN in a breadboard. We use a Saleae Logic Pro 16 to snoop the bus. We run custom normal workloads and attacker code.

1) Synthetic Benchmark: We adapt the Synthetic Benchmark from Cho and Shin [4] to reproduce some of their results. Specifically, we configure a 500 kbps CAN using three TM4C boards as nodes X, V, and A to recreate their 3-node setup. Node X sends message IDs 7 and 9 at a 10 ms period. Node V sends message ID 17 when it receives ID 7 hence also at 10 ms period. Node A is the attacker.

2) SAE Benchmark: As an intermediate step toward real vehicles we adopt a modified SAE Benchmark [35] with sporadic messages omitted. We define message priorities inversely to their periods and use constant valued data fields. We break ties (identical periods) by static prioritization of the subsystems as follows in decreasing priority order: Vehicle Controller (VC), Brakes, Battery, Driver, Inverter/Motor Controller (IMC), and Transmission (Trans). Table I shows the benchmark parameters. Note that, when the subsystems synchronize with each other, every message except A0 has at least one genuine preceded ID. In general, they only synchronize by happenstance.

To allocate the subsystems to boards in our benchtop setup, we analyze their suitability as both victim and attacker by calculating Eq. 1 for each combination of subsystem. The Battery, Brakes, and Trans subsystems can satisfy the role of victim. The VC, Driver, IMC, and Trans subsystems can be the attacker in decreasing order of preference. We place the VC, Driver, and Brakes on separate TM4Cs, IMC on its own BBB, and Battery and Trans together on another BBB.

TABLE I. PARAMETERS FOR MODIFIED SAE BENCHMARK [35]

Sending ECU	VC			Brakes		Battery			Driver		IMC		Trans		
CAN ID (hex)	A0	B0	D0	A1	C1	B2	C2	D2	A3	B3	A4	B4	A5	C5	D5
Size (B)	1	6	1	2	1	1	4	3	1	2	2	2	1	1	1
Period (ms)	5	10	1000	5	100	10	100	1000	5	10	5	10	5	100	1000

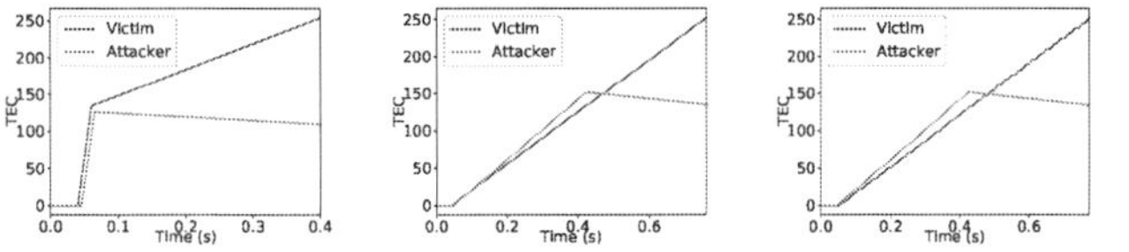

(a) original (b) auto (c) abort transmit error

Fig. 2. TEC increase of dominant bus-off attack with/without retransmissions.

3) F1 Attack Detector: We used the approach described by Cho and Shin [4] to identify consecutive errors (feature F1) as indicative of a bus-off attack. We report the performance of this *F1 attack detector* in each experiment except for the last experiment conducted with a real vehicle because we are unable to observe the internal state of real ECUs.

B. Experiment 1: Bus-Off Attack Reproduction

The first experiment that we conducted is a reproduction of the original bus-off attack. We replicated the attack to conduct this experiment using the Synthetic Benchmark setup. The message ID 9 is the genuine preceded ID of 17. Both messages are transmitted with a period of 10 ms.

We examined 100 classic bus-off attacks implemented as described by Cho and Shin [4]. Fig. 2(a) shows how the victim and attacker TECs grow over time with these attacks; these plots show the mean over the 100 trials, and all results are nearly identical.

The F1 detector identified 100% of the attacks with each synchronization approach and detected 15 retransmissions.

C. Experiment 2: Disabling Retransmissions

As an intermediate step to the full WeepingCAN attack, we first consider the effect of disabling retransmissions while continuing to use dominant bit errors as in the original bus-off attack. Here we evaluate the two approaches for disabling $v_{\mathcal{A}}$'s retransmission: (1) disable automatic retransmissions, and (2) abort transmission on transmit error. We implemented each approach with the TM4C boards. They have TTCAN capability, support interrupts on bit or stuff errors, and can selectively abort messages. We measure performance in terms of two metrics: successful injection rate and injection retransmission rate. Best performance is a high (100%) injection rate and low (0%) retransmission rate as measured by the F1 detector.

We again use the Synthetic Benchmark with dominant bit errors. Node X reliably transmits both preceded messages of 17, therefore $\mathcal{A}$ and $\mathcal{V}$ can be perfectly synchronized, which isolates the variable of retransmission approach.

We examined 100 bus-off attacks with each approach to disable retransmissions and measured the number of successful attacks and visible transmissions by the attacker. We obtain these measurements by monitoring the victim (V) and attacker (A) nodes TEC values: each increase by 8 is a successful injection, while multiples of 8 indicate retransmissions.

Disabling automatic retransmissions is done by configuring the CAN controller. For aborting the transmission on transmit error we clear the transmit message buffer for the attack message in the interrupt handler on a bit or stuff error.

Fig. 2(b) and 2(c) show the increase in TEC for victim and attacker when retransmissions are disabled. Notably, the initial increase in TEC is much longer and smoother, and the attacker's TEC even increases faster than the victim's, but the use of a dominant bit error allows for the original attack to still succeed despite the slower TEC growth of the victim. The attacker transmits messages successfully because of the dominant bit error: both disabling automatic retransmission and aborting on the transmit error result in 18 successful transmissions.

The F1 attack detector identified 0% of the attacks for all three approaches. Thus, although these attacks are still based on dominant bit injections, the F1 feature can be eliminated to avoid existing detection techniques.

D. Experiment 3: Skipping Attack

We now switch gears to study the stealthy attack by investigating the effectiveness of skipping attack iterations with recessive injections. For this experiment we use both the Synthetic Benchmark and the SAE Benchmark. We evaluate effectiveness based on the time needed to complete the attack successfully, the number of completed transmissions of $v_{\mathcal{A}}$, and the F1 detection rate.

Fig. 3 shows mean TEC increases of 100 attacks skipping 2 to 6 cycles per injection (500 total attacks) with a slight modification of the Synthetic Benchmark: node A does not transmit authentic messages thus cannot recover its TEC, so we add two messages that node A transmits at a period of 10 ms but offset by 5 ms from V's transmission of ID 17. Nodes X and V are unmodified.

Nodes A and V transmit a difference of 1 successful message per attack, thus A's TEC increases by 6 and V's by 7 each cycle. This difference is exactly as described in the example of Section III, and the attack can succeed by skipping 2 to 6 iterations as explained previously. None of the trials generated any completed transmissions of $v_{\mathcal{A}}$ and they all successfully put V in bus-off.

The F1 attack detector identified 0% of these attacks and they all had 0 transmissions of $v_{\mathcal{A}}$ prior to bus-off of $\mathcal{V}$.

With the SAE Benchmark, the Battery can be attacked with the VC, Driver, or IMC by skipping 1 to 5 cycles. Brakes and Trans can be attacked by VC, Driver, or IMC by skipping 4 or 5. We conducted 75 WeepingCAN attacks skipping 5 cycles with VC attacking Brakes. The attacker succeeds in 78.1% of the attacks. The minimum and median number of transmissions

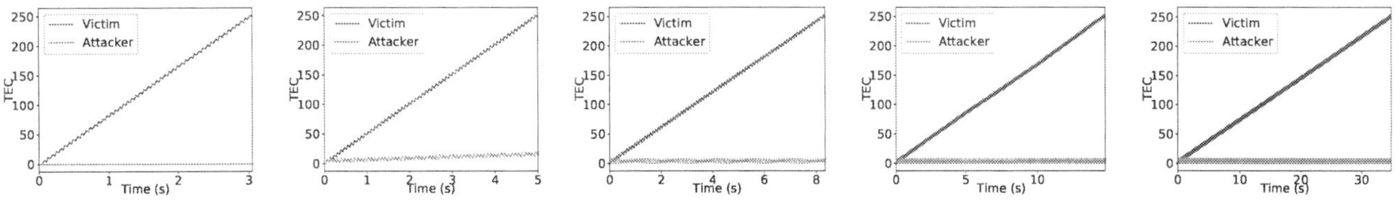

(a) Skip 2 (b) Skip 3 (c) Skip 4 (d) Skip 5 (e) Skip 6

Fig. 3. TEC increase of WeepingCAN attack with skipping. The apparent thickness of the line with increasing skip amounts is due to the slow progression of increasing and then recovering some TEC with each injection. Note the change in timescales on the X axes.

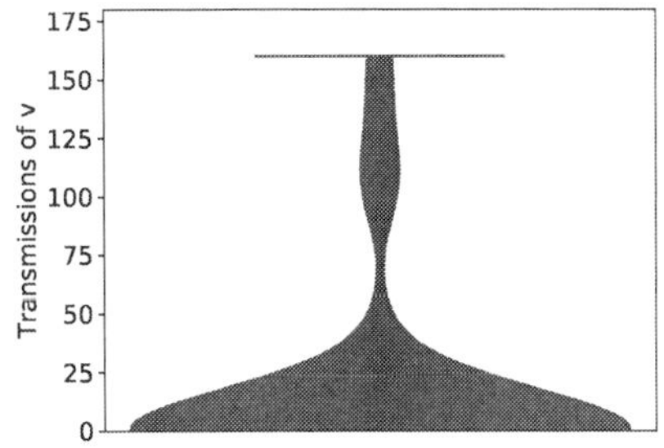

Fig. 4. Distribution of transmissions of the victim's ID during 75 attacks.

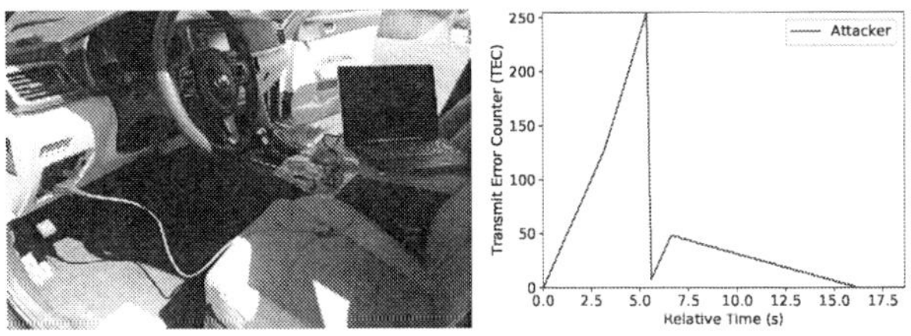

(a) Kia Setup (b) Attacker's TEC

Fig. 5. Evaluation with Real Vehicle (Kia Optima 2016)

of $v_{\mathcal{A}}$ was 0, with a maximum of 160 transmissions. The trials that failed did not manage to synchronize with the victim, which resulted in mis-timed injections. Figure 4 shows a violin plot depicting the distribution of transmissions of $v_{\mathcal{A}}$. Zero transmissions indicates good synchronization and stealthiness, while higher numbers are less stealthy and have been caused by poor synchronization. The F1 attack detector identified 2.7% of the attacks, which we attribute to the lost synchronization. Fig. 4 shows the number of transmissions prior to bus-off for the SAE Benchmark was often but not always 0.

1) Experiment 4: Real Vehicle: As a proof-of-concept, we conducted WeepingCAN on a 2016 Kia Optima (Fig. 5(a)) in a safe environment. We identified a low priority message with a genuine preceded ID transmitted in the accessory mode. The targeted message transmits with a period of 100 ms. We attached a TM4C board configured to attack with the abort on transmit error policy. Although we do not have access to the interior state of the target ECU, we used the bus and attacking board to understand the attack's effectiveness. We attempted WeepingCAN against the low priority message (v) in accessory mode three times with one success. Fig. 5(b) shows the change in the $\mathcal{A}$'s TEC for the successful trial. In this trial, v is not observed on the bus for about 3 seconds, and $\mathcal{A}$ does not transmit any messages until about 7 seconds after starting the attack—the second peak, at which point the attacker loses synchronization with the target. Note that the attacker enters bus-off because it is not transmitting additional messages on the bus, and we immediately reset the attack node and rejoin the bus as soon as allowed. Our results indicate that WeepingCAN is feasible to conduct against ECUs in real vehicles with stealthy and devastating results.

V. Conclusion

We introduced WeepingCAN as a stealthy variant of the original bus-off attack that requires similar capabilities to conduct but lacks the same detectable features to defend against it. WeepingCAN is generalizeable: the attack assumptions are satisfied by modern vehicles that use CAN. We evaluated WeepingCAN in synthetic benchmarks and with a real vehicle, and we found the attack succeeds over 75% of the time under realistic bus loads. In future work, we plan to investigate methods to improve the attack effectiveness and thoroughly explore its stealthiness and detectability. We are interested in considering secure network architectures [2], physical-layer IDS, and secure transceivers as promising methods for attack detection or prevention. WeepingCAN's stealthy nature makes it a challenging problem deserving of further investigation.

Acknowledgment

This work is partially supported by NSF CNS-2011620, NSF OAC-2001789, and Colorado State Bill 18-086.

References

[1] P. Bajpai, R. Enbody, and B. H. Cheng, "Ransomware Targeting Automobiles," in *Proceedings of the Second ACM Workshop on Automotive and Aerial Vehicle Security*. ACM, Mar. 2020, pp. 23–29.

[2] G. Bloom, G. Cena, I. C. Bertolotti, T. Hu, and A. Valenzano, "Supporting security protocols on CAN-based networks," in *2017 IEEE International Conference on Industrial Technology (ICIT)*, Mar. 2017, pp. 1334–1339.

[3] S. Checkoway, D. McCoy, B. Kantor, D. Anderson, H. Shacham, S. Savage, K. Koscher, A. Czeskis, F. Roesner, and T. Kohno, "Comprehensive Experimental Analyses of Automotive Attack Surfaces," in *20th USENIX Security Symposium*. USENIX Association, 2011, pp. 447–462.

[4] K.-T. Cho and K. G. Shin, "Error Handling of In-Vehicle Networks Makes Them Vulnerable," in *Proceedings of the 2016 ACM SIGSAC Conference on Computer and Communications Security*. ACM, 2016, pp. 1044–1055.

[5] ——, "Fingerprinting electronic control units for vehicle intrusion detection," in *25th USENIX Security Symposium (USENIX Security 16)*, 2016, pp. 911–927.

[6] ——, "Viden: Attacker Identification on In-Vehicle Networks," in *Proceedings of the 2017 ACM SIGSAC Conference on Computer and Communications Security*. ACM, Oct. 2017, pp. 1109–1123.

[7] W. Choi, K. Joo, H. J. Jo, M. C. Park, and D. H. Lee, "VoltageIDS: Low-Level Communication Characteristics for Automotive Intrusion Detection System," *IEEE Transactions on Information Forensics and Security*, vol. 13, no. 8, pp. 2114–2129, Aug. 2018.

[8] B. Elend and T. Adamson, "Cyber security enhancing CAN transceivers," in *Proceedings of the 16th International CAN Conference*, 2017.

[9] U. Ezeobi, H. Olufowobi, C. Young, J. Zambreno, and G. Bloom, "Reverse Engineering Controller Area Network Messages using Unsupervised Machine Learning," *IEEE Consumer Electronics Magazine*, pp. 1–1, 2020.

[10] M. Foruhandeh, Y. Man, R. Gerdes, M. Li, and T. Chantem, "SIMPLE: Single-Frame Based Physical Layer Identification for Intrusion Detection and Prevention on in-Vehicle Networks," in *Proceedings of the 35th Annual Computer Security Applications Conference*. ACM, 2019, pp. 229–244.

[11] S. Halder, M. Conti, and S. K. Das, "COIDS: A Clock Offset Based Intrusion Detection System for Controller Area Networks," in *Proceedings of the 21st International Conference on Distributed Computing and Networking*. ACM, Jan. 2020, pp. 1–10.

[12] S. Hu, Q. A. Chen, J. Joung, C. Carlak, Y. Feng, Z. M. Mao, and H. X. Liu, "CVShield: Guarding Sensor Data in Connected Vehicle with Trusted Execution Environment," in *Proceedings of the Second ACM Workshop on Automotive and Aerial Vehicle Security*. New York, NY, USA: Association for Computing Machinery, Mar. 2020, pp. 1–4.

[13] T. Hu, "Deterministic and flexible communication for real-time embedded systems," PhD Thesis, Ph. D Thesis, 2015.

[14] H. J. Jo, J. H. Kim, H.-Y. Choi, W. Choi, D. H. Lee, and I. Lee, "MAuth-CAN: Masquerade-Attack-Proof Authentication for In-Vehicle Networks," *IEEE Transactions on Vehicular Technology*, pp. 1–1, 2019.

[15] M. Kneib, O. Schell, and C. Huth, "EASI: Edge-Based Sender Identification on Resource-Constrained Platforms for Automotive Networks," Feb. 2020.

[16] K. Koscher, A. Czeskis, F. Roesner, S. Patel, T. Kohno, S. Checkoway, D. McCoy, B. Kantor, D. Anderson, H. Shacham, and S. Savage, "Experimental Security Analysis of a Modern Automobile," in *2010 IEEE Symposium on Security and Privacy*, May 2010, pp. 447–462.

[17] T. Koyama, T. Shibahara, K. Hasegawa, Y. Okano, M. Tanaka, and Y. Oshima, "Anomaly Detection for Mixed Transmission CAN Messages Using Quantized Intervals and Absolute Difference of Payloads," in *Proceedings of the ACM Workshop on Automotive Cybersecurity*. ACM, Mar. 2019, pp. 19–24.

[18] S. Kulandaivel, T. Goyal, A. K. Agrawal, and V. Sekar, "CANvas: Fast and Inexpensive Automotive Network Mapping," in *28th USENIX Security Symposium (USENIX Security 19)*. USENIX Association, Aug. 2019, pp. 389–405.

[19] S. Longari, M. Penco, M. Carminati, and S. Zanero, "CopyCAN: An Error-Handling Protocol Based Intrusion Detection System for Controller Area Network," in *Proceedings of the ACM Workshop on Cyber-Physical Systems Security & Privacy*. ACM, 2019, pp. 39–50.

[20] T. Mishra, T. Chantem, and R. Gerdes, "TEECheck: Securing Intra-Vehicular Communication Using Trusted Execution," in *Proceedings of the 28th International Conference on Real-Time Networks and Systems*. New York, NY: ACM, Jun. 2020, pp. 128–138.

[21] S. Mukherjee, J. Walkery, I. Rayz, and J. Daily, "A Precedence Graph-Based Approach to Detect Message Injection Attacks in J1939 Based Networks," in *2017 15th Annual Conference on Privacy, Security and Trust (PST)*, Aug. 2017, pp. 67–6709.

[22] S. Mukherjee, H. Shirazi, I. Ray, J. Daily, and R. Gamble, "Practical DoS Attacks on Embedded Networks in Commercial Vehicles," in *Information Systems Security*, ser. Lecture Notes in Computer Science, I. Ray, M. S. Gaur, M. Conti, D. Sanghi, and V. Kamakoti, Eds. Cham: Springer International Publishing, 2016, pp. 23–42.

[23] M. D. Natale, H. Zeng, P. Giusto, and A. Ghosal, *Understanding and Using the Controller Area Network Communication Protocol: Theory and Practice*. Springer-Verlag, 2012.

[24] H. Olufowobi, G. Bloom, C. Young, and J. Zambreno, "Work-in-Progress: Real-Time Modeling for Intrusion Detection in Automotive Controller Area Network," in *2018 IEEE Real-Time Systems Symposium (RTSS)*, Dec. 2018, pp. 161–164.

[25] H. Olufowobi and G. Bloom, "Chapter 16 - Connected Cars: Automotive Cybersecurity and Privacy for Smart Cities," in *Smart Cities Cybersecurity and Privacy*. Elsevier, Jan. 2019, pp. 227–240.

[26] H. Olufowobi, U. Ezeobi, E. Muhati, G. Robinson, C. Young, J. Zambreno, and G. Bloom, "Anomaly Detection Approach Using Adaptive Cumulative Sum Algorithm for Controller Area Network," in *Proceedings of the ACM Workshop on Automotive Cybersecurity*. ACM, 2019, pp. 25–30.

[27] H. Olufowobi, S. Hounsinou, and G. Bloom, "Controller Area Network Intrusion Prevention System Leveraging Fault Recovery," in *Proceedings of the ACM Workshop on Cyber-Physical Systems Security & Privacy*. ACM, 2019, pp. 63–73.

[28] H. Olufowobi, C. Young, J. Zambreno, and G. Bloom, "SAIDuCANT: Specification-Based Automotive Intrusion Detection Using Controller Area Network (CAN) Timing," *IEEE Transactions on Vehicular Technology*, vol. 69, no. 2, pp. 1484–1494, Feb. 2020.

[29] M. D. Pesé, T. Stacer, C. A. Campos, E. Newberry, D. Chen, and K. G. Shin, "LibreCAN: Automated CAN Message Translator," in *Proceedings of the 2019 ACM SIGSAC Conference on Computer and Communications Security*. ACM, 2019, pp. 2283–2300.

[30] S. U. Sagong, X. Ying, A. Clark, L. Bushnell, and R. Poovendran, "Cloaking the Clock: Emulating Clock Skew in Controller Area Networks," in *2018 ACM/IEEE 9th International Conference on Cyber-Physical Systems (ICCPS)*, Apr. 2018, pp. 32–42.

[31] H. Shirazi, I. Ray, and C. Anderson, "Using Machine Learning to Detect Anomalies in Embedded Networks in Heavy Vehicles," in *Foundations and Practice of Security*, ser. Lecture Notes in Computer Science, A. Benzekri, M. Barbeau, G. Gong, R. Laborde, and J. Garcia-Alfaro, Eds. Cham: Springer International Publishing, 2020, pp. 39–55.

[32] D. Souma, A. Mori, H. Yamamoto, and Y. Hata, "Counter Attacks for Bus-off Attacks," in *Computer Safety, Reliability, and Security*, B. Gallina, A. Skavhaug, E. Schoitsch, and F. Bitsch, Eds. Springer International Publishing, 2018, pp. 319–330.

[33] M. Takada, Y. Osada, and M. Morii, "Counter Attack Against the Bus-Off Attack on CAN," in *2019 14th Asia Joint Conference on Information Security (AsiaJCIS)*, Aug. 2019, pp. 96–102.

[34] A. Taylor, S. Leblanc, and N. Japkowicz, "Anomaly Detection in Automobile Control Network Data with Long Short-Term Memory Networks," in *2016 IEEE International Conference on Data Science and Advanced Analytics (DSAA)*, Oct. 2016, pp. 130–139.

[35] K. Tindell, A. Burns, and A. J. Wellings, "Calculating controller area network (can) message response times," *Control Engineering Practice*, vol. 3, no. 8, pp. 1163–1169, Aug. 1995.

[36] H. Wen, Q. A. Chen, and Z. Lin, "Plug-N-Pwned: Comprehensive Vulnerability Analysis of OBD-II Dongles as A New Over-the-Air Attack Surface in Automotive IoT," 2020, pp. 949–965.

[37] H. Wen, Q. Zhao, Q. A. Chen, and Z. Lin, "Automated cross-platform reverse engineering of can bus commands from mobile apps."

[38] C. Young, H. Olufowobi, G. Bloom, and J. Zambreno, "Automotive Intrusion Detection Based on Constant CAN Message Frequencies Across Vehicle Driving Modes," in *Proceedings of the ACM Workshop on Automotive Cybersecurity*. ACM, 2019, pp. 9–14.

[39] C. Young, J. Zambreno, and G. Bloom, "Towards a Fail-Operational Intrusion Detection System for In-Vehicle Networks," in *Proceedings of the Workshop on Security and Dependability of Critical Embedded Real-Time Systems (CERTS)*, Nov. 2016.

[40] C. Young, J. Zambreno, H. Olufowobi, and G. Bloom, "Survey of Automotive Controller Area Network Intrusion Detection Systems," *IEEE Design Test*, vol. 36, no. 6, pp. 48–55, Dec. 2019.

[41] J. Zhou, P. Joshi, H. Zeng, and R. Li, "BTMonitor: Bit-time-based Intrusion Detection and Attacker Identification in Controller Area Network," Nov. 2019.

Securing CAN Traffic on J1939 Networks

Jeremy Daily, David Nnaji and Ben Ettlinger
Colorado State University
{jeremy.daily,david.nnaji,ben.ettlinger}@colostate.edu

***Abstract*—Controller Area Network (CAN) implementations inherently trust all valid messages on the network. While this feature makes for easy replacement and repair of electronic control units (ECUs), this trust poses some cybersecurity challenges, like making it easy to spoof messages or alter them with a middle-person attack. With an SAE J1939 based network, the meaning of the network messages are often published, which reduces the amount of work needed to reverse engineer the protocol. Furthermore, J1939 is often used on high-value and high-risk cyber-physical systems, like trucks, buses, generator systems, construction, agriculture, forestry, and marine and military systems. Therefore, improving the cybersecurity posture of SAE J1939 networks is crucial for protecting critical infrastructure.**

The approach outlined in this paper for an intrusion detection system (IDS) uses so-called CAN Conditioners at or in each of the vehicle ECUSs that communicate with the Secure Gateway near the vehicle's diagnostic port. Each of the CAN Conditioners and the Secure Gateway includes an allowlist and blocklist procedure to prevent a variety of unauthorized network attacks. In addition, a cipher-based message authentication code (CMAC) is calculated by each node and transmitted across the network using the J1939 Data Security Message parameter group number (PGN). This CMAC message acts as a heartbeat indicator for the Secure Gateway to verify healthy node behavior and unaltered messaging.

Reference prototype hardware and software are described and results from a test implementation on a Class 6 truck with 6.7L diesel engine and an automated transmission are also described. The provisioning process sets up hardware security modules to be able to exchange secrets over the CAN bus using the elliptic-curve Diffie-Hellman protocol (ECDH). Once secrets are exchanged, ephemeral session keys are shared with the Secure Gateway, which keeps track of the CMACs from each CAN Conditioner. If a CMAC fails to match, the Secure Gateway informs the network using the J1939 Diagnostic Message #1 and a message using the J1939 defined Impostor PG Alert parameter group. Results show the IDS can detect alteration of a message or an impersonated message.

I. Introduction

Heavy vehicles are a vital part of the global economy as they are responsible for delivering people and goods to all corners of the world. These vehicles typically use SAE J1939 based networks. The J1939 network is built on top of the CAN2.0b specification and uses 29-bit identifiers. Not only do cybersecurity concerns with CAN based systems apply to J1939, but J1939 specific cybersecurity concerns also exist [1], [2]. In response to these concerns, the National Motor Freight Traffic Association reported on the state of heavy vehicle cybersecurity in a comprehensive whitepaper [3].

A. CAN and J1939 Cybersecurity Vulnerabilities

Together, the ISO 11898 standard and the SAE J1939 recommended practice define the common networking layers of the OSI reference model for heavy vehicle systems. As shown in Fig. 1, SAE J1939 exclusively defines the upper layers of the vehicle model. For example, SAE J1939 provides standardization for non-proprietary Arbitration IDs as well as multi-frame transport protocol messages.

OSI Reference Model	Vehicle Standards
Application	J1939/71 J1939/73
Presentation Session	Null
Transport	J1939/21
Network	J1939/31
Data Link	J1939/21 ISO 11898
Physical	J1939/11 J1939/12 J1939/14 J1939/15 ISO 11898

Fig. 1: Vehicle standards mapped to OSI Network Model.

The fundamental issue being addressed is that CAN messages are trusted by all receiving nodes on the bus. Every message received is treated as if it were already authorized. The CAN messaging protocol is a multi-master network, with all nodes receiving all messages. The only check performed on the message is a cyclic redundancy check (CRC) to validate the integrity of the frame field in the case of bit-flips. All messages are received by all nodes immediately upon sending. Individual modules do not include authentication systems. In SAE J1939 networks, the source address (SA), which is the last byte of the arbitration ID shown in Fig. 2, tells the network which controller application is sending the message. Since this value is self-reported, it can be falsified.

Priority	Reserved	Data Page	PDU Format	PDU Specific	SA
3 bits	1 bit	1 bit	8 bits	8bits	8 bits

Fig. 2: Structure of 29-bit Extended CAN ID.

Workshop on Automotive and Autonomous Vehicle Security (AutoSec) 2021
25 February 2021, Virtual

https://dx.doi.org/10.14722/autosec.2021.23031
www.ndss-symposium.org

This poses a cybersecurity risk because if a node becomes compromised, or if a rogue node is introduced to the network, the control units of the vehicle have no method of determining which messages are authorized and come from the proper source, and which messages are from the attacking node. Due to the historically air-gapped nature of vehicles, this vulnerability has not been a threat until recently, as any attacks would require physical access to the vehicle. Attacks based upon physical access to the system do not scale well. However, with the rise in wireless telematics devices, infotainment systems, and wireless electronic logging devices, new wireless attack surfaces have been introduced to the vehicle CAN network. These wireless attacks may be able to scale, which is a cybersecurity concern.

To combat the potential for cybersecurity attacks against heavy vehicle networks, an intrusion detection system is proposed that introduces traditional network cybersecurity to the legacy CAN protocol using PGNs for Data Security, Imposter PG Alert, and Diagnostic Messages as defined in the SAE Recommended Practice J1939 [4].

This is accomplished using devices at each of the network nodes and another on the diagnostic port. Each device implements a message send allowlist, which prevents its node from sending unauthorized messages, and an incoming message blocklist, which prevents fraudulent messages from reaching the protected node. To monitor the continued cybersecurity health of the devices, each device at the node transmit a message containing a CMAC, which is verified by the secure diagnostic node. Together, these measures mitigate the threat of compromised and rogue nodes on the network.

B. *Background Information*

Functionally, the CAN Conditioners and Secure Gateway devices utilize three useful security concepts: message authentication, firewalls, and intrusion detection. As noted earlier, message authentication is the process of determining if a message has been modified in transit or replayed. Message authentication can also extend to verification that the message came from a legitimate source. CAN uses message CRCs for fault detection but this is largely insufficient to prevent tampering. In modern Internet security, comprehensive authentication is usually accomplished with a combination of multiple techniques including checksums, message authentication codes (MACs), authenticated encryption, or digital signatures. However, constraints within CAN have made direct implementations of these techniques unwieldy. For example, the maximum data payload for a CAN frame is 8-bytes which limits the ability to append cryptographic information like a MAC since these often require at least twice as much data.

Despite this limitation, many message authentication approaches for CAN have been proposed. A review of secure communication approaches in 2018 identified and compared 8 unique methods for implementing MACs from various research publications [5]. For each method, the authors identified the type of algorithm used, the MAC position, MAC size, the computational requirements, and other constraints. CMAC was a commonly selected algorithm among the methods but had the highest computational cost. Despite the variety of methods reviewed, nearly all them lead to increased latency, increased bus load.

AUTOSAR SecOC also mentions CMAC for CAN frames but implementing it would require changes to the existing J1939 standard messaging [6]. Given a requirement for compatibility with legacy systems, approaches that require changes to the J1939 protocol hinder their adoption. Furthermore, many ECUs are required to operate under full bus loads and are resource-limited which prevents the adoption of computationally intensive approaches. However, research has suggested that the calculation times associated with CMACs could be sufficiently offset with the use of hardware-based acceleration [5].

To overcome the deficiencies of using MACs alone, a number of IDSs have been proposed. For example, engineers from NXP Semiconductors have proposed a distributed detection methodology that utilizes CAN message filtering at the transceiver level [7]. In short, the system leverages the NXP TJA115x CAN transceiver's supervisory capabilities to analyze received and transmitted messages of its host ECU in real-time. When faulty behavior is detected, the transceiver will reduce the functionality of its host by sending error frames to the bus [7].

Specifically, the transceiver can be provisioned with an allow and blocklist to prevent spoofing and tampering on the transmit and receive paths. It is also equipped with a message buffering system known as a "leaky-bucket" to minimize the threat of message flooding (DoS) attacks [7]. When these functions are combined into a security model, the result is analogous to a firewalls at each host ECU with added levels of authentication.

II. Needs Analysis and Conceptual Design

To determine the needs and propose a design concept, a threat model is needed. The scope of this project encompasses the internal J1939 heavy vehicle network and its connected ECUs. This means any diagnostic system, as described in [8], is out of scope. As a result, the following attack vectors based on the diagram in Fig. 3 are considered:

1) *Rogue Node.* A malicious node is installed onto J1939 network. The malicious node could be physically installed or the programming on an existing node could be compromised.
2) *Supply Chain.* A new node is installed that has malicious code pre-programmed.
3) *Middle-Person Attack.* A node is installed in the middle of the J1939 network and can alter a message from one side of the network to the other.

Any node on the vehicle can act in ways that violate the rules for normal transmission of messages. Therefore, the need is to detect the violations in a consistent and robust manner. Furthermore, system resilience is considered only up to violation detection as opposed to any additional mitigation.

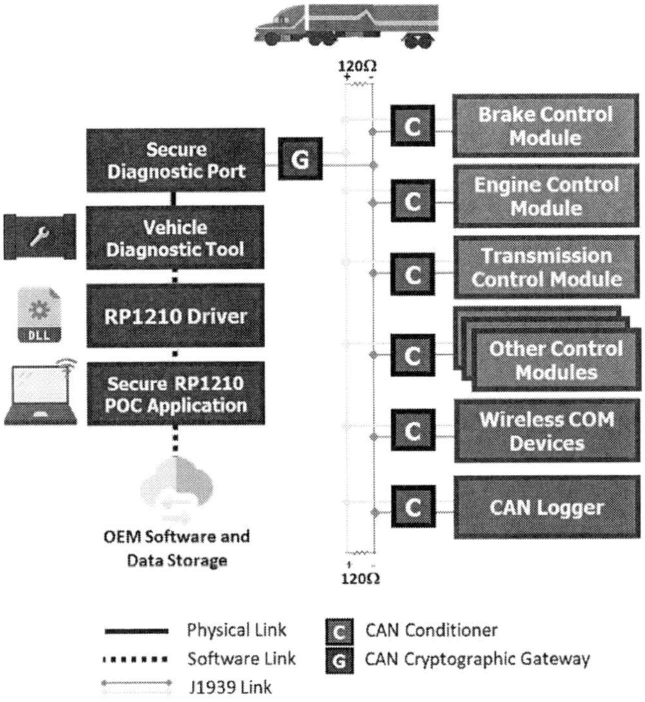

Fig. 3: J1939 network diagram with Secure Diagnostic Connection and Intrusion Detection System Installed

The concept shown in Fig. 3 aims to enforce the rules for the utilization of the CAN bus. The CAN Conditioners, denoted with a "C" are intended to watch and react to the network traffic coming in and out of each node. This concept was proposed by NXP with their "Stinger" CAN Transceiver [7]. This concept implements allowlist for known good messages, blocklists for messages known to not be allowed, and rate limiting to prevent bus flooding and enforce CAN timing.

The secure transceiver approach works only on IDs at this time. However, a middle-person attack can alter message content without detection. To detect message alteration, a message authentication code (MAC) must be calculated and periodically transmitted. Unfortunately, there are few practical ways to embed MACs with 8-byte J1939 frames. As such, the concept is to introduce a sentinel message that contains a MAC for comparison with the received MAC.

The Secure Gateway, denoted with a "G" in Fig. 3, collects all messages and calculates a MAC independent of the CAN Conditioner. The Secure Gateway will compare the MAC it calculates to the MAC it receives to determine if any contents have changed.

III. Requirements

There are two sets of requirements based on the needs of the project. The first set is for the heavy vehicle system and the second set is for cybersecurity. The vehicle system is depicted in Fig. 3. This is a single J1939 specified network connecting typical ECUs on a CAN bus. The system is compliant with SAE J1939 specifications, which means one or more unique controller applications (CAs) reside on an ECU. Each controller application is assigned a SA that is transmitted as the last eight bits in the 29-bit CAN identifier.

CAN Conditioners are installed in the stubs of the wiring harness in such a manner where only one ECU is present on the unprotected side and the J1939 backbone is connected on the other side. This makes the CAN Conditioner like a firewall or gateway device.

In a fashion similar to [9], we define our requirements in two categories, system and cybersecurity.

A. System Requirements

The system is a heavy vehicle using SAE J1939 for in-vehicle networking. The proposed modifications must satisfy the following requirements:

- SR1 CAN Conditioners must be able to support a throughput of 100% busload at 500kbps.
- SR2 Intrusions (i.e. rule violations) should always be detected.
- SR3 False Positives (i.e. detecting a violation when there was not) are not tolerated and should be less than 0.0001%, which is consistent with the reliability of other sensor systems on the vehicle.
- SR4 Longevity - the system must maintain its performance for long periods of operation (i.e. 24 hours) and long vehicle lifetimes (i.e. 20 years).
- SR5 The solution must be applicable to existing and legacy J1939 enabled vehicles. This means CAN frames are restricted to 8 bytes with 29-bit arbitration identifiers.
- SR6 The solution must comply with other vehicle system requirements.

Based on these system requirements, statistics or machine learning based intrusion detection systems are disqualified because the false-positive rate of those approaches is too high. Therefore, deterministic strategies based on message authentication codes are pursued instead.

Another restriction for the solution is the necessity to work with legacy vehicle systems. This eliminates the use of CAN-FD or Automotive Ethernet and the solution is restricted to use the CAN 2.0b specification of SAE J1939.

B. Cybersecurity Requirements

- CS1 Each device must have a unique, unknowable private key that is stored exclusively in a hardware security module (HSM).
- CS2 Randomly generated numbers must have high entropy and unpredictable seeds.
- CS3 No new ciphers or algorithms will be used for cryptographic operations (i.e. use well-known AES, ECC, and RSA ciphers)
- CS4 Session keys must never be transmitted in the clear over the network.

Based on these design requirements, the two components of the conceptual design will be discussed: (1) the Secure Gateway and (2) the CAN Conditioners.

Fig. 4: Hardware prototype utilizing the Teensy 4.0 development board, the ATECC608A security module and 2 CAN transceivers.

IV. Secure Gateway

In [8], Daily and Kulkarni introduced a prototype secure gateway based on the Teensy 4.0 development board and the Microchip ATECC608A hardware security module. The paper detailed a strategy to provision the hardware security module and exchange device keys using the elliptic curve Diffie-Hellman (ECDH) protocol. Once device keys are exchanged, they are used to encipher session keys. These random session keys and initialization vectors are used to setup an AES-128 cipher in CBC mode. This cipher is used to encrypt and decrypt messages from a secure gateway (shown in Fig. 3) to a secure PC diagnostics application. However, the Secure Gateway can also communicate on the J1939 network, albeit not using enciphered traffic.

Since the hardware for the Secure Gateway has two CAN channels, a hardware security module, and a robust processor, it is selected as the hardware for both the CAN Conditioner and Secure Gateway. The detailed hardware prototype schematic is available on Github [10]. A prototype of the hardware is shown in Fig. 4.

V. CAN Conditioners

A. Functional Overview

As seen in Fig. 3, all incoming messages on the CAN bus and outgoing messages from an ECU must go through the CAN Conditioner (or Secure Gateway for diagnostic connections). The CAN Conditioner compares each incoming or outgoing message to the allowlist/blocklist to mitigate spoofing attacks. The allowlists and blocklists are based on the CAN ID, specifically the SA.

If an incoming message to a node, such as the Engine Control Module, contains a blocklisted SA, then the CAN Conditioner does not forward the message to the engine control module. This could be due to a rogue node sending fraudulent engine messages.

If an outgoing message from the protected ECU contains a SA which does not match the SA of its host listed on its allowlist, the CAN Conditioner does not forward the message to the rest of the J1939 network. This could be the case due to a compromised node sending fraudulent messages to the network.

Furthermore, each CAN Conditioner enforces a short pause between transmitting messages. This pause is on the order of 1-3 milliseconds, which is like the "leaky bucket" defense.

B. CMAC Health Monitoring

To augment the protections provided by the CAN Conditioners, each Conditioner generates an individual shared secret with the Secure Gateway node. This shared secret is generated using a Diffie-Hellman key exchange, in which both devices share an encrypted session key, resulting in a unique session key known only to both devices performing the exchange. At all points during the exchange, the information is encrypted and indecipherable in transit. Even if another node captured all key exchange messages, the session key could not be learned due to the use of individual device private keys created when provisioning their HSMs.

Once a session key is securely generated and exchanged between a CAN Conditioner and the Secure Gateway, it is then used by the CAN Conditioner to generate a CMAC. A portion of this CMAC is transmitted across the network. Upon receiving a CMAC portion, the Secure Gateway generates its own CMAC based upon that CAN Conditioner's unique session key. The same bytes of the CMAC generated by the gateway are compared with the received bytes of the CMAC generated on the CAN Conditioner. These two data portions should match, as both the CAN Conditioner and the Secure Gateway generated them using the same session key and nonce.

A new CMAC is then generated and sent once per second using portions of the previous message(s) in the calculation. This results in a unique CMAC being transmitted by the CAN Conditioner and checked by the Secure Gateway once per second. Each node performs these actions independently with the Secure Gateway.

There is a small chance that due to the timing of the CMAC generation, the two nonces used could be different, resulting in conflicting CMACs. However, assuming that is not the case in a CMAC mismatch, the offending node may be identified as malfunctioning or compromised, and this failure to authenticate is logged and further action may take place. If a node stops sending CMAC messages, something has interrupted the process, such as malfunction or a compromise to the device. Again, once detected, further action may be taken to mitigate the potential attack.

C. Secure Key Exchange Process

After the Secure Gateway and CAN Conditioner have been provisioned, connected to a J1939 network, and powered on,

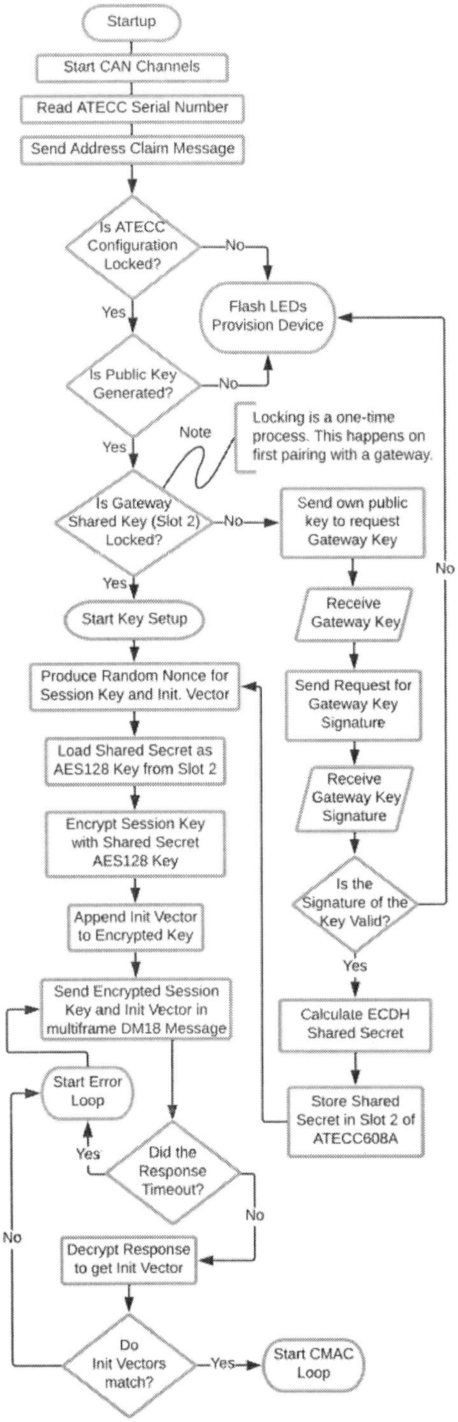

Fig. 5: Flow diagram of the CAN Conditioner startup sequence

the devices will generate their ECC key pairs. When this step is complete, a number of message exchanges take place to establish a secure session. Functionally, these processes are described in detail for the Secure Gateway in Fig. 8 and the CAN Conditioner in Fig. 5.

In sum, the setup of a secure session begins after both de-

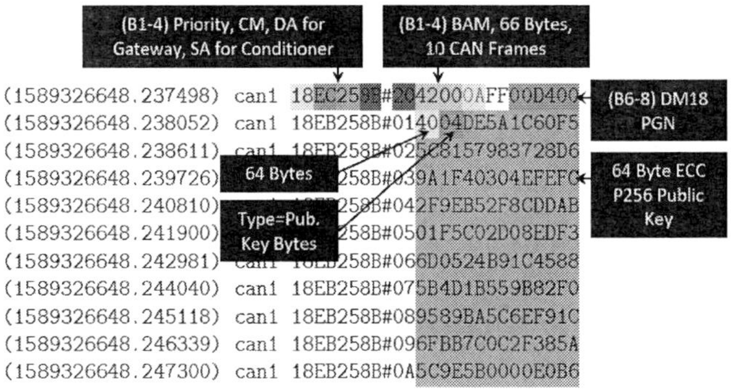

Fig. 6: CAN Conditioner sends its own public key with J1939 transport protocol.

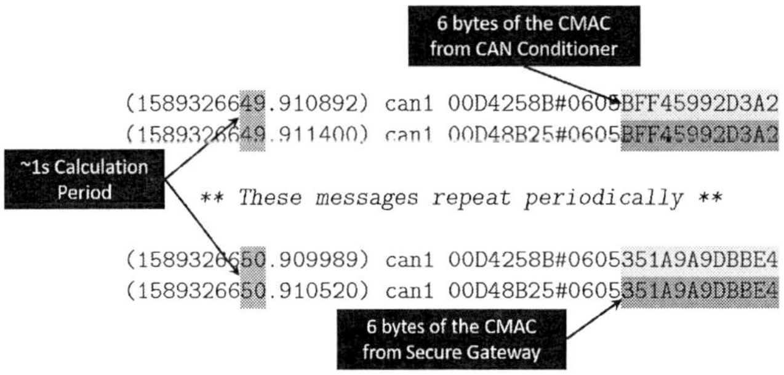

Fig. 7: Periodic CAN Conditioner CMAC messages and Secure Gateway CMAC confirmation responses.

vices have claimed an address and the CAN Conditioner sends its own public key. These messages are broadly facilitated by the transport protocol described in SAE J1939-21 which allows for the transmission of multi-frame messages. It is also facilitated by the data security PGN, DM18, defined in SAE J1939-73, which is used to identify cryptography procedures and information.

An example transmission of the CAN Conditioner public key is shown in Fig. 6. The first message includes the transport message type (CM), destination address for the gateway (0x25), SA of the conditioner (0x8B), the number of segments needed for the rest of the message (10), and the security PGN (0x00D400). The following messages include the segment number, the number of bytes of information (64 bytes), and the key type (public ECC P256). The CAN Conditioner will repeat this message periodically until it receives a response from the Secure Gateway.

When the CAN Conditioner public key is received, the Secure Gateway responds in a similar fashion with its own public key. After both public keys have been exchanged the CAN Conditioner generates a 16-byte AES-128 session key and 10-byte initialization vector using the HSM and sends the pair.

When the Secure Gateway receives the data pair, it calculates an AES encrypted seed and sends it to the CAN Conditioner. If the CAN Conditioner deciphers the encrypted seed and it matches what it sent, then the session is established.

After a secure session is established, the CMAC values are calculated and sent between the two devices. As shown in Fig. 7, these exchanges repeat roughly once per second.

The key features in this process are as follows:

1) Private keys are never known or revealed since they exist in the HSM.
2) Pre-shared secrets are calculated by the HSM but never transmitted.
3) Envelope encryption takes place in the HSM.
4) Session keys are ephemeral and securely shared.
5) Public key exchange only needs to take place upon initial installation.

VI. Test and Evaluation

The Secure Gateway system has two internal counters tracking the number of times the CMAC calculations match and the number of times the CMAC calculations do not match. With these counters, and a controlled experiment, the false positive and false negative rates can be estimated. A false positive is when a CMAC calculation fails to match even though there were no attacks. A false negative is when there was an attack, but the CMAC comparison indicated no messages were changed.

Each SA has its own counter. This means if a node impersonates a controller application that already has a CMAC setup, then the messages using the same SAs will be included in the CMAC calculation on the Secure Gateway. Since the impersonated messages are not used in the CAN Conditioner CMAC (implying they didn't originate from the correct ECU), the CMAC comparison will fail and the system would report a true positive. This feature worked in all tests.

As expected, every time a message was altered, the CMAC calculations did not match. This is an expected result since the false negative rate is on the order of the collision rates in an AES-128 based CMAC, which is acceptably low. Therefore, the requirement for low false negatives is met.

The false positive rate is determined by a ratio of the reported CMAC mismatches to the number of CMACs calculated with no intrusions. Due to the way CMACs are calculated, the timing of the sentinel message containing the CMAC from the CAN Conditioner must provide sufficient gaps such that the same messages are used to calculate the CMAC on the Secure Gateway. If the order of a message is changed, then the CMAC comparison would fail, leading to a false positive. After some initial tuning of the timing, a 20 millisecond gap on either side of the sentinel message lead to a low false positive rate. In one bench test that went for 24 hours, there were 508,762 CMACs that matched and 12 that did not. This is a false positive rate of 0.00236%, which is arguably too much. This would lead to false maintenance actions and operators would tend to ignore the warnings. However, this is a promising preliminary result and similar numbers were found when testing on vehicle. Additional logic regarding the number of messages and better tuning of the timing parameters should drop the false positive rate even lower.

VII. Conclusion

Correcting the security vulnerabilities caused by the inherent trust among devices connected by CAN is an ongoing security challenge among researchers. This paper described a legacy system IDS for CAN2.0b-based systems that aimed to provide stronger authentication of legitimate devices, detect the occurrence of system compromise and minimize the impact of a network attack. This was accomplished through the use of CAN Conditioners and a Secure Gateway device to segment network nodes and verify healthy node behavior. Based on our experiments, this concept shows promising preliminary results towards mitigating rogue nodes, supply chain, and middle-person attacks while minimizing network resource consumption typically associated with cryptography-based approaches. However, further work is needed to reduce the hardware for practical use. With further development, it has the potential to act as a mechanism for enhancing vehicle security.

Acknowledgment

This work is partially supported by the Defense Automotive Technologies Consortium (DATC) through DG Technologies under Award DA2-PA027C. Also partial support from Colorado State Bill 18-086 is gratefully acknowledged.

References

[1] S. Mukherjee, H. Shirazi, I. Ray, J. Daily, R. Gamble, "Practical DoS Attacks on Embedded Networks in Commercial Vehicles," *Int. Conf. Information Systems Security.*, 2016, pp 23-42, doi:10.1007/978-3-319-49806-5_2

[2] Y. Burakova, B. Hass L. Millar, and A. Weimerskirch, (2016) "Truck Hacking: An Experimental Analysis of the SAE J1939 Standard," 10nth USENIX Workshop on Offensive Technologies, [Online]. Available: www.usenix.org/conference/woot16/workshop-program/presentation/burakova

[3] National Motor Freight Traffic Association, Inc., (2015) "A Survey of Heavy Vehicle Cyber Security," Nat. Motor Freight Traffic Association, [Online]. Available: www.nmfta.org/documents/hvcs/nmfta heavy duty vehicle cyber security whitepaper v1.0.3.6.pdf

[4] *J1939 Digital Annex*, SAE Standard No. J1939DA_202001, Jan. 2020.

[5] Q. Hu and F. Lou. (2018). "Review Of Secure Communication Approaches For In-Vehicle Network," Int. Journal of Automotive Technology, 2018 pp. 879-894, doi:10.1007/s1223901800851

[6] *Specification of Secure Onboard Communication*, 654, AUTOSAR, 2017.

[7] Houck, A., "Secure CAN Transceiver," NXP, AMF-AUT-T2854, 2018, [Online]. Available: community.nxp.com/t5/Technology-Days-Training/Secure-CAN-Communication-The-System-Impact-by-Software-Based/ta-p/1104506

[8] J. Daily, P. Kulkarni, "Secure Heavy Vehicle Diagnostics," In *Proc. of the Ground Vehicle Systems Engineering and Technology Symposium (GVSETS)*, NDIA, Novi, MI, Aug. 13-15, 2020.

[9] Ammar, M., Janjua, H., Thangarajan, A., Crispo, B. et al., "Securing the On-Board Diagnostics Port (OBD-II) in Vehicles," SAE Int. J. Transp. Cyber. & Privacy, pp. 83-106, 2019, doi: 10.4271/11-02-02-0009

[10] J. Daily "Secure J1939 Gateway," Last Accessed 11 Jan 2021. [Online]. Available: github.com/SystemsCyber/CANWatermarking

[11] *Electronic Logging Devices and Hours of Service Supporting Documents*, 78292, FMCSA–2010–0167, Department of Transportation, Federal Register, 2015. [Online]. Available: www.govinfo.gov/content/pkg/FR-2015-12-16/pdf/2015-31336.pdf

[12] S. Mukherjee, J. Walker, I. Ray and J. Daily, "A Precedence Graph-Based Approach to Detect Message Injection Attacks in J1939 Based Networks," 2017 15th Annual Conference on Privacy, Security and Trust (PST), Calgary, AB, 2017, pp. 67-6709, doi: 10.1109/PST.2017.00018.

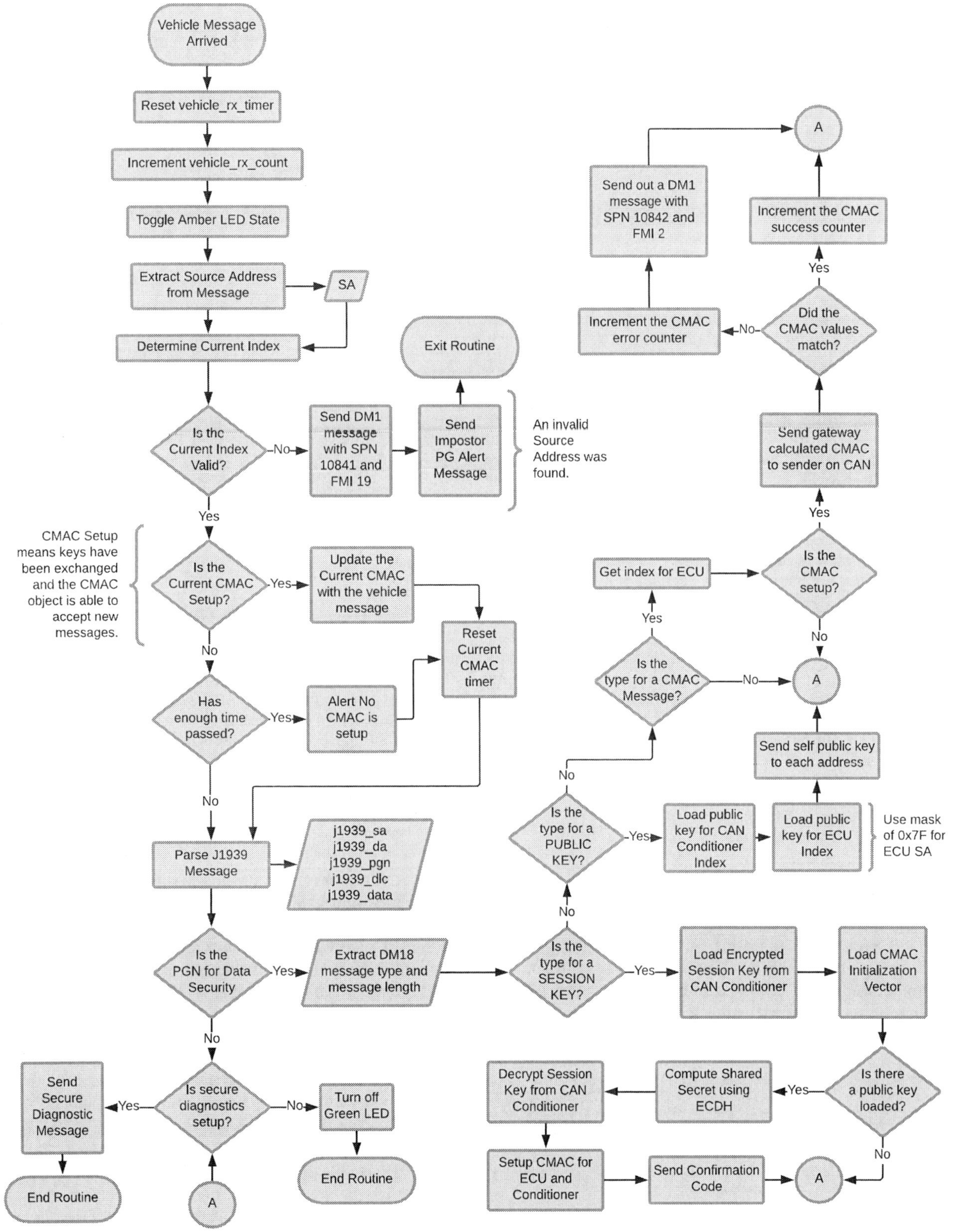

Fig. 8: Flow diagram for the Secure Gateway processing J1939 messages

Time-Based CAN Intrusion Detection Benchmark

Deborah H. Blevins*†, Pablo Moriano*‡, Robert A. Bridges‡, Miki E. Verma‡
Michael D. Iannacone‡, Samuel C Hollifield‡
†University of Kentucky, ‡Oak Ridge National Laboratory
deborah.blevins@uky.edu, {moriano, bridgesra, vermake, iannaconemd, hollifieldsc}@ornl.gov

Abstract—**Modern vehicles are complex cyber-physical systems made of hundreds of electronic control units (ECUs) that communicate over controller area networks (CANs). This inherited complexity has expanded the CAN attack surface which is vulnerable to message injection attacks. These injections change the overall timing characteristics of messages on the bus, and thus, to detect these malicious messages, time-based intrusion detection systems (IDSs) have been proposed. However, time-based IDSs are usually trained and tested on low-fidelity datasets with unrealistic, labeled attacks. This makes difficult the task of evaluating, comparing, and validating IDSs. Here we detail and benchmark four time-based IDSs against the newly published ROAD dataset, the first open CAN IDS dataset with real (non-simulated) stealthy attacks with physically verified effects. We found that methods that perform hypothesis testing by explicitly estimating message timing distributions have lower performance than methods that seek anomalies in a distribution-related statistic. In particular, these "distribution-agnostic" based methods outperform "distribution-based" methods by at least 55% in area under the precision-recall curve (AUC-PR). Our results expand the body of knowledge of CAN time-based IDSs by providing details of these methods and reporting their results when tested on datasets with real advanced attacks. Finally, we develop an after-market plug-in detector using lightweight hardware, which can be used to deploy the best performing IDS method on nearly any vehicle.**

I. Introduction

Modern vehicles are commonly drive-by-wire. That means that the states of vehicle subsystems are constantly being updated through broadcast messages between small dedicated computers called *electronic control units* (ECUs). With the increasing connectivity between ECUs, inherent security risks are becoming evident. Controller Area Network (CAN) is the default protocol used in the automotive industry [3]. It reduces wiring complexity by allowing ECUs to communicate on a common channel or bus with a standard protocol. Due to the continuously growing attack surface and the lack of authentication and lack of encryption, CAN is one of the main means by which adversaries can attack vehicles.

Vehicle complexity increases the attack surface by allowing the execution of (remote) attacks that have been shown to be life threatening. Examples include the injection of malicious messages through cellular networks with the purpose of taking control of targeted vehicles [5, 17] and the demonstrated attacks by Miller and Valasek causing unintended acceleration, deactivation of vehicles' brakes, as well as turning the steering wheel [14, 15]. In addition to these remote attacks, direct access to the CAN bus is generally easy to obtain, and for research purposes, most CAN attacks are administered via adding a node (ECU) through a the standard on-board diagnostic (OBD) II port.

A. Preliminaries

CAN messages or frames have two main parts: an arbitration ID (AID), typically composed of 11 bits, and a data field, composed of up to 64 bits. The AID functions as a label for the frame and serves to determine, by a process called arbitration, which message is received by the CAN bus when messages are transmitted simultaneously. The data communicates the current state of a vehicle system—for example, the anti-lock braking system. Commonly, messages with the same AID are sent regularly—most AIDs occur at their fixed frequency with minor aberrations—and often with redundant data.

CAN attacks have been classified using a three-tiered taxonomy: fabrication, suspension, and masquerade attacks [6]. Here we focus on fabrication attacks that, by definition, add a node (ECU) to the CAN bus and transmits messages with the intention of overloading the bus or overwriting messages to manipulate vehicle functionality. While these are the simplest attacks to execute, their effect on vehicles has been repeatedly proven [16, 23]. Notably, adding messages to the bus changes the time gap between subsequent messages, which leads to our focus—intrusion detection systems (IDSs) targeting fabrication attacks via identifying message timing anomalies.

Due to the redundancy of CAN messages, to "overwrite" a particular AID's message in a fabrication attack (*Targeted ID Attack*), an attacker must either broadcast messages at a rate faster than the true message *(flooding delivery)* or directly after the true message with the target ID is sent *(flam delivery)* [25]. A targeted ID attack using flam delivery is the most stealthy kind of fabrication attack, as the resulting timing perturbation is relatively minor, and thus provide the most difficult fabrication attack testing for time-based detection methods. Denial of service (DOS) and fuzzing attacks use flooding delivery with the goal of overloading the bus rather than targeting a particular ID, resulting in less stealthy fabrication attacks.

This manuscript has been co-authored by UT-Battelle, LLC, under contract DE-AC05-00OR22725 with the US Department of Energy (DOE). The US government retains and the publisher, by accepting the article for publication, acknowledges that the US government retains a nonexclusive, paid-up, irrevocable, worldwide license to publish or reproduce the published form of this manuscript, or allow others to do so, for US government purposes. DOE will provide public access to these results of federally sponsored research in accordance with the DOE Public Access Plan (http://energy.gov/downloads/doe-public-access-plan).

*Deborah H. Blevins and Pablo Moriano, placed in alphabetical order, contributed equally to this work.

Workshop on Automotive and Autonomous Vehicle Security (AutoSec) 2021
25 February 2021, Virtual

https://dx.doi.org/10.14722/autosec.2021.23013
www.ndss-symposium.org

B. Related Work

After early vehicle security work of Hoppe et al. [12], who note that monitoring for increased message frequency poses a potentially effective CAN IDS, initial research began to prove the concept that fabrication attacks can be accurately identified via message timing anomalies. Following works considered simple heuristics based on the counts of messages in a time window [20] or the average observed time gap between messages [8, 16, 23]. Later works began applying more sophisticated statistical machinery to the problem of unsupervised fabrication attack detection via timing-based methods: Tomlinson et al. [24] consider two online methods and one pre-trained unsupervised method, all based on the mean inter-message time gap; Hamada et al. [9] train Gaussian mixture models to identify time gaps in the future that occur with low probability; Olufowobi et al. [18] create a complex simulation for message timing from CPU scheduling research, which unfortunately exhibits low precision (many false alerts); Kuwahara et al. [13] create vectors of message counts in a time window, then use a z-score on nearest neighbor distance to find anomalous windows; Han et al. [10] test survival analysis techniques; Olufowobi et al. [19] use CUMSUM change detection; Young et al. [27] apply the Fast Fourier Transform (FFT) to a square wave representation of messages and find anomalies in the frequency domain representation; Avatefipour et al. [2] test a combination of a modified bat algorithm with a one-class support vector machine (OCSVM).

Noteworthy takeaways from the survey above include:

T1 Very simple methods, e.g. see Moore et al. [16] report strong detection results as do more sophisticated methods, e.g., Olufowobi et al. [19].

T2 Methods that process a time window of data can, depending on implementation, introduce a lag in detection (of up to the length of the time window) and an inability to distinguish specific inter-message time gaps that are anomalous [9, 20].

T3 Few of ~20 proposed methods are evaluated on real (non-simulated), public data, as appropriate public CAN datasets were not available at the time of the earlier research, although a few later works (e.g., [13, 19]) use now-public datasets.

T4 Most of the works fail to cite many directly comparable previous works.

C. Motivation & Contributions

The newly released ROAD Dataset [25] provides real (non-simulated), physically-verified, CAN data with labeled fabrication attacks, in particular many using the stealthy flam delivery. In light of **T1** and **T3**, we leverage this opportunity to benchmark some intuitive, straightforward approaches to time-based detection of fabrication attacks. The methods chosen aim to identify and compare the statistical concepts foundational to time-based CAN IDS methods on a high fidelity dataset. To the best of our knowledge, an analysis benchmarking several different time-based IDS methods has not yet been thoroughly performed.

The contributions of this research are summarized as follows. In light of **T4**, we provide a thorough survey of the previous time-based CAN IDS research targeting fabrication attacks. Second, we provide definitions of four different time-based IDSs, stating the conditions needed to raise alarms in each of the methods. We implement the detailed methods, enabling their further deployment and comparison. Third, we test the implemented methods on a publicly available CAN IDS dataset, ROAD [25]. In contrast with previous work in the area, the test set includes many fabrication attacks that were administered to a real vehicle's CAN with effect to the vehicle physically verified; notably, this dataset is publicly available and does not contain simulated data. Fourth, we compare the proposed time-based IDS methods based on their detection ability. Lastly, we discuss implementation details and the operation of the best performing method in an OBD II plugin. In light of **T2**, this includes detection latency analysis of our Binning detector. We provide access to the analysis scripts for replicability and reproducibility purposes.[1]

II. Methods

In this section, we define the threat model and dataset used throughout the paper (Sec. II-A), the detection methods that we compared (Sec. II-B), an analysis of detection latency (Sec. II-C), and the accuracy metrics we used for comparison (Sec. II-D).

A. Threat Model & Dataset

Cho and Shin [6] provide a widely known CAN attack terminology. Specifically, they used the term *weakly compromised ECU* to denote an ECU that an adversary is able to silence by suspending message transmission. Conversely, they used the term *fully compromised ECU* for an ECU over which an adversary has complete control, including the ability to send fabricated messages and gain memory access.

In this work, we used the ROAD dataset [25] that involve a fully compromised ECU introduced to the CAN bus using the OBD-II port. The ROAD Dataset is the first open dataset with real (non-simulated), stealthy (using flam delivery) fabrication attacks that have physically verified effects on the vehicle. These characteristics make the ROAD dataset ideal for benchmarking time-based IDS methods.

The ROAD dataset consists of 12 ambient captures (log files) containing about three hours of ambient (non-attack) data and 33 attack captures that last in total about 30 minutes. Table I lists contents of attacks and logs in the ROAD dataset, and indicates the subset of logs used in this paper. The ROAD dataset contains several types of attacks (see Table I, bottom): (1) fabrication attacks, including fuzzing attacks and several different targeted ID attacks using flam delivery; (2) masquerade attacks and (3) an advanced "Accelerator" attack. Note that (2) and (3) do not alter timing characteristics and are thus out of scope for this paper. For thorough testing, several of the attacks are run and logged more than once. The ROAD data was obfuscated to ensure anonymity of the vehicle while preserving aspects that are needed for testing IDS methods. For more details on the data collection and obfuscation procedure, refer to the work by Verma et al. [25].

[1] Auxiliary material can be found at https://github.com/pmoriano/can-time-based-ids-benchmark.

TABLE I: Logs in ROAD CAN Intrusion Detection Dataset.

	Description	# Logs	Used	Duration (min)
Training	Dynamometer Various Ambient	10	✓	108.2
	Road Various Ambient	2	✗	70.6
	Total	12	10	178.8
Testing	Accelerator Attack (In Drive)	2	✗	2.7
	Accelerator Attack (In Reverse)	2	✗	3.2
	Correlated Signal Fabrication Attack	3	✓	1.3
	Correlated Signal Masquerade Attack	3	✗	1.3
	Fuzzing Fabrication Attack	3	✓	0.7
	Max Engine Coolant Temp Fabrication Attack	1	✓	0.4
	Max Engine Coolant Temp Masquerade Attack	1	✗	0.4
	Max Speedometer Fabrication Attack	3	✓	3.9
	Max Speedometer Masquerade Attack	3	✗	3.9
	Reverse Light Off Fabrication Attack	3	✓	2.1
	Reverse Light Off Masquerade Attack	3	✗	2.1
	Reverse Light On Fabrication Attack	3	✓	3.2
	Reverse Light On Masquerade Attack	3	✗	3.2
	Total	33	16	28.4

Below we describe the specifics of the data we used from the ROAD dataset for the training and testing phases.

1) Training: Training or ambient data in the ROAD dataset was collected when the vehicle was on the dynamometer or on the road while performing diverse, potentially unusual but benign, driving activities (e.g., unbuckling seatbelts or opening doors while driving). In this work, for training, we used all 10 data logs that were generated on the dynamometer only (see Table I, top). We select only these ambient dynamometer logs since all logs containing attacks, which make up our test data, were collected on a dynamometer.

The time-based IDS methods that we benchmark in this work rely on analyzing inter-message time distributions of each AID. Thus, characterizing inter-message time distributions is an important step during the training phase. Fig. 1 shows the inter-message time distribution of AID `0xD0` (a targeted AID in one of the attacks). We annotate the figure with the values of the mean μ, standard deviation σ, minimum value $\min$, and maximum value $\max$. Fig. 1(a) shows the distribution without removing outliers in training. We notice that although most inter-message times are short (contained in the bar with almost six orders of magnitude), there are a few outliers corresponding to events transmitted at asynchronous rates (more than 50 seconds). Given that these outliers have the potential to skew the inter-message time distributions, we test results with and without outliers.

To remove outliers, we used the Minimum Covariant Determinant (MCD) method [22]. MCD is an estimator of multivariate location (mean) and scatter (covariance) that is robust to outliers in the data and for which a fast algorithm is available. MCD serves as a convenient and efficient tool for identifying and omitting outliers while fitting a Gaussian to the remaining inliers. For removing outliers, we used the EllipticEnvelope class in `SciKit-Learn` [21]. We set the contamination argument to 0.01% to control the proportion of expected outliers. Fig. 1 shows the inter-message time distribution (a) with and (b) without outliers in training. Clearly data in (a) (with outliers) is non-Gaussian; in (b) (without outliers), the Gaussian is plotted in black over the data histogram.

We observe that removing the outliers significantly shrinks the domain of the random variable ($\sigma = 0.352, \max = 179.789$ with outliers versus $\sigma = 0.001, \max = 0.019$ without). By removing outliers, we believe we can ensure a better characterization of the inter-message time distribution, and thereby obtain a better detector. We test this hypothesis by comparing results with and without outliers in Sec. III.

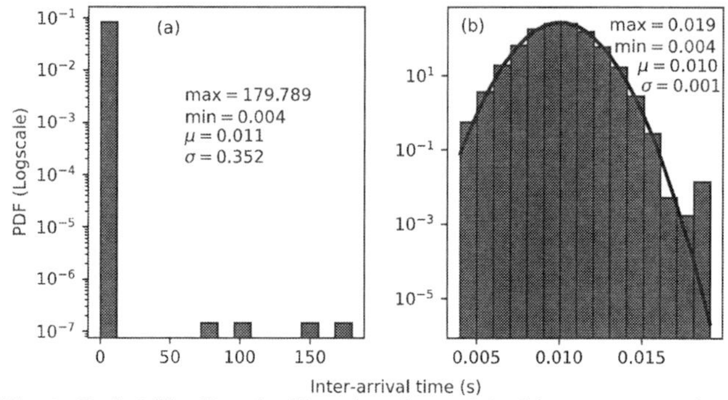

Fig. 1: Probability Density Function (logscale) of inter-message time distributions for AID `0xD0` in the training dataset (a) with outliers and (b) without outliers and with the Gaussian fit of the PDF shown in black. Note that without removing outliers, data is not Gaussian.

2) Testing: We used all 16 available log files for testing time-based detectors (namely, those containing fabrication attacks): the fuzzing attacks and the five different fabrication targeted ID attacks (see Table I, bottom). We aggregated all of these logs for evaluating the performance of the time-based IDS methods. Note that we did not remove outliers in the testing dataset. Importantly, among the 16 logs files that we used for testing, there was a total of 1,588,263 messages, of which 61,516 were attacks. This means that the proportion of positive samples is about 3.9%, which makes the testing dataset highly imbalanced. We revisit the imbalanced effect of the testing dataset in Sec. III.

B. Detection Methods

We tested four detection methods that exploit the timing regularities of CAN messages: Mean Inter-Message Time (Sec. II-B1), Binning (Sec. II-B2), Fitting a Gaussian Distribution (Sec. II-B3), and Kernel Density Estimation (KDE) (Sec. II-B4). While the first two rely on heuristics based on the inter-message times, the latter two follow previous anomaly detection works by fitting a continuous distribution to the inter-message times and detecting time gaps with low p-value [4]. We employ the two-sided p-value (of a sample x given a probability distribution f), denoted by pv_f, where P_f is the probability with respect to f as:

$$pv_f(x) := \int_{\{t:f(t)\leq f(x)\}} f\,dt = P_f\left(\{t : f(t) \leq f(x)\}\right). \quad (1)$$

All methods except for Binning use a two-step process for determining if a message is malicious. **Step (1) Comparison:** this step identifies whether a message is suspicious by comparing it to a threshold identified during training. **Step (2) Check for sufficiency:** this step determines whether the frames identified as suspicious in Step (1) are sufficiently anomalous to warrant an alert. This is done by checking if suspicious inter-message times occur repeatedly; the intuition is that to manifest physical changes, fabrication attacks must have repeated injections to continually overwrite the ambient messages. If sufficiency is confirmed, the messages are marked as malicious.

In this section, let X_{AID} be the set of inter-message times for a particular AID in the ROAD dataset and let x be an arbitrary inter-message time in X_{AID}. Again, μ denotes the average inter-message time for this AID. We run each method using a range of detection thresholds α, where α is defined below for each.

1) Mean Inter-Message Time (Mean): The first method uses the empirical mean μ calculated during training and a given threshold $\alpha \in [0,1]$. **(1) Comparison**: consider if inter-message time $x \leq \alpha\mu$. **(2) Check for sufficiency**: if $x \leq \alpha\mu$ holds for three out of the last six inter-message times, the frame is labeled malicious. We compute results for thresholds $\alpha_i = i/18$ for $i = 1, \ldots, 18$. We use 18 thresholds to be consistent with the distribution-based methods (II-B3, II-B4).

2) Binning: The second method considers the number of messages transmitted during a certain window of time. We let $\alpha_i = (2+i)/2$ for $i = 1, \ldots, 18$. In order to identify the appropriate threshold, for each α_i, we labeled a message malicious when the last six frames arrived in less than $\alpha_i\mu$ seconds. As intuition, note that in a time window of length $\alpha\mu$ we expect α messages to occur. Hence for $\alpha < 6$, this method will alert when extra messages are occurring.

3) Fitting a Gaussian Distribution (Gaussian): The third method fits a Gaussian distribution, f_G, to the inter-message times x (regardless of the shape of the data) and computes the two-sided p-value defined in Eq. 1. Let $S := \{0.001, \ldots, 0.009\} \cup \{0.01, \ldots, 0.09\}$. Detection was run for each $\alpha \in S$ as follows. **(1) Comparison**: for each $x \in X_{\text{AID}}$, compute $pv_{f_G}(x)$ (as in Eq. 1). **(2) Check for sufficiency**: if $pv_{f_G}(x) \leq \alpha$ for three consecutive inter-message times, the frame is labeled malicious.

4) Kernel Density Estimation (KDE): The final method uses a KDE using a Gaussian kernel to establish a probability density function, f_{KDE}, of the inter-message time data. Steps for detection follow the Gaussian method's **(1)** and **(2)** with $pv_{f_{\text{KDE}}}$ instead of pv_{f_G}. Detection results are computed for each $\alpha \in S$ as in the Gaussian method (II-B3).

C. Detection Latency

For all methods except Binning, each frame is scored and alerted; hence, latency is simply the computational time for the detection. Note that the Binning method, by design does not compute counts for moving time windows, but instead stores the previous five message times and asks if the next message occurs too soon, specifically if the last six messages occurred in less than $\alpha\mu$s. Hence, detection latency depends on α. Here we suppose that there is at least one illegitimate frame sent between each pair of ambient frames. If $\alpha \geq 5$ detection is immediate (simply computation time for the algorithm) as the previous five message (all legitimate) will require $\sim 4\mu$ s; thus, the time gap from the first initial illegitimate frame to the sixth previous will be under 5μ. Similarly, the time gap from the second illegitimate frame to the sixth previous is at most 4μ, meaning for $\alpha \in [4,5)$ detection latency is 2μ plus computational time. Finally, the time gap from the third or any subsequent illegitimate frame to the sixth previous message is at most 3μ. This means our detection latency will be at most 3μ plus computation time for $\alpha < 4$. Note that detection accuracy may vary greatly among different values of α. To put this in context, most AID frequencies are on the order of 10Hz to 100Hz, so the latency is a fraction of a second for all thresholds α.

D. Detection Ability Comparison

The basis for the comparison between the time-based IDS methods is based on counting the number of CAN messages that were labeled as true positives (TP), false positives (FP), false negatives (FN), and true negatives (TN). Several important classification metrics are based on these numbers: *Precision*, defined as $\frac{TP}{TP+FP}$, gives the likelihood that a detected message is an attack; *Recall*, defined as $\frac{TP}{TP+FN}$, gives the likelihood that an attack is detected. Since higher precision often comes at the price of higher recall (and vice versa), it is important to consider a balance of both metrics, and the standard balanced metric is the *F1 score*, defined as $2 \times \frac{precision \times recall}{precision + recall}$.

To compare the performance of these time-based methods over a range of detection thresholds (α), we consider the *Precision-Recall (PR) curve*, which plots precision against the recall at different thresholds. We choose to use the PR curve rather than the more commonly used ROC curve, which is less suited to imbalanced datasets [7] (recall that the proportion of attack messages, i.e., positive samples, is about 3.9%). This PR curve illustrates how the accuracy of a method changes at different performance thresholds, and the optimal threshold in terms of F1 score will generally appear towards the furthest top-right point of the curve. In our evaluation, we determine the optimal threshold to be the threshold that results in the highest F1 score.

This curve is also provides an important metric for evaluating a methods head-to-head independent of a specific threshold, namely, the area under the PR curve (AUC-PR), where a higher percentage indicates better overall performance. Note that is is important to consider this threshold-independent metric, since a true unsupervised method cannot consult the test data to determine an optimal threshold. Note that the *baseline* of the PR curve is the proportion of positive samples $\frac{TP+FN}{TP+FN+TN+FP}$.

III. Results

For each method, the PR curve is shown in Fig. 2 and the AUC-PR is given in Table II.

We first consider the method performance independent of a detection threshold. We report the performance comparison between the four methods across every threshold using AUC-PR in Table II, and highlight the method with best performance in bold. Overall, we find that methods that rely heavily on the distribution (i.e., Gaussian and KDE methods) tend to perform much worse and be significantly affected by outliers, as opposed to methods that do not have these distributional assumptions (i.e., Mean and Binning methods). With outliers present, the AUC-PR for both the Gaussian and KDE method are near 0, and while they perform significantly better when these outliers are removed from the training set, both still have a very low AUC-PR of under 15%. Removing outliers also makes the performance of the Mean method slightly better (from 68.90% to 69.05%) but interestingly, it worsens the performance of the Binning method (from 87.63% to 82.18%). The Binning method has the best performance both with and without outliers in training, achieving over 82% in both cases.

We next consider the performance of the methods at different threshold values. This is done illustrate how these thresholds affect the methods and determine the optimal threshold and resulting F1 score for each. Fig. 2 gives a more detailed illustration of the conclusions given above: regardless of the presence of outliers, both Gaussian and KDE methods tend to perform poorly at all detection thresholds, while the

TABLE II: AUC-PR comparison with and without outliers in training. The Binning method (in bold), is the best performing method in both cases.

Method	With Outliers	Without Outliers
Mean	68.90%	69.05%
Binning	**87.63%**	**82.18%**
Gaussian	0.00%	8.99%
KDE	0.02%	13.88%

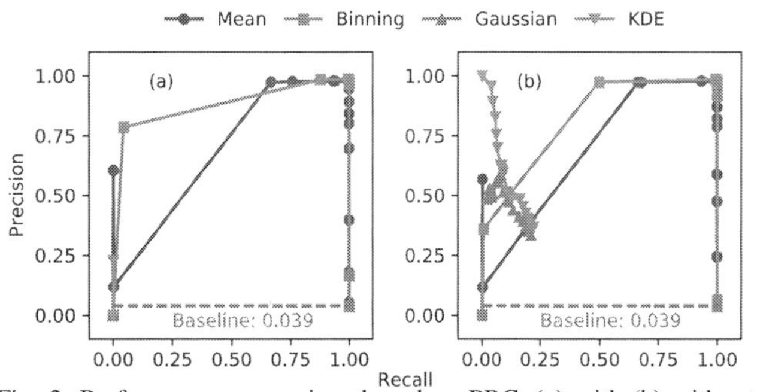

Fig. 2: Performance comparison based on PRC. (a) with (b) without outliers. The Binning method performs best overall.

Mean and Binning methods perform much better, particularly at certain thresholds (indicated by the blue and orange points near $(1.00, 1.00)$).

For the distribution-agnostic methods, we found that the optimal threshold and resulting optimal F1 score were essentially the same with or without outliers present in training. We found that the optimal threshold value for the Mean method is $\alpha = 0.44$, At this threshold, the value of the F1 score is ~98.6% (precision is 97.6% and recall is 99.6%). This means that reporting (as anomalies) messages that are less than 44% of the expected inter-arrival time mean (per AID) produces the best tradeoff between precision and recall. We also found that for the binning method, the optimal value for the threshold α (for this method, the window length) is 3.5. At this threshold, the F1 score is ~99.0% (precision is 98.6% and recall is 99.2%). This means that reporting messages (as anomalies) that do not resemble the expected number of messages in a window of length of 3.5 produces the best tradeoff between precision and recall.

For the distribution-based methods, we consider only the case in which outliers are removed, since these methods are essentially useless without this preprocessing step. The optimal threshold (the p-value) for the Gaussian and KDE methods was 0.09. At this value the F1 score achieved is 25.99% and 27.79%, respectively.

A. *OBD-II Plugin Prototype*

To prove the proposed detector is a viable vehicle-agnostic detector able to run on small edge computing devices efficiently, we implemented the the best performing method, i.e., Binning method (Sec II-B2), on an OBD-II plugin. We devised an edge computing device using a Raspberry Pi 3B+ with Raspbian Buster providing 1GB of RAM, a 1.4GHz ARMv8 processor, and Python support coupled with an interface board, Industrial Berry's CANBerry Dual 2.1 [1] to facilitate CAN communication. Once attached to the CAN bus (plugged into an OBD II of a running vehicle), the device runs an algorithm to identify the CAN's pre-configured bitrate along with other metadata, e.g., the vehicle identification number (VIN). The device then automatically collects CAN data from the vehicle and trains the parameters for each AID's detector. At this point the driver would ideally exercise as much of the vehicle's functionality as possible in order to determine the timing characteristics of the most possible AIDs. Once trained, the device can deploy the time-based detectors in real time and receive alerts visually via LEDs, with metadata and logs of the alerts stored on the prototype. The stages of the process are started/stopped with a switch on the device. The implementation into hardware follow our previous work [26]. We provide a demonstration video of the hardware running the Binning detector on a passenger vehicle while implementing an attack online (https://www.youtube.com/watch?v=mQxkycW0mV4).

IV. Discussion

Recalling the takeaways from our survey of the related literature, Sec. I-B, specifically, **T1** (simple detectors have garnered strong results) and **T4** (few previous works use real, public, physically-verified, high-fidelity attack datasets for testing), we formally define, implement, comparatively evaluate four different time-based intrusion detection system (IDS) methods on the ROAD Dataset [25], a publicly available CAN dataset with labeled attacks. The Mean method (II-B1) represents the many initial works that use heuristics based on differences from the average inter-message timing, while the Binning method (II-B2) represents the early methods that count messages in a time-window. As these both rely heavily on the learned mean inter-message time, a logical next step is to leverage also the second moment, variance, specifically, fitting a Gaussian to training data and detecting events in the tail (II-B3). Peeking at the training data (Fig. 1) we note that outliers may ruin the Gaussian fit. Alternatively, one may argue that non-Gaussian data should be fit with a more flexible class of distributions. To this end we also tested an analogous detector based on the very flexible kernel density estimate (KDE) method (both with and without outliers in training) to test this hypothesis.

Unsurprisingly considering previous works, the two simple, distribution-agnostic (Mean, Binning) achieve strong results (F1 scores of 0.986, 0.990, respectively). Moreover, our results with and without outliers in the training data show the methods are fairly robust to outliers as their results are not substantially affected. Perhaps shockingly, the two distribution-based methods pale in comparison. Our analysis of results when fitting these distributions to training data with and without outliers shows that these poor detection results exhibit only minor improvements (F1 scores of 0.260, 0.278, respectively); hence, they are not amended by this pre-processing maneuver. Rather, it seems that the tails of the Gaussian (and KDE, whose tails are near identical) are insufficient to characterize these. In the case of the Gaussian, these result suggest that considering the inter-message time as a fraction of the mean is an informative statistic but as a z-score is not, perhaps because the variance is so small in these distributions. As the tails of the Gaussian and KDE distributions are similar, this provides intuition for the poor results of these distributional methods.

Overall, these results suggest that counting methods are perhaps slightly better than those that consider inter-message timing, and more dramatically, the heuristic/distribution-agnostic methods far outperform those that explicitly seek tails of an estimated distribution. Inspecting the testing data reveals an artifact of flam attacks (that send one illegitimate message just after a legitimate message); i.e., they force the attack inter-message times to be a bi-modal distribution.

The following are some limitations of our study. First, we do not consider CAN messages without fixed timing. Second, the ROAD dataset only includes data from a single car. It is clear from the research that these techniques will succeed on a wide variety of vehicles, but specifics, e.g., the optimal thresholds found via our test data, may or may not translate to other vehicles. Third, as these are unsupervised methods, how to set the threshold with no attack data is a real-world need that we do not address. Finally, the methods we tested are exclusively of a time-based nature and the scope of our paper is limited to fabrication attacks. These methods are not intended to detect attacks that do not alter message frequencies, e.g., masquerade attacks. For detecting such anomalous event messages, methods should also take into account changes in the payload (e.g., see [11]).

To the best of our knowledge, the results from this research show for the first time a systematic comparison of time-based detection methods on an open CAN IDS dataset with verified real-world attacks. While this may seem like a solved problem we note that the results of the Binning and Mean detectors (and likely most all previous works) are in fact insufficient when put in context. Referring to the Dataset Section (II-A), the test data was $\sim$12.3 minutes of driving data comprised of $\sim$1.6M CAN messages. With the optimal Binning detector's precision of 98.6%, this still produces approximately $0.014 \times 1.6/12.3$M = 1,821 alerts per minute. In short, systematically pushing the state of the art in this area is still needed, and we hope this benchmark of the straightforward approaches in the area helps. In summary, our results indicate that future researchers may wish to focus on counting algorithms that can increase precision at (ideally) no expense to recall, and statistical machinery that relies on distributional estimates.

References

[1] "CAN bus shield for raspberry with 2 can interfaces," http://www.industrialberry.com/canberrydual-v2-1/.

[2] O. Avatefipour, A. S. Al-Sumaiti, A. M. El-Sherbeeny, E. M. Awwad, M. A. Elmeligy *et al.*, "An intelligent secured framework for cyberattack detection in electric vehicles can bus using machine learning," *IEEE Access*, 2019.

[3] R. Bosch *et al.*, "CAN specification version 2.0," *Rober Bousch GmbH, Postfach*, vol. 300240, p. 72, 1991.

[4] R. A. Bridges, J. D. Jamieson, and J. W. Reed, "Setting the threshold for high throughput detectors: A mathematical approach for ensembles of dynamic, heterogeneous, probabilistic anomaly detectors," in *Proceedings of the IEEE International Conference on Big Data*, 2017, pp. 1071–1078.

[5] S. Checkoway, D. McCoy, B. Kantor, D. Anderson, H. Shacham, S. Savage, K. Koscher *et al.*, "Comprehensive experimental analyses of automotive attack surfaces," in *Proceeding of the USENIX Security Symposium*, 2011, pp. 447–462.

[6] K.-T. Cho and K. G. Shin, "Fingerprinting electronic control units for vehicle intrusion detection," in *Proceedings of the 25th USENIX Security Symposium*, 2016, pp. 911–927.

[7] J. Davis and M. Goadrich, "The relationship between precision-recall and roc curves," in *Proceedings of the 23rd international conference on Machine learning*, 2006, pp. 233–240.

[8] M. Gmiden, M. H. Gmiden, and H. Trabelsi, "An intrusion detection method for securing in-vehicle can bus," in *2016 17th IEEE International Conference on Sciences and Techniques of Automatic Control and Computer Engineering*, Dec 2016.

[9] Y. Hamada, M. Inoue, H. Ueda, Y. Miyashita, and Y. Hata, "Anomaly-based intrusion detection using the density estimation of reception cycle periods for in-vehicle networks," *SAE Int. J. Transp. Cybersecur. Privacy*, vol. 1, no. 1, pp. 39–56, May 2018.

[10] M. L. Han, B. I. Kwak, and H. K. Kim, "Anomaly intrusion detection method for vehicular networks based on survival analysis," *Veh. Commun.*, vol. 14, pp. 52–63, Oct 2018.

[11] M. Hanselmann, T. Strauss, K. Dormann, and H. Ulmer, "CANet: An unsupervised intrusion detection system for high dimensional CAN bus data," *IEEE Access*, vol. 8, 2020.

[12] T. Hoppe, S. Kiltz, and J. Dittmann, "Applying intrusion detection to automotive it early insights and remaining challenges," *Journal of Information Assurance and Security (JIAS)*, vol. 4, no. 6, pp. 226–235, 2009.

[13] T. Kuwahara, Y. Baba, H. Kashima, T. Kishikawa, J. Tsurumi *et al.*, "Supervised and unsupervised intrusion detection based on can message frequencies for in-vehicle network," *Journal of Information Processing*, vol. 26, 2018.

[14] C. Miller and C. Valasek, "Remote exploitation of an unaltered passenger vehicle," *Black Hat USA*, vol. 2015, p. 91, 2015.

[15] ——, "CAN message injection: OG dynamite edition," *Tech. Rep.*, 2016.

[16] M. R. Moore, R. A. Bridges, F. L. Combs, M. S. Starr, and S. J. Prowell, "Modeling inter-signal arrival times for accurate detection of CAN bus signal injection attacks: a data-driven approach to in-vehicle intrusion detection," in *Proceedings of the 12th Annual Conference on Cyber and Information Security Research*, 2017.

[17] S. Nie, L. Liu, and Y. Du, "Free-fall: Hacking tesla from wireless to CAN bus," *Briefing, Black Hat USA*, vol. 25, pp. 1–16, 2017.

[18] H. Olufowobi, G. Bloom, C. Young, and J. Zambreno, "Work-in-progress: Real-time modeling for intrusion detection in automotive controller area network," in *2018 IEEE Real-Time Systems Symposium*, Dec 2018, pp. 161–164.

[19] H. Olufowobi, U. Ezeobi, E. Muhati, G. Robinson, C. Young *et al.*, "Anomaly detection approach using adaptive cumulative sum algorithm for controller area network," in *Proceedings of the ACM Workshop on Automotive Cybersecurity*, 2019, pp. 25–30.

[20] S. Otsuka, T. Ishigooka, Y. Oishi, and K. Sasazawa, "CAN Security: Cost-Effective Intrusion Detection for Real-Time Control Systems," SAE Technical Paper, Tech. Rep., Apr 2014.

[21] F. Pedregosa *et al.*, "Scikit-learn: Machine learning in Python," *J. Mach. Learn. Res.*, vol. 12, pp. 2825–2830, 2011.

[22] P. J. Rousseeuw and K. V. Driessen, "A fast algorithm for the minimum covariance determinant estimator," *Technometrics*, vol. 41, no. 3, pp. 212–223, 1999.

[23] H. M. Song, H. R. Kim, and H. K. Kim, "Intrusion detection system based on the analysis of time intervals of CAN messages for in-vehicle network," in *Proceedings of the International Conference on Information Networking*, 2016.

[24] A. Tomlinson, J. Bryans, S. A. Shaikh, and H. K. Kalutarage, "Detection of Automotive CAN Cyber-Attacks by Identifying Packet Timing Anomalies in Time Windows," in *Proceedings of the 48th Annual IEEE/IFIP International Conference on Dependable Systems and Networks Workshops*, 2018.

[25] M. E. Verma, M. D. Iannacone, R. A. Bridges, S. C. Hollifield, B. Kay, and F. L. Combs, "ROAD: the real ORNL automotive dynamometer controller area network intrusion detection dataset (with a comprehensive CAN IDS dataset survey & guide)," *arXiv: 2012.14600 [cs]*, Dec 2020.

[26] M. E. Verma, R. A. Bridges, J. J. Sosnowski, S. C. Hollifield, and M. D. Iannacone, "CAN-D: A modular four-step pipeline for comprehensively decoding controller area network data," *arXiv:2006.05993 [cs, eess]*, Jun 2020.

[27] C. Young, H. Olufowobi, G. Bloom, and J. Zambreno, "Automotive intrusion detection based on constant can message frequencies across vehicle driving modes," in *Proceedings of the ACM Workshop on Automotive Cybersecurity*, 2019, pp. 9–14.

Demo: Detecting Illicit Drone Video Filming Using Cryptanalysis

Ben Nassi,[1] Raz Ben-Netanel,[1] Adi Shamir,[2] Yuval Elovici[1]
[1] Ben-Gurion University of the Negev, [2] Weizmann Institute of Science
nassib@post.bgu.ac.il, razx@post.bgu.ac.il, adi.shamir@weizmann.ac.il, and elovici@inter.net.il

Video 1 - https://youtu.be/4icQwducz68 **Video 2** - https://youtu.be/9PVaDpMsyQE

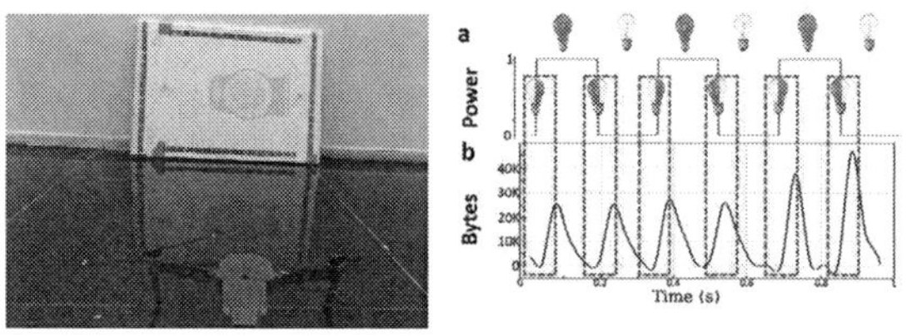

Fig. 1. Left: A drone placed in front of a whiteboard with an attached LED strip. Right: (a) the flickering LED strip that operates at 3 Hz creates (b) six bursts in the intercepted bitrate signal extracted from the drone.

***Abstract*—In this demo, we demonstrate that cryptanalysis can be used to determine whether a passing drone is used for spying, by analyzing the drone's encrypted video channel. We also show that a spying drone can be detected when the victim is located in a house or traveling in a car, with the use of a flickering light.**

IN an era in which drones are flying among us, a new question arises [1]: how can we determine whether a passing drone is being used by its operator for a legitimate purpose (e.g., delivering a pizza) or an illegitimate purpose (e.g., taking a peek at a person showering in his/her own house)? In this demo, we demonstrate that cryptanalysis can be used to determine whether a passing drone is used for spying, by analyzing the drone's encrypted video channel.

First, we show how the side effect of the H.264 video compression algorithm, the variable bitrate, can be utilized to detect whether a drone's camera is used to film an object, by analyzing the traffic of the video channel. To do this, we position a DJI Mavic Pro in front of a whiteboard with an attached LED strip connected to Arduino Uno (see Fig. 1). The LED strip is programmed to flicker at 3 Hz. We extract the bitrate signal by sniffing encrypted Wi-Fi packets sent from the drone to its controller using Airmon-ng.

We use the intercepted encrypted packets in order to extract a time series, using unencrypted metadata from each packet: (1) the packet arrival time, and (2) the size. Fig. 1 presents the results of this experiment. As can be seen, a 3 Hz flickering LED strip creates a 6 Hz phenomenon within the intercepted bitrate signal by producing six bursts per second. Each time the LED strip is turned on/off, a larger amount of data is sent from the drone, which is expressed as a burst of bytes in the time domain. Based on the results of this experiment, we conclude that by attaching a flicker to an object, we can detect whether a drone's camera is used to film the object, by analyzing the video channel, even if the traffic is encrypted.

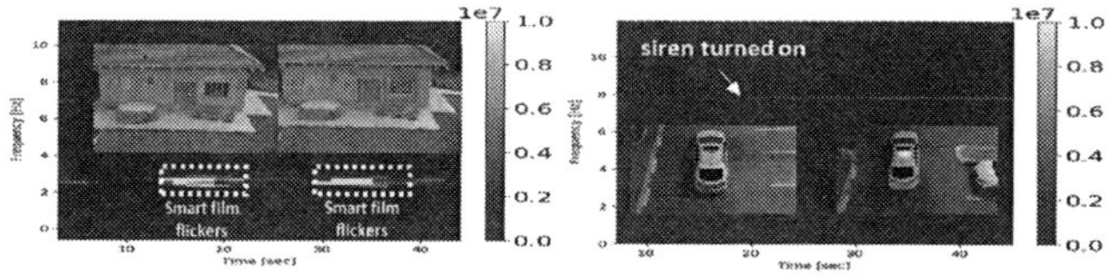

Fig. 2. spectrograms of the intercepted bitrate signal obtained from the intercepted bitrate signal when a drone was used to spy on the victim that was located in his house (left) and in his car (right).

Next, we demonstrate how a smart film attached to a window can be used to detect whether a drone is used to film a private house from a neighboring property. In this experiment, smart film (film that changes its state from transparent to mat and vice versa) that has been installed on a victim's living room window is used for flickering. A video of this experiment can been in the link above. Fig. 2 presents a spectrogram of the intercepted bitrate signal that was extracted during this experiment. The effect of the flickering film on the intercepted bitrate signal shows how a spying drone can be detected by a victim located in a house.

Finally, we demonstrate how a siren installed on top of a car can be used to detect whether a drone is used to film a subject while he/she is traveling in a car. A video of this experiment can been in the link above. Fig. 2 presents a spectrogram of the intercepted bitrate signal that was extracted during this experiment. The effect of the flickering siren on the intercepted bitrate signal shows how a spying drone can be detected by a victim traveling in a car.

The extended version of this paper can be found in [2], [3].

References

[1] B. Nassi, R. Bitton, R. Masuoka, A. Shabtai, and Y. Elovici, "Sok: Security and privacy in the age of commercial drones," in *2021 2021 IEEE Symposium on Security and Privacy (SP)*. Los Alamitos, CA, USA: IEEE Computer Society, may 2021, pp. 73–90.

[2] B. Nassi, R. Ben-Netanel, A. Shamir, and Y. Elovici, "Drones' cryptanalysis-smashing cryptography with a flicker," in *2019 IEEE Symposium on Security and Privacy (SP)*. IEEE, 2019, pp. 1397–1414.

[3] R. Ben Netanel, B. Nassi, A. Shamir, and Y. Elovici, "Detecting spying drones," *IEEE Security Privacy*, vol. 19, no. 1, pp. 65–73, 2021.

Workshop on Automotive and Autonomous Vehicle Security (AutoSec) 2021
25 February 2021, Virtual

https://dx.doi.org/10.14722/autosec.2021.23003
www.ndss-symposium.org

Demo: Attacking Tesla Model X's Autopilot Using Compromised Advertisement

Ben Nassi[1], Yisroel Mirsky[1,2], Dudi Nassi[1], Raz Ben-Netanel[1], Oleg Drokin[3], Yuval Elovici[1]
[1] Ben-Gurion University of the Negev, [2] Georgia Tech, [3] Independent Researcher
{nassib, yisroel, razx, nassid, elovici}@post.bgu.ac.il, green@linuxhacker.ru
Video Demonstration: https://youtu.be/-E0t_s6bT_4

Abstract—**In this demo, we demonstrate how attackers can remotely apply split-second phantom attacks by embedding phantom road signs into an advertisement presented on an Internet connected digital billboard which causes Tesla's autopilot to suddenly stop the car in the middle of a road.**

IN this demo, we identify a limitation of AI models that can be exploited by attackers to perform a new type of attack called a "split-second phantom attack." This attack exploits a weakness of advanced driving assistance systems (ADASs) where (1) digitally displayed imagery is perceived as a real object (i.e., phantom imagery), and (2) the imagery only has to appear briefly (for a few milliseconds) in order to be detected by the ADAS. One might argue that the authenticity of phantoms can be determined by commercial ADASs that use sensor fusion by cross-correlating the camera sensor with data obtained from depth sensors (e.g., radar, LiDAR, and ultrasonic sensors), however we show that the most advanced semi-autonomous vehicle, the Tesla Model X, resolves the disagreement between the camera and the integrated depth sensors regarding a phantom by treating the phantom as real, despite the fact that it does not have any depth.

We demonstrate the attack via a digital billboard by embedding a phantom into an existing advertisement and displaying it for a few milliseconds in a way that the imagery itself is hard to perceive. We picked a random McDonald's advertisement from YouTube. We embedded a stop sign into nine consecutive frames (500 ms) of the advertisement in order to attack the Tesla Model X.

The experiment was conducted on a road on our university campus after we received the proper approvals from the security department. The attacker used a 42 inch TV screen (which was used to simulate a digital billboard and was plugged into another car for electricity) that was placed in the middle of the road. We used this setup to demonstrate the attack, since we had no intention of hacking a real digital billboard in this study. The experiment was conducted as follows: We engaged Tesla's autopilot at the beginning of the road. The Tesla approached the middle of the road where the TV screen presented the compromised McDonald's advertisement (with the embedded 500 ms stop sign). Fig. 1 presents a snapshot from the 500 ms that the phantom was presented on the upper left corner on the screen. The attack was successful, since Tesla's autopilot identified the phantom stop sign and immediately triggered the car to stop in the middle of the road. The reader can view a video of the experiment and the compromised advertisements in link above.

Fig. 1. Top: The compromised frame in the advertisement with the embedded phantom road sign. Bottom: Tesla's autopilot triggers the car to stop suddenly after a phantom stop sign was detected in the upper left corner of the digital billboard.

The extended version of this paper, that includes the algorithm that was used to detect the most suitable frame to embed the phantom, can be found in [1], [2].

Workshop on Automotive and Autonomous Vehicle Security (AutoSec) 2021
25 February 2021, Virtual

https://dx.doi.org/10.14722/autosec.2021.23004
www.ndss-symposium.org

References

[1] B. Nassi, Y. Mirsky, D. Nassi, R. Ben-Netanel, O. Drokin, and Y. Elovici, "Phantom of the adas: Securing advanced driver-assistance systems from split-second phantom attacks," in *Proceedings of the 2020 ACM SIGSAC Conference on Computer and Communications Security*, ser. CCS '20. New York, NY, USA: Association for Computing Machinery, 2020, p. 293–308. [Online]. Available: https://doi.org/10.1145/3372297.3423359

[2] B. Nassi, D. Nassi, R. Ben-Netanel, Y. Mirsky, O. Drokin, and Y. Elovici, "Phantom of the adas: Phantom attacks on driver-assistance systems."

Demo: Securing Heavy Vehicle Diagnostics

Jeremy Daily, David Nnaji and Ben Ettlinger
Colorado State University
{jeremy.daily,david.nnaji,ben.ettlinger}@colostate.edu

Abstract—**Diagnostics and maintenance systems create frequent, legitimate, and intermittent connections to a vehicle's communication network. These connections are typically made with a vehicle diagnostics adapter (VDA), which serves to translate vehicle network communications to a Windows based service computer running diagnostics software. With heavy vehicles, the diagnostic systems are written and maintained by the supplier of the electronic control units. This means there may be multiple different software packages needed to maintain a heavy vehicle. However, all of these software systems use an interface defined by the American Trucking Association (ATA) through their Technology and Maintenance Council (TMC) using Recommended Practice (RP) number 1210, the Windows API for vehicle diagnostics. Therefore, most diagnostics and maintenance communications on a heavy vehicles utilize a third-party VDA with little to no cybersecurity controls. The firmware and drivers for the VDA can be entry points for cyber attacks. In this demonstration, a vehicle diagnostics session is attacked using the VDA firmware, VDA PC driver, and a middle-person attack. A proposed secure diagnostics gateway is demonstrated to secure the diagnostics communications between the heavy vehicle network and the diagnostics application, thus defending against attacks on vulnerable VDA components. Furthermore, the maintenance operations are often trusted and an attacker gains physical access to the vehicle with the unknowing technician. Since these diagnostic systems are connected to the Internet and run Windows, the traditional security issues associated with Windows PCs are now part of the heavy vehicle.**

I. Demonstration

In [1], Daily and Kulkarni introduced a prototype secure gateway based on the Teensy 4.0 development board and the Microchip ATECC608A hardware security module. The paper detailed a strategy to provision the hardware security module and exchange device keys using the elliptic curve Diffie-Hellman (ECDH) protocol. Once device keys are exchanged, they are used to encipher session keys. These random session keys an initialization vectors are used to setup an AES-128 cipher in CBC mode. This cipher is used to encrypt and decrypt messages from a secure gateway (shown in Fig. 1) to a secure PC diagnostics application. This protects the data in the external vehicle connections and the Windows subsystems.

However, AES-128 requires 16 byte blocks to be transmitted. Therefore, a scheme will be demonstrated that packs one CAN frame into two CAN messages to be sent in sequence to get the requisite 16 bytes across the wire. Since the 16-byte enciphered CAN frame includes a CRC-16, incorrect deciphering will invalidate the CRC and the message is dropped. With this approach, exfiltration, manipulation, and pattern matching of CAN messages in the VDA communications are thwarted.

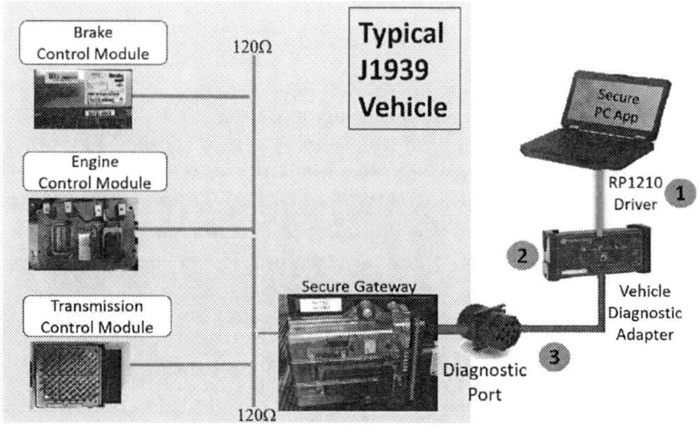

Fig. 1: Typical heavy vehicle diagnostic system architecture with three potential attack vectors: 1) the RP1210 DLL, 2) malicious VDA firmware, and 3) a middle-person device.

Two modes of key exchange will be demonstrated. One mode uses an on-line server to compute the session key and share it with the PC Application using a TLS connection. An off-line mode requires the user to check out the keys needed for the ECDH. However, these private PEM keys are encrypted to minimize risk of being leaked. To decrypt the PEM keys needed for the ECDH, the gateway must be in the circuit. In other words, part of the PEM key encryption requires the hardware security module on the secure gateway.

The demonstration will show how the secure channel will mitigate attacks on single CAN frames and multi-frame messages. A special version of the RP1210 driver is used as a shim DLL that looks for J1939 Engine Hours and manipulates that single frame message. Additionally, the shim DLL looks for a transport layer message carrying a VIN, which is altered. With the secure gateway in place and a compatible diagnostics software application, these attacks are mitigated. The result is increased confidence in the sanctity of vehicle diagnostics data as it flows through a Windows computer.

References

[1] J. Daily, P. Kulkarni, "Secure Heavy Vehicle Diagnostics", In Proceedings of the Ground Vehicle Systems Engineering and Technology Symposium (GVSETS), NDIA, Novi, MI, Aug. 13-15, 2020.

Workshop on Automotive and Autonomous Vehicle Security (AutoSec) 2021
25 February 2021, Virtual

https://dx.doi.org/10.14722/autosec.2021.23020
www.ndss-symposium.org

Demo: Impact of Stealthy Attacks on Autonomous Robotic Vehicle Missions

Pritam Dash, Mehdi Karimibiuki, and Karthik Pattabiraman
University of British Columbia

I. Motivation and Key Insights

Robotic Vehicles (RV) use sensors to measure their physical states and derive the appropriate actuator signals for autonomous navigation and other control operations. Unfortunately, attackers can manipulate sensor and actuator signals through malicious code injection [2], sensor spoofing [7], and acoustic noise injection [6].

Model-based techniques have been recently proposed to detect attacks against RVs. Control Invariants (CI) [3] and Extended Kalman Filter (EKF) [1] are techniques that use control-based estimations to derive invariants and monitor the RV's runtime behaviour to detect attacks. In this paper, we demonstrate three stealthy attacks, namely false data injection (FDI), artificial delay (AD), and switch mode (SM) attacks, based on the findings of our previous work [4], [5]. The stealthy attacks evade the CI and EKF detection techniques and result in significant adverse impact on the RV's mission (e.g., significant deviations from the target or result in a crash).

Our main insight is that by design, CI and EKF techniques have to tolerate some degree of deviation from the planned trajectory due to environmental factors such as wind or sensor noise, and hence set a threshold for flagging errors between model estimations and observed behaviour as attacks. Further, we found that the control based estimation techniques fail to accurately model RV's runtime behavior. Because of the model inaccuracies, CI and EKF techniques set a high threshold, and perform stateless analysis in order to avoid false alarms. This opens up new vulnerabilities, and allows attackers to launch stealthy sensor and actuator attacks against RVs.

The FDI attack injects bias values to sensor and actuator measurements, such that the deviations in the control output (e.g., Euler angles, motor rotation rates) are always maintained under the detection threshold. The AD attack injects intermittent delays in the reception of the RV's gyroscopic sensor measurements, which will, in turn influence the estimation of RV's angular orientation while eluding detection. The SM attack injects strong bias values into actuators when the RV switches it's modes of operation (e.g., when a drone switches from steady flight to landing). By launching stealthy attacks over a prolonged duration the attacker will be able to cause mission failure or adversely influence RV's performance.

Autonomous RVs are deployed in variety of industrial sectors such as agriculture, package delivery etc. Further, RVs are projected to be deployed in mission-critical tasks such as drug delivery and disaster relief. Therefore, it is critical to protect RVs from attacks in order to maximize their performance and prevent adverse consequences. Our findings show that using inaccurate models for invariant analysis in non-linear RV systems, opens the door to new vulnerabilities.

II. Attack Impact

We demonstrate the three stealthy attacks on 6 RVs including 3 real RVs (2 drones and a rover) in presence of both CI and EKF techniques. We found that the stealthy attacks can cause severe disruptions in RV missions while remaining undetected [1]. For example, we found that the FDI attack can deviate RVs by 8 to 15 meters from its target for short RV missions (50 meters), and by more than 160 meters for long RV missions (5 kilometers). Similarly, the AD attack increases the mission duration of a rover and drone by more than 65% and 30% respectively. Finally, the SM attack, when launched at vulnerable states during a drone mission, can result in a crash (in more than 50% of the cases in our experiments).

References

[1] P.-J. Bristeau, E. Dorveaux, D. Vissière, and N. Petit, "Hardware and software architecture for state estimation on an experimental low-cost small-scaled helicopter," *Control Engineering Practice*, vol. 18, no. 7, pp. 733 – 746, 2010, special Issue on Aerial Robotics.

[2] N. Carlini, A. Barresi, M. Payer, D. Wagner, and T. R. Gross, "Control-flow bending: On the effectiveness of control-flow integrity," in *24th USENIX Security Symposium (USENIX Security 15)*. Washington, D.C.: USENIX Association, Aug. 2015, pp. 161–176.

[3] H. Choi, W.-C. Lee, Y. Aafer, F. Fei, Z. Tu, X. Zhang, D. Xu, and X. Deng, "Detecting attacks against robotic vehicles: A control invariant approach," in *Proceedings of the 2018 ACM SIGSAC Conference on Computer and Communications Security*, ser. CCS '18. New York, NY, USA: ACM, 2018, pp. 801–816.

[4] P. Dash, M. Karimibiuki, and K. Pattabiraman, "Out of control: Stealthy attacks against robotic vehicles protected by control-based techniques," in *Proceedings of the 35th Annual Computer Security Applications Conference*, ser. ACSAC '19. New York, NY, USA: ACM, 2019.

[5] P. Dash, M. Karimibiuki, K. Pattabiraman, "Stealthy attacks against robotic vehicles protected by control-based intrusion detection techniques," *Digital Threats: Research and Practice*, vol. 2, no. 1, Jan. 2021.

[6] Y. Son, H. Shin, D. Kim, Y. Park, J. Noh, K. Choi, J. Choi, and Y. Kim, "Rocking drones with intentional sound noise on gyroscopic sensors," in *24th USENIX Security Symposium (USENIX Security 15)*. Washington, D.C.: USENIX Association, 2015, pp. 881–896.

[7] N. O. Tippenhauer, C. Pöpper, K. B. Rasmussen, and S. Capkun, "On the requirements for successful gps spoofing attacks," in *Proceedings of the 18th ACM Conference on Computer and Communications Security*, ser. CCS '11. New York, NY, USA: ACM, 2011, pp. 75–86.

[1]Videos showing the attacks. The stealthy attacks code can be found at https://github.com/DependableSystemsLab/stealthy-attacks

Workshop on Automotive and Autonomous Vehicle Security (AutoSec) 2021
25 February 2021, Virtual

https://dx.doi.org/10.14722/autosec.2021.23014
www.ndss-symposium.org

WIP: Deployability Improvement, Stealthiness User Study, and Safety Impact Assessment on Real Vehicle for Dirty Road Patch Attack

Takami Sato*, Junjie Shen*, Ningfei Wang, Yunhan Jack Jia†, Xue Lin‡, and Qi Alfred Chen
Univesity of California, Irvine; †ByteDance; ‡Northeastern University

***Abstract*—Automated Lane Centering (ALC) systems are convenient and widely deployed today, but also highly security and safety critical. Recently, Dirty Road Patch (DRP) attack is proposed as a state-of-the-art adversarial attack against ALC systems. In this work, we report our recent progress of improving the DRP attack on attack deployability, attack stealthiness, and effectiveness on real vehicle. We also discuss future directions.**

I. Introduction

Automated Lane Centering (ALC) is a Level-2 driving automation technology that automatically steers a vehicle to keep it centered in the traffic lane. Due to its high convenience for human drivers, today it is widely available on various vehicle models such as Tesla, GM Cadillac, etc. While convenient, such system is highly security and safety critical: When the ALC system starts to make wrong steering decisions, the human driver may not have enough reaction time to prevent safety hazards such as driving off road or colliding into vehicles in adjacent lanes. Thus, it is imperative and urgent to understand the security property of ALC systems.

Dirty Road Patch (DRP) attack [1] is recently proposed as a domain-specific adversarial attack to Deep Neural Network (DNN) based ALC systems. This attack identifies *dirty road patches* as an attack vector for physical-world adversarial attacks on ALC systems due to 2 unique advantages: (1) Road patches can appear to be legitimately deployed on traffic lanes in the physical world, e.g., for fixing road cracks; and (2) Since it is common for real-world roads to have dirt or white stains, using similar dirty patterns as the input permutations can allow the malicious road patch to appear more normal and thus stealthier. With the attack vector, the DRP attack systematically generates a malicious surface pattern mimicking the normal dirty patterns and achieves high attack effectiveness against a production ALC system. However, it is known that the DRP attack has major limitations on deployability, attack stealth, and effectiveness against real vehicles.

In this work, we report our recent progress to address such limitations of the DRP attack. In §II, we design a multi-piece mode that can significantly reduce the attacker's effort in deploying attacks while maintaining a high attack success rate. In §III, we conduct a user study to more rigorously evaluate the stealthiness of the DRP attack. In §IV, we assess safety impact on real vehicle by injecting attack traces into an ALC system installed in a real vehicle to simulate other driver assistance features that are commonly used with ALC at the same time in real-world driving, for example, Lane Departure Warning (LDW), Adaptive Cruise Control (ACC), Forward Collision Warning (FCW), and Automatic Emergency Braking (AEB). Finally, we discuss the future research directions in §V.

*The first two authors contributed equally.

Workshop on Automotive and Autonomous Vehicle Security (AutoSec) 2021
25 February 2021, Virtual

https://dx.doi.org/10.14722/autosec.2021.23027
www.ndss-symposium.org

II. Attack Deployability Improvement.

To deploy the attack, the direct approach is to print the malicious dirty patterns on one single road patch and deploy it at once. However, if the required patch size is large, it may not be easy to be quickly deployed at once, which may increase the risk of being noticed by police officers or road guards. To improve this, we design an optional *multi-piece patch attack* mode, which allows the attackers to deploy the DRP attack with multiple small pieces of road patches. In this mode, the attacker can specify (1) the size of a small piece that they can quickly deploy at once, denoted as $size_p$, and (2) the total number of such pieces based on their affordable deployment efforts and risks, denoted as N_p. Fig. 1 shows an example multi-piece patch attack from the driver's view, which includes 8 pieces of quickly-deployable small road patches. With this, the attacker can deploy one small piece at a time to avoid drawing too much attention, and can also parallelize the deployment of different pieces to further accelerate the process.

Evaluation methodology and setup. First, we consider a road patch of size 1.6-1.8 m wide and 6-8 m long as a *deployment unit* for 1-2 people at a time, based on normal arm span and available adhesive road patch lengths online.Different from a legitimate road patch deployment, the attacker does not need to fill asphalt and stamp the road, which are the most time-consuming steps. Instead, she only needs to place the patch on the road surface, and this step only takes 5-10 seconds for the defined deployment unit above based on demo videos of the adhesive patch deployment. With this, we can then estimate the deployment effort for 1-2 people by calculating the number of deployment units for a given attack road patch. We start from an attack patch size of 5.4m×36m (width×length), the size used in previous sections, and then vary the allowed number of deployment units in the patch area using multi-piece patch attack mode to evaluate the trade-off between deployability and attack effectiveness.

Results. Table I shows the experiment results with 4 to

TABLE I: Evaluation results for attack deployability using multi-piece patch attack mode. Piece #: Allowed number of 1.8m×7.2m patches for the attack; 15 pieces cover the entire deployable area.

Piece #	Succ. rate	Succ. time (s)	Deploy. time improvement
15 (full)	100%	0.89	-
12	98.8%	0.94	-20%
8	93.8%	1.28	-47%
6	76.3%	1.63	-60%

Fig. 1: Driver's view in multi-piece patch attack mode (§II) at 2.5 seconds before the attack succeeds. The attack in the figure has 8 pieces of 1.8m×7.2m road patches, each requiring only 5-10 sec to deploy for 1-2 people.

15 deployment units. To fully cover the 5.4m wide and 36m long patch placement area, 15 deployment units, each for a piece of 1.8m×7.2m patch, are required for 1-2 people. When the allowed piece number decreases, the attack success rate decreases accordingly since the perturbable area size becomes smaller. Interestingly, the success rate is still as high as 93.8% when only 8 pieces are allowed, which is able to significantly reduce the original deployment efforts by nearly 50%. This suggests that it is not necessary to cover the entire attack deployable area to achieve a high success rate for the DRP attack, which thus concretely shows the benefit of our multi-piece patch attack mode design in improving deployability. Fig. 1 shows an example DRP attack with such 8 pieces of 1.8m×7.2m road patches from the driver's view. To deploy 8 such pieces, the attacker only needs to find opportunities to block the road for 1-2 min in total. To maximize the stealthiness, such an effort can be spread up to 8 different times, each for a single piece or more. Each time, a single piece only requires a 5-10 seconds vacant period of the target road, which is common in the U.S. since the majority of the driving scenarios in the U.S. are *free-flow* scenarios, where a vehicle has at least 5-9 seconds headway. In the late night, such opportunities can be even more frequent.

III. Attack Stealthiness User Study

We conduct a user study to more directly evaluate the stealthiness of the DRP attack. We have gone through the IRB process and our study is determined as in the IRB Exempt category since it does not involve the collection of any Personally Identifiable Information (PII) or target any sensitive population.

Evaluation methodology. We use the generated attacks on real-world driving traces to perform the user study. For an attack scenario, we ask the participants to imagine that they are driving with the ALC system taking control, and then show a sequence of image frames with the malicious road patch from the driver's view at 3, 2.5, 2, 1.5, and 1 second(s) before the attack succeeds. Here, 1 second before the attack succeeds is right before the attack starts to take effect. At this point, the patch is placed at 7 m away from the vehicle. For each image frame, we ask whether they will decide to take over the driving to avoid danger or potential safety risks. These questions are also asked for the image frames with a benign road patch that only has the base color without the malicious dirty patterns as a control group.

Since our attack is designed for drivers who are in favor of using ALC system in normal cases, the same set of questions are asked at the beginning for the original image frames without attack, and we only accept a participant if she does not choose to take over the driving for these cases. This process also helps filter out ill-behaved participants who just provide random answers. Since DRP is a new form of attack vectors on the road, we do not tell the participants that the study is related to security attacks. Instead, we only tell them that our focus is on surveying driver's decisions under ALC systems for different road surface patterns such as road patches and scratches. At the beginning of the study, we also provide an introduction of ALC systems with demo videos to ensure that the participants fully understand what driving technology we are surveying about. To understand the distribution of the participant background, we also ask demographic information and background information related to driving and ALC usage. None of the questions in our study involve PII or target any sensitive population; our study is thus determined as in the IRB Exempt category.

Evaluation setup. We use Amazon Mechanical Turk to perform this study, and in total collected 100 participants. All of them have driving experience, which is confirmed by asking them the age when first licensed and the weekly driving mileage. A local-road driving trace is used in this study, and for the scenarios with attack, we evaluate 3 stealthiness levels (i.e., $\lambda = 10^{-2}, 10^{-3}, 10^{-4}$ as defined in [1]). The survey is available at [2]. Among the 100 participants, 56% are male and 44% are female. The average age is 32.3 years old. 79% of them have experienced at least one ALC system, among which Tesla Autopilot has the largest share (28%). Statistics of ALC experiment and demographic information are shown in Fig. 3.

Results. Fig. 2 shows the study results. As shown, the closer it is to the attack success time, the more participants choose to take over the driving in the attacked scenarios since the dirty patterns become increasingly larger and clearer. Among the 3 stealthiness levels, the driver decisions are consistent with our design: the lowest stealthiness level ($\lambda = 10^{-4}$) has the highest take-over rate, while the highest level ($\lambda = 10^{-2}$) has the lowest. In particular, we find that even for the lowest stealthiness level ($\lambda = 10^{-4}$), only *less than 25%* of the participants decide to take over before the attack starts to take effect. At this stealthiness level the white dirty patterns are quite dense and prominent. Thus, these results suggest that the majority of human drivers today do not treat dirty road patches as road conditions where ALC systems cannot handle.

As discussed in [3], 2.5 seconds is commonly used as the average driver reaction time to road hazard. Thus, at 2.5

seconds or more before the attack succeeds, the human driver still has a chance to take over the driving to prevent the damage in common cases, as long as she can realize that it is a road hazard. However, our results show that only less than 20% of the participants decide to take over at 2.5 and 3 seconds before our attack succeeds even for the lowest stealthiness level. In particular, when the stealthiness levels are $\lambda = 10^{-2}$ and $\lambda = 10^{-3}$, the take-over rates at these 2 time points are similar to the rates for the benign road patch with only the base color. This suggests that at the time when there is still a chance to prevent the damage in common cases, our attack patches at $\lambda = 10^{-2}$ and 10^{-3} *appear to be as innocent as normal clean road patches to human drivers*. In these cases, the take-over rates are only *less than 15%*, which are from participants who will take over even for normal clean road patches. Note that the take-over rates in practice are likely to be lower than this since (1) this study is performed for a local-road scenario, while the road patches in highway scenarios are much farther and thus much less noticeable as shown in Fig. 7 in [1], and (2) the road patches in this study are digitally synthesized into the image frames, which may appear less natural and thus may more easily alert the participants.

Discussion. While we try our best to evaluate the stealthiness of the DRP attack, our user study has 3 potential limitations: (1) The participants may not represent the normal drivers. Unfortunately, we cannot fully address this limitation as long as we use cloud-sourcing. To the best of our ability, we use the responses for normal cases to filter out people who are not in favor of using ALC systems and those who answer random responses. However, this filtering may introduce a bias to the participants. While we intentionally target people who are supportive to use ALC systems, the results of the user study may change in the future along with the spread of ALC systems. (2) Our patch may increase the attention level of drivers from a distance due to its noisy appearance of our patch, and it could reduce the reaction time to less than 2.5 sec. We agree that such a case may occur, but we consider that it only has a minor impact. The driver's reaction time (2.5 sec) consists of 1.75 sec of perception time and 0.75 sec of physical reaction time [3]. In the target scenario, our attack starts to take effect at 1 second before the attack succeeds. In this case, the driver needs to react within 0.25 sec to avoid the DRP attack, which requires a significant reduction from 1.75 sec perception time since the attention level can only improve the perception time. (3) The multi-piece patch mode may draw more driver's attention. In the user study, we only evaluate the stealthiness of the single-piece patch. If the multi-piece patch mode harms the stealthiness, we need to find the best balance between the stealthiness and deployability.

IV. Safety Impact on Real Vehicle

While the simulation-based evaluation is able to show severe safety impacts of our attack, it does not simulate other driver assistance features that are commonly used with ALC at the same time in real-world driving, for example Lane Departure Warning (LDW), Adaptive Cruise Control (ACC), Forward Collision Warning (FCW), and Automatic Emergency Braking (AEB). This makes it unclear whether the safety damages discussed in [1] are still possible when these features are used, especially the safety-protection ones such as AEB. In this section, we thus use a real vehicle to more directly understand the safety impact.

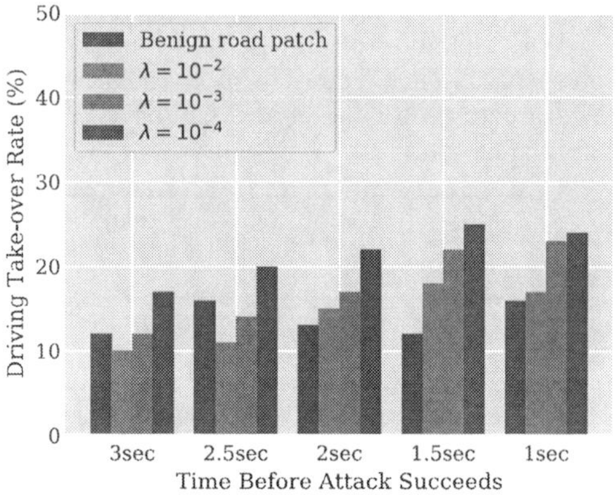

Fig. 2: Results of the attack stealthiness user study. Driving take-over rate is the percentage of participants who choose to take over the driving at a particular time point before the attack succeeds.

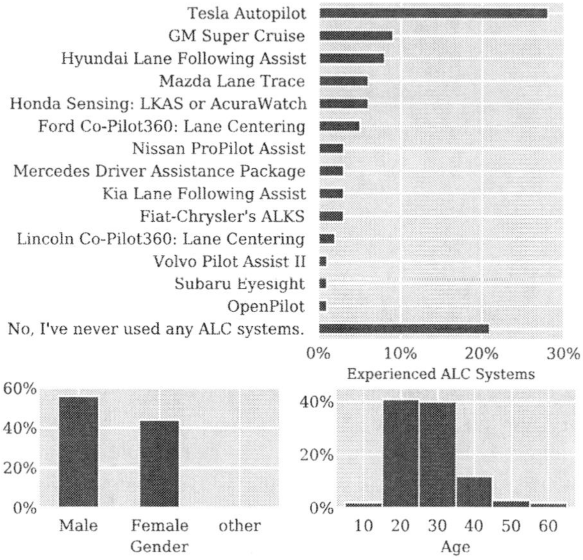

Fig. 3: Statistics of the ALC system experience and demographic information in the attack stealthiness user study.

Evaluation methodology. We install OpenPilot on a Toyota 2019 Camry, in which case OpenPilot provides ALC, LDW, and ACC, and the Camry's stock features provide AEB and FCW [4]. We then use this real-world driving setup to perform experiments on a rarely-used dead-end road, which has a double-yellow line in the middle and can only be used for U-turn. The driver's view of this road is shown on the left of Fig 4. In our miniature-scale experiment in [1], the attack realizability from the physically-printed patch to the lane detection (LD) model output has already been validated under 12 different lighting conditions. Thus, in this experiment we evaluate the safety impact by directly injecting an attack trace at the LD model output level. This can also avoid blocking the road for sticking printed patches to the ground and cleaning them up, which can easily affect other vehicles. Note that attack trace injection is also a common practice in physical-world attack evaluation for cyber-physical systems.

To create safety-critical driving scenarios, we place cardboard boxes adjacent to but outside of the current lane as shown in Fig 4, which can mimic road barriers and obstacles

Fig. 4: Safety impact evaluation for our attack on a Toyota 2019 Camry with OpenPilot engaged. Even with other driver assistance features such as Automatic Emergency Braking (AEB), our attack still causes collisions in all the 10 trials.

in opposite direction while not causing damages to the vehicle and driver safety. Similar setup is also used in today's vehicle crash tests [5], [6]. While the cardboard boxes are smaller than the object used in [5], [6], our setup has enough potential to damage the vehicle, e.g., the attacker can put heavy weights in the boxes. To ensure that we do not affect other vehicles, we place the cardboard boxes only when the entry point of this dead-end road has no other driving vehicles in sight, and quickly remove them right after our vehicle passes them as required by the road code of conduct.

Experiment setup. We perform experiments in day time with and without attack, each 10 times. The driving speed is kept at ~28 mph, the minimum speed for engaging OpenPilot on our Camry. The injected attack trace is generated from our simulation environment at the same driving speed.

Results. Our experiment results show that our attack causes the vehicle to hit the cardboard boxes in all the 10 attack trials (100% collision rate), including 5 front and 5 side collisions. The collision variations are caused by randomness in the dynamic vehicle control and the timing differences in OpenPilot engaging and attack launching. In contrast, in the trials without attack, OpenPilot can always drive correctly and does not hit or even touch the objects in any of the 10 trials.

These results thus show that driver assistance features such as LDW, ACC, FCW, and AEB are not able to effectively prevent the safety damages caused by our attack on ALC. We examine the attack process and find that LDW is not triggered since it relies on the same lane detection module as ALC and thus are affected simultaneously by our attack. ACC does not take any action since it does not detect a front vehicle to follow and adjust speed in these experiments. FCW is triggered 5 times out of the 10 collisions, but it is only a warning and thus cannot prevent the collision by itself. Moreover, in our experiments FCW is triggered only *0.46 sec* before the collision on average, which is far too short to allow human drivers to react considering the 2.5-second average driver reaction time to road hazard.

In our Camry model, FCW and AEB are turned on together as a bundled safety feature.However, while we have observed some triggering of FCW, we were not able to observe any triggering of AEB among the 10 attack trials, leading to a *100% false negative rate*. We check the vehicle manual and find that this may be because the AEB feature (called *pre-collision braking* for Toyota) is used very conservatively: it is triggered only when the possibility of a collision is *extremely high*. This observation is also consistent with the previously-reported high failure rate (60%) for AEB features on popular car models today [7]. Such conservative use of AEB can reduce false alarms and thus avoid mistaken sudden emergency brakes in normal driving, but also makes it difficult to effectively preventing the safety damages caused by our attack — in our experiments, it was not able to prevent any of the 10 collisions. The video recordings for these real-vehicle experiments are available at **https://youtu.be/OT8seN6pZj4** and **https://youtu.be/Ph42FIaadFo**.

V. Conclusion and Future Directions

In this paper, we address the limitations of the DRP attack from 3 improvements and further evaluation: the multi-piece patch mode, conduct attack stealthiness user study, and safety impact on real vehicle. The multi-piece patch mode can improve the attack deployability significantly. The attack with 8 pieces can reduce the original deployment time by nearly 50%. The stealthiness user study reveals that the DRP attack can appear to be as innocent as normal clean road patches to human drivers and the take-over rates by human drivers can be only less than 15%. The safety impact on real vehicle demonstrates that that driver assistance features such as LDW, ACC, FCW, and AEB are not able to effectively prevent the safety damages caused by the DRP attack on ALC. These results indicate that DNN-based ALC systems have security risks against adversarial attacks in the real world.

To improve the robustness of ALC systems, we plan to explore 2 domain-specific defense strategies in future directions: (1) We will design an attack detection and warning system, which detects cracks or dirty patterns on the road and warn the drivers if such patterns can mislead ALC systems. The challenge in this defense is that the system needs to warn the driver before the driver's reaction time (2.5 sec). (2) We think leveraging HD maps could be a feasible solution for Level-2 AD systems as Level-4 AD systems today heavily utilize HD maps [8]. If such a map can be available, a follow-up research question is how to effectively detect our attack without raising too many false alarms, since mismatched lane information can also occur in benign cases We will conduct a systematic exploration of these directions in future work.

Acknowledgements

This research was supported in part by the National Science Foundation under grants CNS-1850533, CNS-1929771, CNS-1932464, and USDOT UTC Grant 69A3552047138.

References

[1] T. Sato, J. Shen, N. Wang, Y. J. Jia, X. Lin, and Q. A. Chen, "Hold tight and never let go: Security of deep learning based automated lane centering under physical-world attack," *arXiv:2009.06701*, 2020.

[2] "Driver Take-Over Decision Survey with Automated Lane Centering System in our Attack Stealthiness User Study," https://storage.googleapis.com/driving-decision-survey/driving_decision_survey.pdf, 2020.

[3] S. of California Department of Motor Vehicles, *California Commercial Driver Handbook: Section 2 – Driving Safely*, 2019. [Online]. Available: https://www.dmv.ca.gov/portal/uploads/2020/06/comlhdbk.pdf

[4] "OpenPilot," https://github.com/commaai/openpilot, 2018.

[5] "Toyota Safety Sense Pre-Collision System (PCS) Settings and Controls," https://youtu.be/IY4g_zG1Qj0, 2017.

[6] C. Miller and C. Valasek, "A Survey of Remote Automotive Attack Surfaces," https://youtu.be/tnYO4U0h_wY?t=1840, 2015.

[7] "Does Your Car Have Automated Emergency Braking? It's a Big Fail for Pedestrians," https://zd.net/2MoUqpd, 2019.

[8] "Building Maps for a Self-Driving Car," https://link.medium.com/Bo5pCOov95, 2016.

Model-Agnostic Defense for Lane Detection against Adversarial Attack

Henry Xu
University of California, Berkeley
henryxu@berkeley.edu

An Ju
University of California, Berkeley
an_ju@berkeley.edu

David Wagner
University of California, Berkeley
daw@cs.berkeley.edu

***Abstract*—Susceptibility of neural networks to adversarial attack prompts serious safety concerns for lane detection efforts, a domain where such models have been widely applied. Recent work on adversarial road patches have successfully induced perception of lane lines with arbitrary form, presenting an avenue for rogue control of vehicle behavior. In this paper, we propose a modular lane verification system that can catch such threats before the autonomous driving system is misled while remaining agnostic to the particular lane detection model. Our experiments show that implementing the system with a simple convolutional neural network (CNN) can defend against a wide gamut of attacks on lane detection models. With a 10% impact to inference time, we can detect 96% of bounded non-adaptive attacks, 90% of bounded adaptive attacks, and 98% of patch attacks while preserving accurate identification at least 95% of true lanes, indicating that our proposed verification system is effective at mitigating lane detection security risks with minimal overhead.**

I. Introduction

End-to-end lane detection methods have shown great promise; however, their shared foundation with deep neural networks imply a shared weakness to adversarial examples [16]. Given the importance of accurate lane detection in downstream control decisions for autonomous vehicles, a successful attack on lane perception could result in undesirable or outright dangerous vehicle behavior. In particular, we are interested in attacks that could interfere with vehicle guidance through the generation of malicious lane lines, where attack success is marked not by alarm, as is the case when lane lines cannot be found, but by a false sense of normalcy. With no defense, as is the case with current state-of-the-art efforts, a lane detection pipeline is unable to make any judgement of lane validity, and thus the perceived fake lanes are indistinguishable from real. To defend against such attacks, we propose a system for lane verification as illustrated in Figure 1, with the goal not to recover the original lanes, but to minimize instances of lane detection model false confidence.

Our lane verification model is fast, lightweight, and applicable to any existing lane detection effort. The simplicity of our verification model imparts very little inference overhead, and its modular nature allows for independent training that avoids the costs associated with redesigning and retraining the large and complex neural networks commonly seen in industrial lane detection systems.

The modularity carries the additional benefit of being lane detection model-agnostic, paving a path for integration into any lane detection pipeline. Given the constant improvement and refinement of lane detection techniques, detaching our defense from a particular architecture allows it to remain viable as the underlying methods become more sophisticated.

Our system is motivated by the framing of secure lane detection as two complementary tasks: lane detection and lane verification. The former requires discerning the locations of a variable number of lanes in a constantly changing environment; the latter boils down to binary classification: given a set of lane coordinates, determine if they correspond to a lane that is either real or fake. Instead of further complicating the optimization problem faced by existing lane detection models by introducing the secondary goal of security on top of their initial purpose, we propose moving the task of verification into a separate bespoke model, allowing each part of the pipeline to focus on maximizing individual performance without compromise. Since the task of lane verification can take lane coordinates as given and only needs to return a binary result, it can be accomplished by models much simpler and faster than those required for lane detection.

Our experiments show that simple convolutional models are sufficient to significantly improve lane detection pipeline robustness to both digital and physical attack as pictured in Figure 2. When evaluated against a L_p bounded attack and two patch-based attacks, our model can detect over 95% of attacks with minimal impact to model accuracy and inference time. These results suggest that our model is capable of defending against a variety of attack types, including unknown threats.

In summary, strong performance of our defense against both nonadaptive and adaptive versions of such threats indicates that such a system could offer security to lane detection models at very little expense.

Our primary contributions are as follows:

- We propose a simple lane verification defense that can be integrated into the pipeline of any lane detection effort with no retraining of the underlying model required. Its independent and lightweight nature provides marginal inference overhead and allows for quick security updates when new attacks arise.
- We show empirically that verification provides significant lane detection security with minimal cost.

Workshop on Automotive and Autonomous Vehicle Security (AutoSec) 2021
25 February 2021, Virtual

https://dx.doi.org/10.14722/autosec.2021.23032
www.ndss-symposium.org

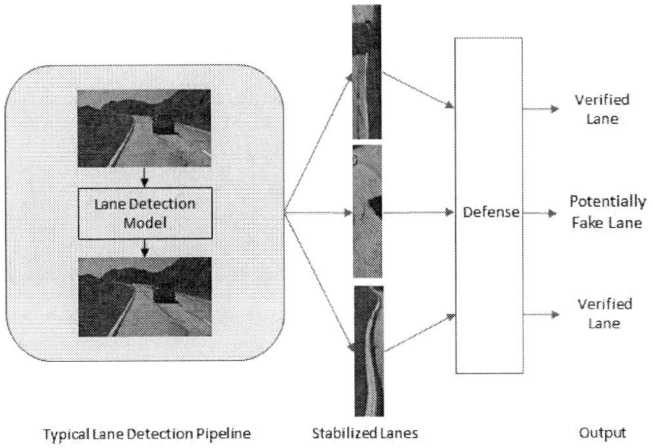

Fig. 1. Our proposed defense augmentation to a general lane detection model.

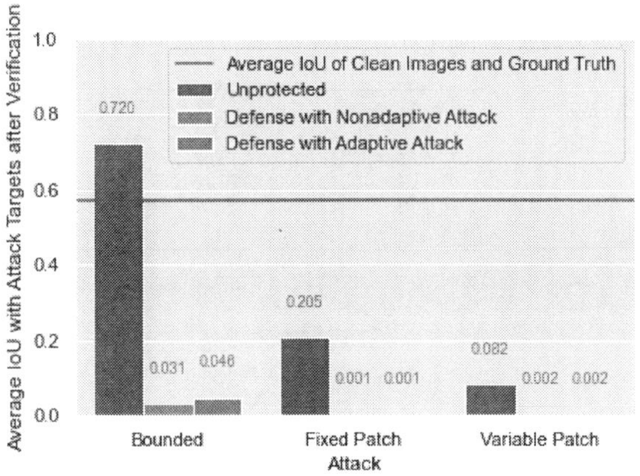

Fig. 2. Defense Performance. Our defense is able to filter out all but a handful of adversarial attacks that would otherwise fool unprotected lane detection models. Intersection over Union (IoU) between detected lanes and attack targets is our chosen attack metric due to its measurement of both how well the induced fake lane matches the target fake lane and how much of the original scene was preserved, providing a sense of amount of control an attacker has over the scene. The bounded attack before verification surpasses the IoU achieved by the lane detection model on real lanes, suggesting the adversarial fake lanes are indistinguishable from real ones to the model. While patch attack IoU is relatively muted compared to that of bounded attack due to its largely local impact, it can still cause significant lane deviation as shown in Figure 6.

II. Related Work

While work on lane detection model defenses is sparse, there is extensive related work on end-to-end detection models and some work on lane detection attacks which have been summarized below.

A. End-to-End Lane Detection Models

Convolutional neural network-based lane detection models typically frame the core task as one of image segmentation, with the goal to label each pixel as one of N classes, each class corresponding to a distinct lane. In the end-to-end formulation, the segmentation is accompanied by a parallel binary labelling of lane existence, allowing the model to narrow down where exactly the lane is within pixels of the same segmentation class. By doing so, an end-to-end lane detection model is able to take a scene and return predictions of lane line locations. Proposed models largely differ on neural network architecture choices and postprocessing cleanup procedures, the details of which our defense treats as a black box.

Given the methodological similarities between the top lane detection models on the TuSimple dataset, we chose to test our proposed defense with LaneNet as proposed by Neven et al. [10] due to its near state-of-the-art performance at time of writing and result reproduction accessibility. We achieve accuracy within 2% of Neven et al.'s results before adding our defense. Note that due to the lane detection model-agnostic nature of our defense, the results from our experiments should be applicable to any other model we could have chosen, such as [5], [6], and [7].

B. Image Comprehension Model Attacks and Defenses

The framing of lane detection as a task of image segmentation suggests a sharing of similar security weaknesses, and recent work has shown image comprehension models to be very susceptible to adversarial attack. Adversarial examples, shown to be incredibly effective for image classification, have been shown to be extendable to image segmentation, with [3] specifying a framework generalizing their generation across a variety of tasks, including segmentation, and [16] finding attack success across a variety of segmentation networks. Successful attack need not change every pixel as discovered in [2], and classification can easily be corrupted with a patch a fraction of the total size of the image. Defenses, such as adversarial training, as suggested and explored by [4], [11], [9], and [15] against adversarial attack, often involve retraining the entire model which is costly given the ever increasing complexity of state-of-the-art techniques.

C. Lane Detection Model Attacks

Regarding adversarial attacks on lane detection models in particular, recent work has used image segmentation attack methods to great effect. [12] details how a bounded patch, disguisable in practice as road dirt, could be used to fool lane detection models before the passenger catches on. The adversarial patches we test our defense on differ in their much smaller size and unboundedness compared to the full lane covering required by [12]. Although our metric of attack success show the patches are unable to achieve our goal of reshaping all the lanes in the scene, our results do reaffirm that patch attack-based lane deviation is a valid threat necessitating defense.

III. Method

A. Defense

Our proposed defense takes place at the end of an existing lane detection pipeline, at which point a set of candidate lanes have been identified by the lane detection model. Upon attack success, these candidate lanes are corrupted and may include a mix of real and fake lanes. The goal of our defense is to verify the real lanes and filter out the fake lanes before further autonomous vehicle systems make potentially hazardous decisions based on faulty information.

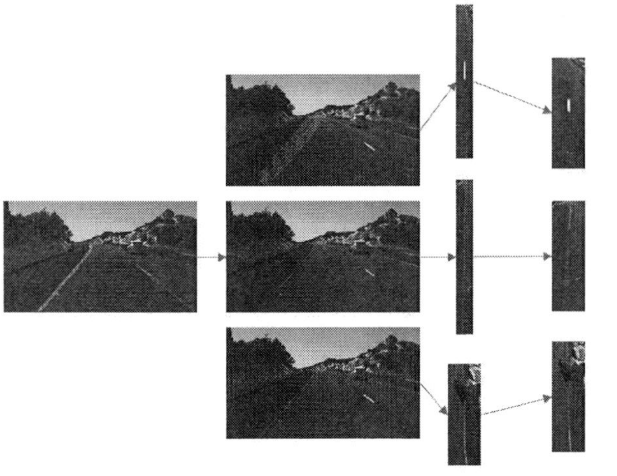

Fig. 3. Lane Stabilization. Stabilized lanes are classified as either real or fake by the verification system.

1) Stabilizing Lanes: The defense takes detected lanes as input; however, due to the nature of perspective and exacerbated by the fact that lane lines can curve either left or right, extracting lanes using masks formed from the pixel-level segmentation as provided by the lane detection model results in lane lines that can take an arbitrary number of forms, lending itself to a classification problem with an unbounded domain. To address this issue, we construct a stabilized image of each lane as follows:

1) Given a set of points corresponding to a lane, we first perform a least squares polynomial regression to get its underlying shape.
2) For each pixel that lies on the curve, we compute the derivative of the polynomial at that point, and extract the pixels corresponding to the line centered around the point on the curve and rotated by the angle formed by the derivative and the horizontal axis.
3) Rotating each extracted line such that the pixels in each line are lined up horizontally, we can then stack the horizontal lines vertically to obtain a stabilized image of the lane that is not influenced by perspective or lane curvature.

While inverse perspective transforms [1] can mitigate perspective distortions as well, we found little benefit from applying a fixed homography before extracting the stabilized lanes. Figure 4 shows examples of positive and negative samples generated by our stabilization process.

2) Training: Given the absence of applicable existing datasets, to generate a training dataset for the defense, we extract stabilized real and fake lanes from a dataset labelled for lane detection, using the ground truth labels as the basis for real lanes and generating curves that start from real lanes but deviate as they move away from the camera as the basis for fake lanes. While each scene only has a fixed number of real lanes, an arbitrary number of fake lanes can be generated from them, creating an imbalance in real versus fake lanes. A potential enhancement of the defense could involve tailoring fake lane design in anticipation of specific attacks.

Fig. 4. Examples of positive and negative examples generated by the lane stabilization process for the defense training dataset.

To address class imbalance, the defense is trained using focal loss as described in [8] with hyperparameters determined experimentally. To improve robustness, we employ adversarial training [9] with an emphasis on missed fake lane detection via asymmetric weighting of the loss function.

B. Nonadaptive Threat Model

We propose two different threat models dependent on attacker access to lane detection equipment. The threats share the goal of perturbing the original scene such that the binary segmentation component of an end-to-end lane detection model is disrupted, allowing the attacker to inducing an arbitrary lane existence pattern of their choosing. Due to the downstream dependence of lane detection models on lane existence, the attack can fatally disrupt lane detection model function. All attacks are carried out using Projected Gradient Descent [9] until convergence.

The attacks are nonadaptive, meaning that they do not target our verification model. We describe adaptive versions of our attacks [13] in the following section.

1) L-Infinity Attack: In our first threat model, the attacker is able to manipulate any pixel in the input image, but is constrained by a bound on the size of perturbation for each pixel, akin to digital corruption of the input or a lens filter over the camera.

2) Patch Attack: The attacker is able to manipulate a subset of pixels in the input image, but is not constrained by a bound on the size of perturbation for each pixel. We can further break the subset of pixels into two sizes: fixed and variable. In a fixed size patch attack, there is a fixed number of pixels the attacker can modify, akin to having a patch on the lens of the camera. In a variable size patch attack, the number of pixels able to be modified is a function of distance away from the camera, akin to being able to lay a physical patch on the road in the scene. We can simulate such an attack by scaling patch size against how lane width and lane marker height change as a function of pixel height.

C. Adaptive Threat Model

The lane stabilization procedure poses an issue for differentiability when planning an adaptive attack in which the attacker seeks to outmaneuver the defense. Specifically, the

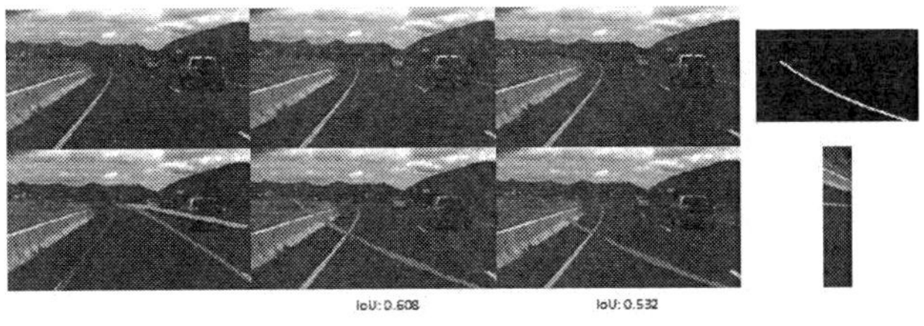

Fig. 5. Example of L-infinity bounded attack. From left to right, the vertical pairs of images represent clean, nonadaptive, and adaptive attack, with the lane detection model output superimposed on the second row, and IoU values below. IoU values are with respect to the upper rightmost image of the target lane binary segmentation map, and the resulting stabilized lane is shown below. Under bounded attack, the attacker is able to assert full control over the scene and induce arbitrary lane configurations.

backpropagation when attacking the defense is unresolvable at the point of lane stabilization. We instead propose an adaptive threat model that takes place in two stages that can extend any of the nonadaptive threat models proposed above. Without loss of generality, we discuss the adaptive threat in the context of an L-infinity attack.

1) The first stage is an L-infinity attack on the lane detection model, with the goal to induce an arbitrary binary segmentation map of our choosing. The output is a perturbed scene in which the lane detection model identifies the arbitrary lane we choose.
2) Once the first stage has converged, the pixels corresponding to the arbitrary lane are extracted from the perturbed scene. The lane is then stabilized as described in the process above, and subject to the second stage of the attack. The goal of the second stage is to find a perturbation to the stabilized lane such that the defense is fooled into thinking the arbitrary lane is real. Upon convergence of the L-infinity attack on the defense, the resulting perturbation on the stabilized lane is mapped back to the original location of the pixels that form the stabilized lane in the perturbed scene output from the first stage.

The final result is a perturbed scene designed to both convince the lane detection model of the existence of a fake lane and the defense that the perceived fake line is real.

IV. Experiments

A. Datasets

The lane detection model, LaneNet, is trained on the TuSimple dataset [14], which consists of 3,626 training images and 2,782 testing images taken from a camera mounted on the front of a vehicle. The images are scaled to be of size 512x288.

The defense is trained on stabilized lanes extracted from the TuSimple dataset. Each stabilized lane is fit with a polynomial of degree 3 and resized to be of size 128x40.

B. Implementation Details

The defense model takes the form of a 3-layer convolutional neural network, intentionally designed to contrast against the numerous layers and weights used for lane detection

Fig. 6. Examples of fixed and variable size adaptive patch attacks. Each group of four images has the original and applied patch on the first row, and the corresponding binary segmentation maps on the second. The target lane is dotted in green, with the patch's bounding box outlined in red. IoU values are below each applied patch segmentation map, with the resulting stabilized lane shown to the right of each group. While full scene control is limited, the results are substantial enough to cause rogue vehicle behavior.

segmentation. Inputs to the defense take the form of stabilized lanes of size 128x40. The network is comprised of two convolutional layers and one linear layer. Both convolutional layers use a 3x3 filter size with stride 3 and no padding, with BatchNorm and ReLU applied after each.

Both LaneNet and defense model are trained using one GPU (GTX 1080). LaneNet is implemented as specified in [10], with no modifications for robustness, keeping in line with the modular nature of our defense.

All attacks are performed until convergence is achieved. Parameter details are as follows:

1) The L-infinity attack is bounded by a per-pixel perturbation of at most 8/255, where the input image's pixels have a range of $[0, 1]$.
2) The fixed size patch attack is a 100x100 square with no bound on pixel deviations inside the square. The square is centered around a point on the targeted arbitrary lane.
3) The variable size patch attack is specified by a 100x100 square at the foot of the camera, corresponding to roughly a 3-foot by 3-foot physical patch. For each scene, an arbitrary distance from the camera is selected, and the square is scaled down accordingly.

C. Evaluation

We evaluate performance of the defense on the test set of TuSimple. For each scene in the original dataset, LaneNet is used to identify lanes in clean and attacked variants. The identified lanes are stabilized and fed to the defense for

TABLE I. DEFENSE RESULTS. FALSE POSITIVE RATE (FPR) REFERS TO REAL LANES THE DEFENSE MISTAKENLY FLAGGED AS FAKE, WHEREAS FALSE NEGATIVE RATE (FNR) REFERS TO FAKE LANES THE DEFENSE BELIEVED TO BE REAL. AS A MEASURE OF POST-DEFENSE ATTACK SUCCESS, THE FALSE NEGATIVE (FN) AVERAGE IOU IS THE AVERAGE IOU BETWEEN ALL ATTACKED SCENES AND TARGETS ONCE FLAGGED LANES HAVE REMOVED.

	Defense Metrics		*Attack Metric*
Bounded Attack	**FPR**	**FNR**	**FN Average IoU**
Unprotected	0	1	0.720
Nonadaptive	0.040	0.039	0.031
Adaptive	0.043	0.098	0.046

	Defense Metrics		*Attack Success Metric*
Patch Attack	**FPR**	**FNR**	**FN Average IoU**
Fixed Size Unprotected	0	1	0.205
Fixed Size Nonadaptive	0.039	0.005	0.001
Fixed Size Adaptive	0.042	0.005	0.001
Variable Size Unprotected	0	1	0.082
Variable Size Nonadaptive	0.053	0.017	0.002
Variable Size Adaptive	0.045	0.023	0.002

TABLE II. SELECTED DEFENSE ROC CURVE RESULTS. FALSE POSITIVE RATE (FPR) REFERS TO REAL LANES THE DEFENSE MISTAKENLY FLAGGED AS FAKE, WHEREAS FALSE NEGATIVE RATE (FNR) REFERS TO FAKE LANES THE DEFENSE BELIEVED TO BE REAL. $\downarrow$ - LOWER IS BETTER $\uparrow$ - HIGHER IS BETTER.

		Bounded Attack		*Adaptive Patch Attack*	
		Nonadaptive	Adaptive	Fixed Size	Variable Size
FNR at 0.01 FPR	$\downarrow$	0.160	0.496	0.071	0.099
FNR at 0.02 FPR	$\downarrow$	0.075	0.210	0.021	0.056
FNR at 0.05 FPR	$\downarrow$	0.036	0.082	0.005	0.020
FNR at 0.10 FPR	$\downarrow$	0.026	0.048	0.003	0.010
Area Under Curve	$\uparrow$	0.984	0.971	0.996	0.993

classification. We report fake lane missed detection rates (false negative) and real lane misclassification rates (false positive) at a classification threshold such that we see a 5% real lane misclassification rate in a validation set. Additionally, we report the average intersection over Union (IoU) values between all lanes in attacked scenes and attack targets once flagged lanes have been removed. IoU values were of interest due to their dual purpose of measuring how much of the target was achieved and how much of the original scene was preserved, providing a sense of attacker control over the scene.

V. RESULTS

A. L-Infinity Attack

We observe that success is almost certain under bounded attack, with all traces of the real lanes wiped out and the induced fake lanes matching target fake lanes with an average IOU of 0.720. Note that after typical lane detection model postprocessing cleanup procedures, induced fake lane and the target fake lane have almost identical stabilized forms. Examples of scenes and their corresponding binary segmentation maps before and after targeted attack are in Figure 5.

Table I shows defense results under bounded attack. With an unprotected model, fake lanes slip by undetected 100% of the time. Under nonadaptive attack, the defense is very capable of detecting fake lanes while very rarely mistaking real lanes for fake. We do see some gains in attack strength under adaptive attack; however, we are still able to detect 90.2% of fake lanes. Table II shows selected ROC curve data.

B. Patch Attack

1) Fixed Size: The fixed patch attack results reveal a strong reliance of LaneNet on spatially local features. Unlike the previous L-infinity attack, which could manipulate the entire scene to achieve its goal, the patch attack is unable to induce change outside of a small region around the patch location. An example of the attack can be found in the first half of Figure 6. To improve attack stability, the polynomial curve used to stabilize the lane for the defense is pulled from the target binary segmentation map instead of being fitted from what the patch attack is able to induce. Note that while the patch attack does not do well against our attack success metric of full scene control, the achieved result is still capable of causing undesired lane deviation.

Table I shows defense results under fixed patch attack. Similar to the bounded attack, we see strong detection rates for nonadaptive attack with a minor drop when subject to adaptive attack. Table II shows selected ROC curve data for the fixed size adaptive attack.

2) Variable Size: Variable patch attack success follows a similar trend to that of the fixed size patch attack, with the region of effect largely localized around the patch location. An example of the variable patch attack can be found in the second half of Figure 6. The same strategy to improve attack stability as described in the previous section is employed when preparing the lane for verification by the defense.

Table I shows defense results under variable patch attack. Mirroring both previous attacks, robust nonadaptive attack detection rates are accompanied by slightly weaker results when under adaptive attack. Although variable patch sizes are generally smaller than the fixed patch, the former attack is slightly stronger than the latter with respect to false positive and false negative rates despite the smaller attack IoU on the unprotected model, suggesting the fixed patch being a more noticeable anomaly harder for the adaptive attack to overcome. Table II shows selected ROC curve data for the adaptive attack.

C. Speed

The addition of our defense saw a marginal impact on pipeline inference time, experiencing a drop in output from 29.8 to 27 frames per second. Due to differences in system configuration, we were unable to achieve the 50 frames per second as presented in [10], but as a rough estimate, the 3ms inference time of our defense as measured locally would translate to a drop from 52.6 to 45.5 frames per second using the pipeline timings provided by [10].

D. Ablation Studies

1) Adaptive Attack Cycling: Given that the second stage of the adaptive attack is unable to assess its impact on the first stage, it is possible that there exists adverse feedback between the two stages. To evaluate the extent of this feedback, we test a bounded attack where the stages are cycled up to four times. Results are in the first half of Table III. Comparing them with the figures in Table I, we note that the false positive and false negative rates are slightly better for the defense in the cycled attack, suggesting that while repeated cycling may be helping first stage output, the effect is outweighed by an adverse impact

TABLE III. ABLATION RESULTS. FALSE POSITIVE RATE (FPR) REFERS TO REAL LANES THE DEFENSE MISTAKENLY FLAGGED AS FAKE, WHEREAS FALSE NEGATIVE RATE (FNR) REFERS TO FAKE LANES THE DEFENSE BELIEVED TO BE REAL. AS A MEASURE OF POST-DEFENSE ATTACK SUCCESS, THE FALSE NEGATIVE (FN) AVERAGE IOU IS THE AVERAGE IOU BETWEEN ALL ATTACKED SCENES AND TARGETS ONCE FLAGGED LANES HAVE REMOVED.

	Defense Metrics		*Attack Success Metric*
Cycled Adaptive Attack	**FPR**	**FNR**	**FN Average IoU**
Bounded	0.042	0.044	0.030

	Defense Metrics		*Attack Success Metric*
Linear Defense	**FPR**	**FNR**	**FN Average IoU**
Nonadaptive Bounded	0.049	0.966	0.720
Nonadaptive Fixed Size Patch	0.045	0.879	0.180
Nonadaptive Variable Size Patch	0.052	0.921	0.075

to the efficacy of the second stage. Since polynomial fitting cleans up much of the noise in the binary segmentation map, first stage gains may provide marginal benefits to overall attack strength.

2) Simpler Defense Architecture: We found that although the philosophy of our defense encourages simple defense designs, purely linear models struggle with the task of lane classification as shown in the second half of Table III. This result hints again at the highly local nature of lane detection as previously seen in Figure 6, a property linear layers are less adept at taking advantage of compared to the convolutional layers used in our 3-layer model.

VI. CONCLUSION

Our proposed defense sits on top of existing lane detection models and can defend against adversarial attacks with minimal impact to lane detection capabilities.

The orthogonal nature of the defense allows it to be trained independently from the underlying lane detection model, eliminating the cost of retraining. Amid the rising complexity of image processing models, our defense can provide security with very little overhead. Taking only lane locations as inputs, the defense does not depend on a particular lane detection model's features or assumptions, streamlining integration into any lane detection pipeline. The lightweight nature of the defense promotes fast inference and quick updates as new attacks arise.

Under a bounded threat model that is able to fully take over the scene, we show that a simple 3-layer model employing our defense structure on top of LaneNet can detect over 90% of attacks while maintaining a maximum 5% impact to clean accuracy. Under a patch-based threat model where attacker control is limited but still capable of causing undesired lane deviation, our defense is able to identify 98% of abnormal activity while preserving the same 5% threshold. In such situations where the lane detection model would have otherwise passed fake lanes off as real to the autonomous control system, our model is able to call attention to potentially malicious actors.

Future work could involve designing a differentiable adaptive attack and collecting performance of our proposed defense on a larger sample of lane detection models. An application of transfer learning could be explored by training the defense on a separate dataset from the lane detection model and examining performance. While our defense is able to alert the vehicle to the presence of an attack, it does not provide guidance on the safest response, which we leave as an open question. Variants in the architecture of the verification system may also be worth investigating; for example, defense model enhanced with domain-specific knowledge of the highly local nature of lane detection could see further improvement in verification accuracy. Finally, a similar system could prove useful for bolstering robustness against corruption.

ACKNOWLEDGMENT

This work was supported by generous gifts from the Hewlett Foundation through the Center for Long-Term Cybersecurity, from the Berkeley Drive Project, and from Google.

REFERENCES

[1] M. Bertozz, A. Broggi, and A. Fascioli, "Stereo inverse perspective mapping: theory and applications," *Image and Vision Computing*, vol. 16, no. 8, pp. 585 – 590, 1998. [Online]. Available: http://www.sciencedirect.com/science/article/pii/S0262885697000930

[2] T. B. Brown, D. Mané, A. Roy, M. Abadi, and J. Gilmer, "Adversarial patch," 2018.

[3] M. Cisse, Y. Adi, N. Neverova, and J. Keshet, "Houdini: Fooling deep structured prediction models," 2017.

[4] I. J. Goodfellow, J. Shlens, and C. Szegedy, "Explaining and harnessing adversarial examples," 2015.

[5] Y. Hou, Z. Ma, C. Liu, and C. C. Loy, "Learning lightweight lane detection cnns by self attention distillation," 2019.

[6] S. Jung, S. Choi, M. A. Khan, and J. Choo, "Towards lightweight lane detection by optimizing spatial embedding," 2020.

[7] Y. Ko, Y. Lee, S. Azam, F. Munir, M. Jeon, and W. Pedrycz, "Key points estimation and point instance segmentation approach for lane detection," 2020.

[8] T. Lin, P. Goyal, R. B. Girshick, K. He, and P. Dollár, "Focal loss for dense object detection," *CoRR*, vol. abs/1708.02002, 2017. [Online]. Available: http://arxiv.org/abs/1708.02002

[9] A. Madry, A. Makelov, L. Schmidt, D. Tsipras, and A. Vladu, "Towards deep learning models resistant to adversarial attacks," in *International Conference on Learning Representations*, 2018. [Online]. Available: https://openreview.net/forum?id=rJzIBfZAb

[10] D. Neven, B. D. Brabandere, S. Georgoulis, M. Proesmans, and L. V. Gool, "Towards end-to-end lane detection: an instance segmentation approach," in *2018 IEEE Intelligent Vehicles Symposium (IV)*, 2018, pp. 286–291.

[11] A. Nøkland, "Improving back-propagation by adding an adversarial gradient," 2016.

[12] T. Sato, J. Shen, N. Wang, Y. J. Jia, X. Lin, and Q. A. Chen, "Hold tight and never let go: Security of deep learning based automated lane centering under physical-world attack," 2020.

[13] F. Tramer, N. Carlini, W. Brendel, and A. Madry, "On adaptive attacks to adversarial example defenses," 2020.

[14] TuSimple. [Online]. Available: http://benchmark.tusimple.ai/

[15] Y. Wang, X. Ma, J. Bailey, J. Yi, B. Zhou, and Q. Gu, "On the convergence and robustness of adversarial training," in *Proceedings of the 36th International Conference on Machine Learning*, ser. Proceedings of Machine Learning Research, K. Chaudhuri and R. Salakhutdinov, Eds., vol. 97. Long Beach, California, USA: PMLR, 09–15 Jun 2019, pp. 6586–6595. [Online]. Available: http://proceedings.mlr.press/v97/wang19i.html

[16] C. Xie, J. Wang, Z. Zhang, Y. Zhou, L. Xie, and A. L. Yuille, "Adversarial examples for semantic segmentation and object detection," *CoRR*, vol. abs/1703.08603, 2017. [Online]. Available: http://arxiv.org/abs/1703.08603

WIP: End-to-End Analysis of Adversarial Attacks to Automated Lane Centering Systems

Hengyi Liang*, Ruochen Jiao*, Takami Sato†, Junjie Shen†, Qi Alfred Chen†, Qi Zhu
Northwestern University   † University of California, Irvine

***Abstract*—Machine learning techniques, particularly those based on deep neural networks (DNNs), are widely adopted in the development of advanced driver-assistance systems (ADAS) and autonomous vehicles. While providing significant improvement over traditional methods in average performance, the usage of DNNs also presents great challenges to system safety, especially given the uncertainty of the surrounding environment, the disturbance to system operations, and the current lack of methodologies for predicting DNN behavior. In particular, adversarial attacks to the sensing input may cause errors in systems' perception of the environment and lead to system failure. However, existing works mainly focus on analyzing the impact of such attacks on the sensing and perception results and designing mitigation strategies accordingly. We argue that as system safety is ultimately determined by the actions it takes, it is essential to take an end-to-end approach and address adversarial attacks with the consideration of the entire ADAS or autonomous driving pipeline, from sensing and perception to planing, navigation and control. In this paper, we present our initial findings in quantitatively analyzing the impact of a type of adversarial attack (that leverages road patch) on system planning and control, and discuss some of the possible directions to systematically address such attack with an end-to-end view.**

I. Introduction

Recent years witnessed significant advancement of autonomous driving techniques and advanced driver-assistance systems (ADAS), with widely-adopted applications such as Adaptive Cruise Control (ACC), Forward Collision-Avoidance Assistance (FCA), and Automated Lane Centering (ALC). Such systems typically consist of a pipeline of sensing, perception, planning, and control modules. They rely on on-board sensors to collect data at real time, use perception algorithms to process the data and understand the environment, and then make planning and control decisions for the vehicle. In these systems, deep neural networks (DNNs) are used prevalently, especially for perception tasks such as lane detection and object detection, due to their high level of average accuracy. Moreover, there have also been increasing application of DNNs to other modules, such as prediction, planning, and control.

However, the safety and security of these learning-based ADAS and autonomous systems can hardly be guaranteed or even quantitatively analyzed, given the various uncertainties in the system and its surrounding environment, such as the inherent uncertainties from the dynamic environment, the disturbances to system operations from environment interference, transient errors, malicious attacks, and the current lack of methodologies for predicting the DNN behavior [1], [2].

* These two authors contribute equally to the work.

Workshop on Automotive and Autonomous Vehicle Security (AutoSec) 2021
25 February 2021, Virtual

https://dx.doi.org/10.14722/autosec.2021.23034
www.ndss-symposium.org

In the literature, there has been a large body of works demonstrating the vulnerability of DNNs to external disturbances and adversarial attacks [3]–[6]. In particular, some recent works try to attack DNN-based ADAS and autonomous systems by adding adversarial perturbations to the physical environment in a stealthy way [7], [8]. The adversarial patterns are carefully designed so that they can make the perception module render wrong results while themselves can hardly be noticed by human – one such example is the dirty road patch attack shown in [8]. The wrong perception results caused by these attacks will then affect the downstream planning, navigation, and control decisions, and possibly cause dangerous situations and accidents (e.g., causing victim vehicle to drive off the road or collide with other objects).

Most prior defense works either focus on 1) making the neural networks themselves more robust against adversarial attacks [9], [10] or 2) trying to detect anomaly in the input data [11], [12]. While it is clear that the impact of those adversarial attacks on system safety has to be eventually reflected through vehicle planning, navigation, and control, there is currently a lack of *systematic and quantitative* methods to analyze such impact throughout the end-to-end ADAS and autonomous driving pipeline and to design mitigation strategies accordingly. In this work, we focus on the safety and robustness of the entire system and explore holistic end-to-end methods for the analysis and mitigation of adversarial attacks to driving assistance systems. We analyze how the perturbation from sensor data propagates through the pipeline and affect the final control actions (e.g., steering decisions). Our overall goals in this area include the following:

1) Analyzing the impact of each module on system safety and identifying proper interfaces between modules that can be utilized to improve system safety and robustness.
2) Proposing a system-level framework to improve the safety of DNN-based driving assistance systems, e.g., by quantifying the perception uncertainty and adapting planning and control accordingly.
3) Evaluating our proposed approach on a production-grade simulation environment (e.g., OpenPilot [13] combined with LGSVL [14]).

This work-in-progress paper mainly focuses on the first goal. We analyze the ALC system as a representative ADAS application, identify how the uncertainty/confidence changes under various adversarial scenarios from the dirty road patch attack, and discuss potential methods to improve system safety and robustness.

II. System Model

In this paper, we use the ALC system as a demonstrating example. We believe that our analysis methodology could also be applied to other autonomous driving functionalities (e.g., localization), where there are uncertainties from external environment. The ALC is a popular Level 2 autonomous driving system that is widely available for modern vehicles. For example, many OEM vehicles such as Mercedes-Benz C-class, Tesla and GM CT6 come with lane centering feature. Moreover, there are also third party open-source autonomous driving software stacks (e.g., OpenPilot, Baidu Apollo, Autoware) that integrate ALC.

Figure 1 shows an ALC system structure that involves three major modules: *perception*, *planning* and *control*. The perception module takes sensor data as input and then detects lane lines and predicts any other objects on the road (e.g., vehicles, obstacles). The planning module mainly calculates the desired trajectory based on the output of perception module. The control module then calculates a desired steering angle and speed that will be applied to the vehicle actuators. In the following, we use the ALC system in OpenPilot as an example and briefly introduce each module.

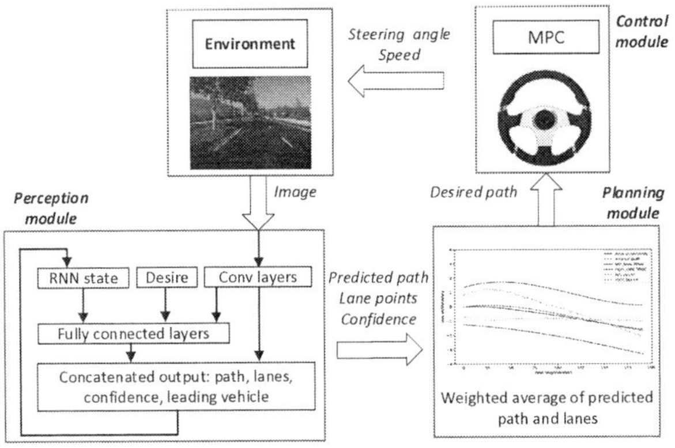

Fig. 1: The end-to-end pipeline of automated lane centering.

A. DNN-based Lane Detection Module

Traditional perception module uses edge detection algorithms to detect lane lines from images captured by the front camera [15]. In recent years, DNN-based lane detection models have achieved the state-of-the-art accuracy and been widely adopted in production-level ALC systems. Since lane lines do not change significantly across consecutive frames, recurrent neural networks (RNNs) ares typically used to make the prediction more stable. The perception module in Figure 1 highlights the input-output relation of the OpenPilot lane detection model. Particularly, a convolutional neural network (CNN) is used to process current image data and then a combination of the CNN output and the last RNN state is fed to a fully connected network. OpenPilot lane detection model leverages Multiple Hypotheses Prediction (MHP) [16] to capture ambiguity in the prediction. The output of the lane detection model contains 1) 192 predicted lane line points, in the form of mean and standard variance, for each lane, 2) the confidence value for each predicted lane line, 3) a predicted driving path, and 4) information related to the leading vehicle. After the lane detection inference, a post-process is followed to fit the points into lane line curves. Specifically, in OpenPilot, the weighted least square regression method is used.

B. Planning Module

The planning module generates the desired path for the next period. For ALC, this means that the desired path should be the center of the detected left lane and right lane and the steering angle should keep the vehicle following the desired path. As mentioned earlier, the perception module handles the ambiguity of prediction by outputting confidence scores for the left lane and the right lane. In the OpenPilot planning module, this information is used to generate the final desired path as a weighted sum of the predicted lanes and the predicted path. Intuitively, if the prediction is less confident on the predicted lanes, then the final desired path relies on the predicted path; otherwise, if the prediction has high confidence on the predicted left lane and right lane, the final desired path will be close to the center of the predicted left lane and right lane.

C. Control Module

The main goal of the control module is to calculate the vehicle maneuver for the next period and convert it into a command that will be applied to vehicle actuators, e.g., steering, throttle, and brake command to the chassis. For lateral control, after obtaining the desired path from the path planner, a controller is used to calculate the corresponding steering angle based on the desired path. In OpenPilot, model predictive control (MPC) is used to calculate the steering angle. The constraints include 1) simplified system dynamics, 2) vehicle heading constraints, and 3) maximum steering angle constraints. In our simulation environment, due to the constraint of the mechanical unit, we consider that the steering rate is limited by a maximum value. The throttle is generated by a PID controller by setting an appropriate reference speed.

III. Threat Model

In this paper, we mainly consider attacks achieved through physical domain. Specifically, we assume that attacker cannot hack into the victim vehicle and should not be able to modify the software of the victim vehicle directly. However, the attacker has the ability to modify the physical environment that can be captured by the sensors equipped on the victim vehicle (e.g., cameras). The attacker's goal is to carefully change the appearance of certain object such that 1) the object can hardly be noticed by human driver, 2) and it can cause the ADAS or autonomous driving system to drive off the road. There are many adversarial attacks against deep learning based tasks such as image classification and object detection, but we focus on attacks specially targeting deep learning based driving assistance systems so as to analyze and evaluate the safety of those systems. For example, the work in [7] can generate an adversarial billboard to cause steering angle error; the work in [8] is able to generate a gray scale dirty patch on road such that vehicles passing through the patch will deviate (either left or right). In the following experiments, we use the dirty road patch attack as a case study, and we believe that our approach may be extended for other types of physical world attacks.

In fact, the optimization-based physical attack in [8] is the first attack that is systematically designed for the ALC system. Specifically, the attackers first collect the input image and predicted steering angle of the ALC on a certain road. Using these images, the knowledge of the ALC system, and the kinematic model of the vehicle, they can optimize an adversarial patch to make the vehicle deviate from the original trajectory to the greatest extent. In the experiment, it can lead the vehicle out of the lane boundary within 1 second (which means the lateral deviation is larger than 0.735m in highway) with high success rate.

Fig. 2: Image of the adversarial patch captured by front camera.

IV. Experiments and Observations

As a preliminary case study, we perform the ALC attack in a simulation environment. We bridge the product-level simulator LGSVL with OpenPilot and put a carefully designed patch on the road [8]. During each simulation step, we obtain the image frame captured by the front camera (a demo frame is shown in Figure 2) and the vehicle status through the API provided by the LGSVL simulator. We then pass these data to OpenPilot. OpenPilot ALC will calculate a desired steering angle for the next simulation step. Then, the steering command is sent back to LGSVL through the API.

To evaluate the effectiveness of the attack, we conduct a series of experiments with different settings of the patch. Figure 3 shows the trajectory of the ego vehicle when we put the patch on different locations of the road. The maximum lateral deviation is over 1 meter, which will cause the vehicle to drive into the opposite lane. Although the ego vehicle finally drives back to its original lane after it has passed through the dirty patch area, this behavior is extremely dangerous. Then, we gradually reduce the perturbation area of the patch. Here, the perturbation area ratio (PAR) denotes the percentage of the pixels on the patch that can be perturbed. For example, 30% PAR means that only 30% of pixels can be perturbed while the rest 70% pixels have the same color as the road. Figure 4 shows the trajectory of the ego vehicle under different level of PAR. The ego vehicle drives off the road when PAR is 50% or 30%. When PAR is 10%, the ego vehicle can stay in the lane but the patch still can impact its stability.

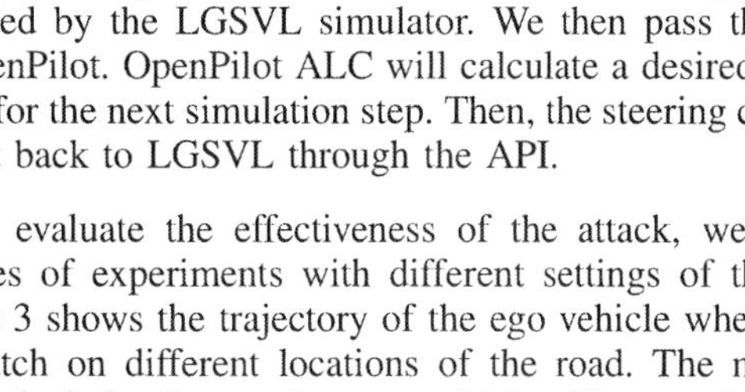

Fig. 3: The trajectory of the vehicle when the dirty patch is placed on different locations of the road.

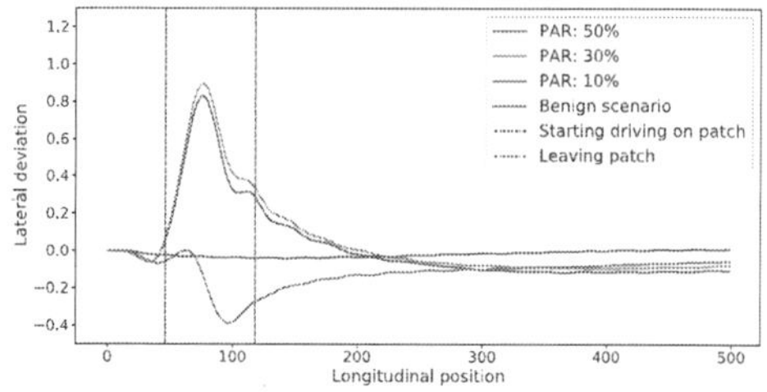

Fig. 4: The trajectory of the vehicle when the dirty patch is designed with different values of the PAR.

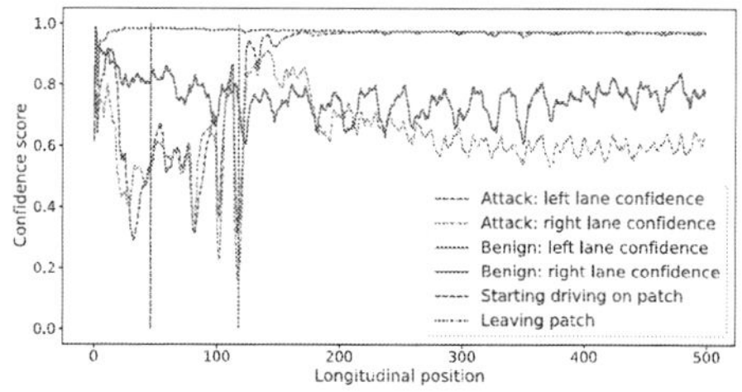

Fig. 5: The confidence of the perception module drops significantly when the ego vehicle is approaching the patch.

To study how the adversarial attack can lead the vehicle to deviate, we inspect the interface between each module and try to reason about how the impact of the adversarial attack can propagate through each module.

Perception Confidence: We first check the result of the perception module. In OpenPilot, the MHP model is trained with binary cross entropy loss, which means the output can indicate the confidence in whether there are lane lines [17]. Through our experiments with different settings of the patch, we notice a general phenomenon: the confidence scores for both left lane and right lane drop significantly when the vehicle is approaching the patch, as shown in Figure 5, while the confidence score will almost stay stable under benign situation or ineffective attack. The dashed green line in Figure 5 indicates the starting point of the patch. As we can see, the confidence score drops even before the vehicle is on the patch (e.g., when the vehicle is at around 30 meters). However, when the confidence score drops, the vehicle has not started to deviate. This observation indicates that the impact of adversarial attack comes earlier than when the driver can perceive.

Biased Desired Path: We then inspect the result of path planner and try to figure out how the perception confidence may affect the final desired trajectory. Figure 6 is the result of one frame when the vehicle is approaching the patch. The predicted left lane, predicted right lane and the predicted path are the results generated by the perception module. As we can see, these three curves lean to the left (i.e., the positive direction of the y axis). If the vehicle just follows the predicted path, it will definitely drive into the opposite lane. By analyzing the code of the path planner, we find that OpenPilot tries to leverage the confidence scores as weights. The final desired path can be considered as a weighted sum of the predicted left lane, predicted right lane, and the predicted path. However, as we observe that the confidence score for predicted lanes drops significantly, the final desired path will largely depend on the predicted path, which is bent to wrong

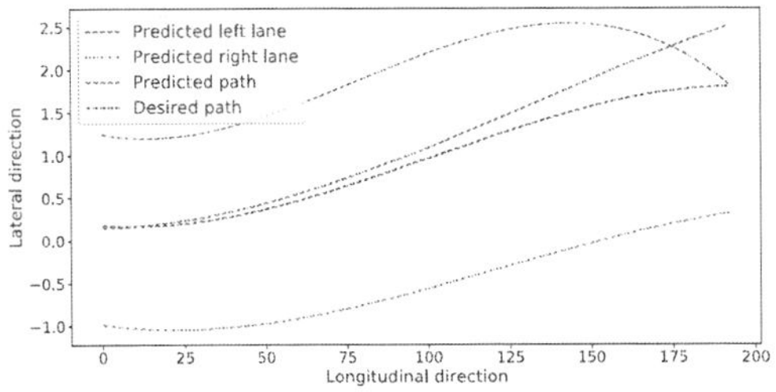

Fig. 6: Desired trajectory generated by OpenPilot path planner deviates towards left when the vehicle is approaching the patch.

direction. Since the desired path is biased, the MPC controller cannot calculate a correct steering angle for the next step.

Potential Mitigation Methods: Based on the preliminary experiments and observations, we find that the confidence score can work as a triggering signal to indicate the presence of adversarial attack or anomalous noises in this case. We believe that an end-to-end approach is needed to mitigate the attacks, and there are some potential directions:

1) We may try to quantify/estimate the uncertainty of the DNN-based perception module, including both epistemic uncertainty (caused by unbalanced distribution of the training data) and aleatory uncertainty (caused by noises of input data). Such estimated uncertainty can then be used by the planning and control module to improve system safety.
2) We may develop an adaptation strategy to holistically adjust each module to mitigate the impact of adversarial attacks.
3) In the perception module, we may use other sensors' data (e.g., from LiDAR and GPS) to compensate the result of cameras, especially when the confidence is low.
4) We may leverage the temporal and spatial correlation of consecutive inputs to detect the anomaly of current sensor data or even re-use more reliable results from recent data samples. Besides, the RNN can be modified to make better use of the temporal correlation and assign more weights on frames with high confidence and less uncertainty.

V. Conclusion and Future Work Plan

We argue that it is essential to address adversarial attacks on driving assistance systems from an end-to-end perspective, by quantitatively analyzing the impact of those attacks across the ADAS or autonomous driving pipeline and designing mitigation strategies in a holistic manner. In our preliminary work, we studied an ALC system, analyzed how different modules interact under dirty road patch attacks, and identified a sensitive signal that can be leveraged to detect those attacks. We are currently working on better quantifying the uncertainty of the perception module and using it to guide the adaption of the planning and control module for improving system safety. In future, we also plan to study other ADAS and autonomous driving applications and try to generalize our approach.

Acknowledgment

We gratefully acknowledge the support from CNS-1839511, CNS-1834701, IIS-1724341, CNS-1850533, CNS-1929771, CNS-1932464, USDOT UTC Grant 69A3552047138, and ONR grant N00014-19-1-2496.

References

[1] Q. Zhu, W. Li, H. Kim, Y. Xiang, K. Wardega, Z. Wang, Y. Wang, H. Liang, C. Huang, J. Fan, and H. Choi, "Know the unknowns: Addressing disturbances and uncertainties in autonomous systems : Invited paper," in *ICCAD*, 2020, pp. 1–9.

[2] Q. Zhu, C. Huang, R. Jiao, S. Lan, H. Liang, X. Liu, Y. Wang, Z. Wang, and S. Xu, "Safety-assured design and adaptation of learning-enabled autonomous systems," *ASP-DAC*, 2021.

[3] A. Kurakin, I. Goodfellow, and S. Bengio, "Adversarial examples in the physical world," 2017.

[4] S.-M. Moosavi-Dezfooli, A. Fawzi, and P. Frossard, "Deepfool: A simple and accurate method to fool deep neural networks," in *Proceedings of the IEEE Conference on Computer Vision and Pattern Recognition (CVPR)*, June 2016.

[5] N. Papernot, P. McDaniel, S. Jha, M. Fredrikson, Z. B. Celik, and A. Swami, "The limitations of deep learning in adversarial settings," in *2016 IEEE European Symposium on Security and Privacy (EuroS P)*, 2016, pp. 372–387.

[6] K. Eykholt, I. Evtimov, E. Fernandes, B. Li, A. Rahmati, C. Xiao, A. Prakash, T. Kohno, and D. Song, "Robust physical-world attacks on deep learning visual classification," in *Proceedings of the IEEE Conference on Computer Vision and Pattern Recognition (CVPR)*, June 2018.

[7] H. Zhou, W. Li, Z. Kong, J. Guo, Y. Zhang, B. Yu, L. Zhang, and C. Liu, "Deepbillboard: Systematic physical-world testing of autonomous driving systems," in *Proceedings of the ACM/IEEE 42nd International Conference on Software Engineering*, ser. ICSE '20. New York, NY, USA: Association for Computing Machinery, 2020, p. 347–358.

[8] T. Sato, J. Shen, N. Wang, Y. J. Jia, X. Lin, and Q. A. Chen, "Hold tight and never let go: Security of deep learning based automated lane centering under physical-world attack," *arXiv preprint arXiv:2009.06701*, 2020.

[9] I. J. Goodfellow, J. Shlens, and C. Szegedy, "Explaining and harnessing adversarial examples," 2015.

[10] N. Papernot, P. McDaniel, X. Wu, S. Jha, and A. Swami, "Distillation as a defense to adversarial perturbations against deep neural networks," in *2016 IEEE Symposium on Security and Privacy (SP)*, 2016, pp. 582–597.

[11] K. Lee, K. Lee, H. Lee, and J. Shin, "A simple unified framework for detecting out-of-distribution samples and adversarial attacks," in *Advances in Neural Information Processing Systems*, S. Bengio, H. Wallach, H. Larochelle, K. Grauman, N. Cesa-Bianchi, and R. Garnett, Eds., vol. 31. Curran Associates, Inc., 2018, pp. 7167–7177.

[12] Z. Zheng and P. Hong, "Robust detection of adversarial attacks by modeling the intrinsic properties of deep neural networks," in *Advances in Neural Information Processing Systems*, S. Bengio, H. Wallach, H. Larochelle, K. Grauman, N. Cesa-Bianchi, and R. Garnett, Eds., vol. 31. Curran Associates, Inc., 2018, pp. 7913–7922.

[13] "Openpilot," https://comma.ai/.

[14] G. Rong, B. H. Shin, H. Tabatabaee, Q. Lu, S. Lemke, M. Možeiko, E. Boise, G. Uhm, M. Gerow, S. Mehta, E. Agafonov, T. H. Kim, E. Sterner, K. Ushiroda, M. Reyes, D. Zelenkovsky, and S. Kim, "Lgsvl simulator: A high fidelity simulator for autonomous driving," 2020.

[15] J. B. McDonald, "Application of the hough transform to lane detection and following on high speed roads," in *in Motorway Driving Scenarios", in Proceeding of Irish Signals and Systems Conference*, 2001.

[16] C. Rupprecht, I. Laina, R. DiPietro, M. Baust, F. Tombari, N. Navab, and G. D. Hager, "Learning in an uncertain world: Representing ambiguity through multiple hypotheses," in *Proceedings of the IEEE International Conference on Computer Vision*, 2017, pp. 3591–3600.

[17] D. Ramos, J. Franco-Pedroso, A. Lozano-Diez, and J. Gonzalez-Rodriguez, "Deconstructing cross-entropy for probabilistic binary classifiers," *Entropy*, vol. 20, no. 3, p. 208, 2018.

Demo: Automated Tracking System For LiDAR Spoofing Attacks On Moving Targets

Yulong Cao*, Jiaxiang Ma*, Kevin Fu*, Rampazzi Sara† and Morley Mao*
* {yulongc, mmmjx, kevinfu, zmao}@umich.edu, University of Michigan, Ann Arbor, MI, USA
† srampazzi@ufl.edu, University of Florida, Gainesville, FL, USA

***Abstract*—Recent studies have demonstrated that LiDAR sensors are vulnerable to spoofing attacks, in which adversaries spoof fake points to fool the car's perception system to see nonexistent obstacles. However, these attacks are generally conducted on static or simulated scenarios. Therefore, in this demo, we perform the first LiDAR spoofing attack on moving targets. We implemented a minimal tracking system integrated with the spoofer device to perform laser-based attacks on Lidar sensors. The demo shows how it is possible to inject up to 100 fake cloud points under three different scenarios.**

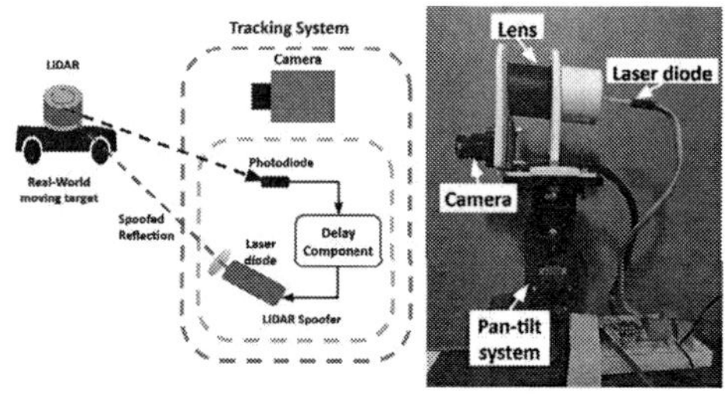

Fig. 1. Spoofing attack overview with laser integrated to the pan-tilt system.

I. Introduction

Advanced driver-assistance (ADA) systems used in autonomous vehicles leverage LiDAR sensors technology for obstacle detection. Prior research has shown that spinning LiDARs are vulnerable to laser spoofing attacks. In particular, Cao et al. [4] demonstrated how to selectively inject fake points to a LiDAR in order to fool the LiDAR-based perception system of autonomous vehicles into perceiving nonexistent obstacles. Such LiDAR spoofing attacks can lead to dangerous automatic emergency maneuvers such as steering or activate the brakes that may injure passengers, other vehicles, and pedestrians. However, these attacks were demonstrated in static scenarios (e.g. the LiDAR sensor in a fixed position). Thus, it is unclear whether such attacks can be successfully performed if the victim's vehicle is moving. In order to investigate this scenario, we designed and built a minimal automated tracking system (see Figure 1) integrated to an optimized version of the spoofer device developed by Cao et al. [4] to perform laser attacks in dynamic settings (e.g. moving robotic systems). The developed tracker is composed of a LI-USB30-AR023ZWDR camera [1] to detect the LiDAR location and a pan-tilt system PTX-ATX18 [2] to automatically aim a 905 nm pulsed laser diode with integrated driver. In this demonstration, we verify the feasibility of the laser spoofing attack in dynamic settings. The developed tracking system can be used in future studies to investigate LiDAR spoofing attacks in real-world scenarios.

II. Tracking System Overview

We adopted the SSD Inception v2 COCO model [3] to detect the LiDAR location. We trained the model using a custom dataset consisting of 320 LiDAR images publicly available, captured with different scenarios. To further increment the size of the dataset, we used standard image data augmentations techniques such as horizontal flipping and random crop. The model achieves a mean average precision (mAP) of 0.8 at intersection over union (IOU) of 0.5 in the test set. To predict a smoother bounding box of the LiDAR over continuous frames, we implemented the SORT model [5] to track the LiDAR using the prediction results of the object detector. We then extracted the spatial coordinates of the LiDAR based on the camera parameters to calculate the pan-tilt system movement for aiming the laser to the target direction keeping the LiDAR sensor at the center of the camera frame.

III. Demonstration

We performed the laser spoofing attack demonstration[1] tracking a Velodyne VLP-16 PUCK on top of a Neato Botvac D85 Robot while proceeding on a straight line in three different indoor scenarios: (1) at the maximum robot speed of 0.11 m/s, (2) up to 4 meter away from the spoofer, and (3) under different environmental light conditions. In all the scenarios the spoofer device were able to continuously spoof up to 100 fake points, confirming the feasibility of the attack on moving targets.

Acknowledgment

This research was funded by NSF Grants CNS-2031077 and CNS-1930041, and awards from Facebook and UM MCity.

References

[1] "LIUSB30AR023ZWDR Datasheet," https://www.leopardimaging.com/.

[2] "PhantomX Robot Turret Kit," https://www.trossenrobotics.com/.

[3] "TensorFlow 1 Detection Model Zoo," https://github.com/tensorflow/-models/blob/master/research/-object_detection/g3doc/tf1_detection_zoo.md.

[4] Y. Cao, C. Xiao, B. Cyr, Y. Zhou, W. Park, S. Rampazzi, Q. A. Chen, K. Fu, and Z. M. Mao, "Adversarial sensor attack on lidar-based perception in autonomous driving," in *ACM SIGSAC CCS*, 2019.

[5] N. Wojke, A. Bewley, and D. Paulus, "Simple online and realtime tracking with a deep association metric," in *IEEE ICIP*, 2017.

[1] Demo videos available at https://sites.google.com/view/lidarspoofingattack

Workshop on Automotive and Autonomous Vehicle Security (AutoSec) 2021
25 February 2021, Virtual
https://dx.doi.org/10.14722/autosec.2021.23019
www.ndss-symposium.org

Demo: Security of Camera-based Perception for Autonomous Driving under Adversarial Attack

Christopher DiPalma
UC Irvine
cdipalma@uci.edu

Ningfei Wang
UC Irvine
ningfei.wang@uci.edu

Takami Sato
UC Irvine
takamis@uci.edu

Qi Alfred Chen
UC Irvine
alfchen@uci.edu

***Abstract*—Robust perception is crucial for autonomous vehicle security. In this work, we design a practical adversarial patch attack against camera-based obstacle detection. We identify that the back of a box truck is an effective attack vector. We also improve attack robustness by considering a variety of input frames associated with the attack scenario. This demo includes videos that show our attack can cause end-to-end consequences on a representative autonomous driving system in a simulator.**

I. Introduction

Autonomous vehicles have become increasingly prominent, and their safety is becoming critical. A fundamental pillar to ensure safe Autonomous Driving (AD) systems is perception, which leverages sensors such as cameras and LiDARs (Light Detection and Ranging) to detect surrounding obstacles in real time. LiDAR excels at detecting obstacles, but it can be prohibitively expensive. As such, many companies have invested in camera-based perception. For example, Tesla and Apollo Lite both apply camera-based perception without LiDAR.

In this demo, we illustrate the effects of adversarial obstacle hiding attack on camera-based perception in an AD system. While several prior works succeed in attacking camera-based object detectors in an AD context, they mostly target traffic sign detection [1], which can be handled via High Definition (HD) map rather than camera-based perception in high-level AD systems [2]. We instead place an adversarial patch on the back of a box truck to make such box truck bypass camera-based AD perception. This demo builds upon prior works by demonstrating end-to-end attack impacts through a production-grade AD simulator, and by using a specialized Expectation over Transformation (EoT) closely relevant to the attack scenario to improve patch robustness. All demonstrations are performed in a production-grade AD simulator and generated for a representative AD system, Baidu Apollo [2], which is ranked in the top 4 leading AD developers along with Waymo, Ford, and Cruise.

II. Threat Model and Attack Goal

Threat Model. As with previous attacks for AD perception [1], we assume the attacker has full knowledge of the camera-based AD perception used in the victim AD system. We also assume the attacker can place an adversarial patch on the back of a box truck, and can collect the required sensor data on the target road beforehand to facilitate the attack.

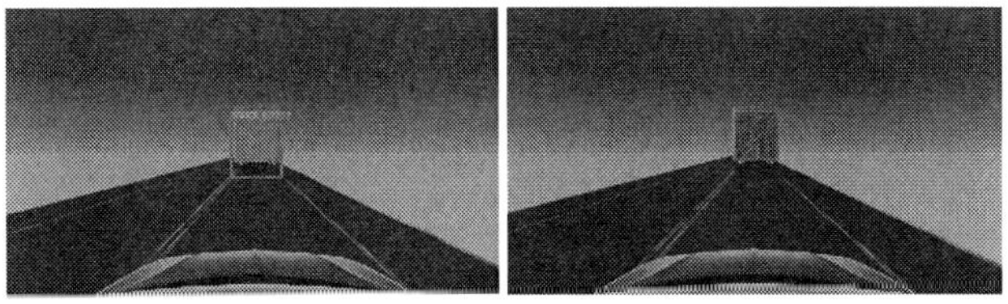

(a) Box truck with benign patch (b) Box truck with adv. patch

Fig. 1: Snapshots from attack demo videos.

Attack Goal. The attacker's goal is to cause the victim AV to fail in detecting such box truck with the adversarial patch and thus collide into it. This thus directly threatens the safety of the passengers in the victim AV.

III. Attack Design

We add an adversarial patch to the back of a box truck. This patch is generated against camera-based perception in AD system with the objective to minimize detection confidence of the truck over multiple frames. To improve the success rate of the attack, we use EoT [3] to apply 3D perspective rotation, random resize, and crop, along with other distortions.

IV. Demonstration Plan

We will provide videos[1] to demonstrate end-to-end attack impact in an AD system by launching the attack against a Baidu Apollo AV running in production-grade AD simulator LGSVL. We also provide screenshots as per Fig. 1 for both benign and adversarial cases. In Fig. 1 (a), the victim AV can detect the box truck with benign patch and stop before it. However, in Fig. 1 (b), the victim AV cannot detect the box truck with adversarial patch and will thus crash into it.

Acknowledgment

We would like to thank Junjie Shen and the anonymous reviewers for providing valuable feedback on our work. This research was supported in part by the National Science Foundation under grants CNS-1850533, CNS-1929771, CNS-1932464, and USDOT UTC Grant 69A3552047138.

References

[1] Y. Zhao, H. Zhu, R. Liang, Q. Shen, S. Zhang, and K. Chen, "Seeing isn't Believing: Towards More Robust Adversarial Attack Against Real World Object Detectors," in *ACM CCS*, 2019, pp. 1989–2004.

[2] "Baidu Apollo," https://apollo.auto/.

[3] A. Athalye, L. Engstrom, A. Ilyas, and K. Kwok, "Synthesizing Robust Adversarial Examples," in *ICML*, 2018.

Workshop on Automotive and Autonomous Vehicle Security (AutoSec) 2021
25 February 2021, Virtual

https://dx.doi.org/10.14722/autosec.2021.23018
www.ndss-symposium.org

[1] https://youtu.be/T-dvXFJ3rCg

Spoofing Mobileye 630's Video Camera Using a Projector

Ben Nassi, Dudi Nassi, Raz Ben-Netanel, Yuval Elovici
The Department of Software and Information Systems Engineering, Ben-Gurion University of the Negev
nassib@post.bgu.ac.il, nassid@post.bgu.ac.il, razx@post.bgu.ac.il, elovici@bgu.ac.il
Video Demonstration - https://youtu.be/C-JxNHKqgtk

Abstract—**In this paper, we evaluate the robustness of Mobileye 630 PRO, the most popular off-the-shelf ADAS on the market today, to camera spoofing attacks applied using a projector. We show that Mobileye 630 issues false notifications about road signs projected in proximity to the car that the system is installed in. We assess how changes of the road signs (e.g., changes in color, shape, projection speed, diameter and ambient light) affect the outcome of an attack. We find that while Mobileye 630 PRO rejects fake projected road signs that consists of non-original shapes and objects, it accepts fake projected road signs that consists of non-original colors. We demonstrate how attackers can leverage these findings to apply a remote attack in a realistic scenario by using a drone that carries a portable projector which projects the spoofed traffic sign on a building located in proximity to a passing car equipped with Mobileye 630. Our experiments show that it is possible to fool Mobileye 630 PRO to issue false notification about a traffic sign projected from a drone.**

I. Introduction

Advanced driver assistance systems (ADASs) [1] are electronic systems that aid automobile drivers while they are driving. Such systems aim to help drivers by: 1) issuing alerts (e.g., collision avoidance) regarding potential threats and 2) recognizing upcoming traffic signs. ADASs have already become an integral part of the current car generation, and they will provide automated functionalities for the next generation of cars (autonomous vehicles).

Security of ADAS have recently attracted attention of researchers that has begun to investigate the their robustness to various attacks. Recent studies [2], [3], [4], [5] showed that ADAS alerts and notifications can be spoofed by applying adversarial machine learning techniques to traffic signs, allowing attackers to control the output of the ADAS for their benefit. The application of the methods suggested in these studies exposes drivers that respond to ADAS alerts and notifications and other nearby drivers and pedestrians to variety of risks that can cause accidents. However, the suggested attacks are complicated and require deep understanding of the ADAS used in order to manipulate it. In addition, the nature of the attacks necessitated that the attacker be located near the traffic sign in order to perform the attack. Because of this, the attacks suggested in the recent studies have not appeared in the wild. We wonder whether a complicated attack is really needed to manipulate an ADAS?

In this paper, we evaluate the robustness of Mobileye 630 PRO, the most popular off-the-shelf ADAS on the market today, to camera spoofing attacks applied using a projector. We show that attackers can use a projector in order to inject traffic signs into Mobileye 630 causing this system to issue false warnings. We performed various experiments and assessed the influence of color, shape, projection speed, diameter, and ambient light on the outcome of the attack by mounting a projector onto a drone and injecting traffic signs into the ADAS of a real driving car.

We make the following contributions: First, unlike other studies in this area that trained a classifier and found vulnerabilities to attack the ADAS, we evaluated the practicality of our attack against Mobileye, a real off-the-shelf ADAS. Second, our vector attack doesn't require the attacker to be in the attack location; we demonstrate a remote attack that can be executed by a drone.

II. Related Work

In this section, we describe related work on attacks against ADASs and provide an overview of adversarial attacks. Computer vision object detectors are integrated to ADAS and used to detect traffic signs from a video stream. Many of these detectors are trained using deep learning techniques. Several studies created adversarial instances to trick such deep learning classifiers and showed that this type of classifier is vulnerable to spoofing attacks. *Petrakieva et al.* [2] demonstrated how perturbations that are often too small to be perceptible to humans can fool deep learning models. *Sitawarin et al.* [6] showed that they could embed two traffic signs in one traffic sign with a dedicated array of lens that causes a different traffic sign to appear depending on the angle of view. *Eykholt et al.* [7] and *Lu et al.* [3] showed that physical artifacts (e.g., stickers, graffiti) misled computer vision classifiers. In the abovementioned studies, the researchers only trained dedicated models by themselves and identified instances that could exploit them using white-box techniques. Furthermore, the researchers did not show the effectiveness of the attack against an off-the-shelf ADAS. In contrast, we demonstrate our attack against

Workshop on Automotive and Autonomous Vehicle Security (AutoSec) 2021
25 February 2021, Virtual

https://dx.doi.org/10.14722/autosec.2021.23007
www.ndss-symposium.org

the Mobileye system and mislead it so it recognizes spoofed traffic signs using black-box techniques.

Attacks against ADAS are not, however, limited to misleading the classifier using an adversarial traffic sign. *Petit et al.* [4] presented two attack vectors against car's sensors such as LiDAR and cameras. They were able to show that: 1) a laser directed at the camera can destroy the optical sensor permanently, and 2) LiDAR's output can be spoofed using infrared light. *Yan et al.* [8] demonstrated various spoofing attacks against a camera, ultrasonic sensor, and radar that can cause Tesla's Model S to misperceive the distance of nearby obstacles. However, it is not possible to perform the suggested attacks [4], [8] on a driving car due to the complexity of the attacks because: 1) they require deploying devices at specific ranges from the attacked car, and 2) the attacker must connect the hardware directly to a driving autonomous car which can be a major challenge due to the driving speed. A recent study [5] misdirected an autopiloted vehicle, taking it in the wrong direction. The authors placed interference patches (small stickers) on the ground at two way route, causing the vehicle to turn in to the opposite lane. In this case, the attacker must physically put the stickers on the road; in contrast, our attack vector doesn't require the attacker to be on site, since the drone can be deployed remotely.

Other famous attacks against cars that are not related to our work are [9], [10], which were based on compromising the firmware of the car or an internal device. Our attack model is much lighter than these attacks, since it does not require us to hack to those systems.

III. Threat Model

We consider an attacker as any malicious entity with the aim of attacking a driving car with equipped with Mobileye 630 PRO. The attacker can inject spoofed traffic signs into Mobileye using a portable projector mounted on a drone. The attacker's goals can be to: 1) harm or manipulate the car of a specific victim, or 2) cause environmental chaos (e.g., harm multiple cars in a specific region such as a city, neighborhood, highway, etc.).

IV. Mobileye Analysis

Here we analyze the robustness of Mobileye 630 PRO against various projected road signs. Mobileye is an external ADAS that provides function-specific vehicle automation (Level 0). The Mobileye 630 PRO contains two main components. The first is a camera, which is installed on the windshield, under the rear view mirror, and the second is a small display which is placed in front of the driver and provides visual and audible alerts about the surroundings as needed. Mobileye has the following features: lane departure warning, pedestrian collision warning, forward collision warning, headway monitoring and warning, intelligent high beam control, and traffic sign recognition. In this section we focus on testing the robustness of its traffic sign recognition.

In the following subsections, we learn the effect of environmental factors (ambient light, distance) on the result of the attack. In addition, we test the robustness of the Mobileye for classifying traffic signs that do not exist.

A. Experimental Setup

Fig. 1. Experimental setup: the projected sign is boxed in red, and the attacked vehicle is boxed in yellow

In this subsection, we describe the setup for the experiments performed. For convenience we used a white projector screen, in order as screen for the projected traffic sign. A portable projector was used to provide the sign's content. The injection method, as described in Section III, is comprised of the projector and screen. The portable projector was placed on a tripod about 2.5 meters from the screen and projected a traffic sign onto the center of the screen; while the sign was projected in this way we drove the car (a Renault Captur equipped with Mobileye 630 PRO) in a straight line at a speed of approximately 25 km/h. Figure 1 presents an illustration of our experimental setup.

B. Influence of the Projected Sign's Diameter

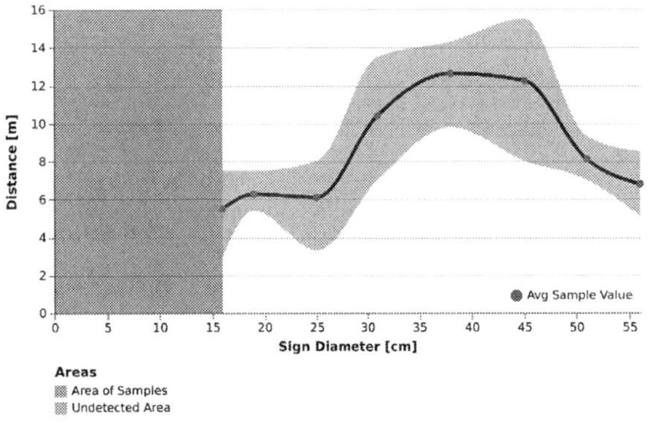

Fig. 2. Influence of the sign's diameter

1) Experimental Setup: In this case, we investigate whether the size of the projected sign influences the distance from which the Mobileye 630 PRO's sensor can detect the projected sign. We repeated the experiment five times, projecting a different sized sign each time, and calculated the average detection distance.

2) Results: Figure 2 presents the results of this experiment. As can be seen, if the sign is too small (less than 16 cm in diameter) the Mobileye 630 Pro sensor didn't detect it at all. The red dots in the graph symbolize the average distance at which we managed to mislead the sensor, and the grey area shows the range of the entire samples set.

3) Conclusion: The diameter range is wide and provides a lot of room for error when projecting a traffic sign. Based on our measurements, the distance can range from approximately 5-16 meters.

C. Influence of the Color of the Projected Sign

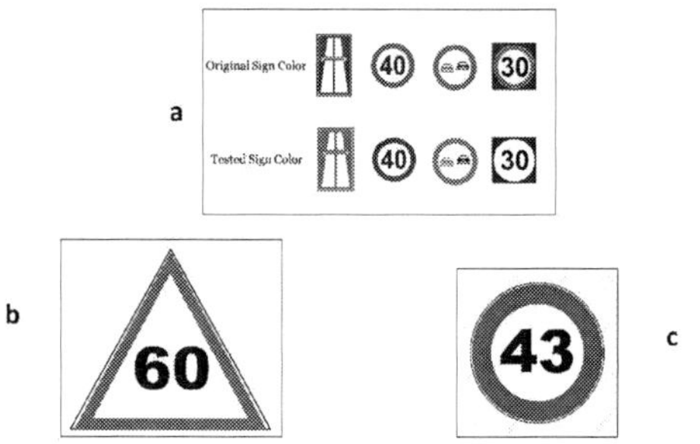

Fig. 3. (a) examples of different colored traffic signs, (b) an example of a different traffic sign shape, (c) an example of an incorrect or unrecognized speed limit value

1) Experimental Setup: Here we assess whether the Mobileye 630 PRO sensor is sensitive to the color of the sign. We tried various colors as seen in (Figure 3a). First we projected the sign with its true colors, and then we verified that the Mobileye 630 PRO sensor managed to recognize the sign. Next, we projected the same sign but this time with a color scheme which is different from the real one.

2) Results: We could see, quite quickly, that Mobileye is not sensitive to color, since all of the signs tested managed to mislead the sensor (even the black and white speed limit sign seen in, Figure 3a).

3) Conclusion: Based on these results we conclude that the Mobileye 630 PRO sensor only considers the shape of a sign when trying to classify the sign's content.

D. Influence of the Projected Sign's Shape

1) Experimental Setup: In this case, we evaluate whether the Mobileye 630 PRO sensor can detect signs which do not take the form of their original shape. For this experiment we simply took a speed limit sign and modified its shape (as seen in Figure 4b). This experiment was binary, i.e., we only wanted to know if the sign can be detected or not.

2) Results: We utilized a total of seven different shapes (a triangle, rectangle, pentagon, and hexagon, as well as three other more unusual shapes - a star, arrow, and random polygon). The Mobileye 630 PRO's sensor was unable to detect any of these shapes.

3) Conclusion: We can conclude the Mobileye system considers just the shape of the sign and isn't fooled by unknown shapes.

4) Experimental Setup: In this case, we tested the effect of ambient light, utilizing 20 samples (drives) from every hour of the day to check our injection success rate.

5) Results: Figure 4 presents the results of this experiment; success is considered a sample (drive) in which Mobileye recognized the projected sign.

6) Conclusion: Based on our analysis of these results we can conclude that is possible to inject a spoofed traffic sign at all hours of the day, but performance is best later in the day (in the evening and at night). One thing that should be considered with regard to ambient light is the equipment used, since the opacity of the projected sign depends on the ambient light as well as the projector used (a better success rate may be achieved with a better projector).

E. Influence of the Speed of the Projection Time

1) Experimental Setup: Here we assessed the speed of the projection time that is needed to fool the system. We conducted a few experiments that measured the amount of time required for injection.

2) Results: We discovered that a projection speed of 100 ms is sufficient for fooling the system. We were unable to fool the system with faster projection speeds probably due to the frame per second rate of the optical sensor of the Mobileye.

3) Conclusion: The fast projection speed causes the attack vector on the target to be very easy to inject and doesn't require staying for to long.

F. Influence of the Number on the Projected Sign

1) Experimental Setup: In this case, we investigate whether the Mobileye 630 PRO sensor can also detect speed limit signs with speed values that are not used in the real world (e.g. Figure 3.c).

2) Results: Table 1 presents the results of this experiment.

3) Conclusion: Based on these results, we can conclude that incorrect speed limit signs are effective at misleading the system. The system do not ignore them and classify them as other similar traffic signs.

V. Attacking a Car While Driving

In this section, we demonstrate how attackers can spoof Mobileye 630 PRO's video camera remotely using drone.

1) Experimental setup: We mounted a portable projector on a drone (DJI Matrice 600) (Figure 4). In this experimental setup our car (a Renault Captur equipped with Mobileye 630 PRO) was driven in an urban environment as the attacker operated a drone, positioning the drone so the spoofed speed limit sign can be injected into the Mobileye sensor. The attacker projected the incorrect speed limit sign (see Figure 4), managing to mislead the Mobileye sensor which recognized the sign as a 90 km/h speed limit sign (see Figure 5). The implemented attack vector can be seen in an uploaded video of the attack [1].

[1] https://youtu.be/C-JxNHKqgtk

Fig. 4. Left: Influence of Ambient Light. Middle: the drone with the projector used in our experiments, Right: the moment of the attack (the projected road sign is boxed in blue, the attacker's drone is boxed in purple, and the victim's car is boxed in red).

TABLE I
DETECTION OF INCORRECT SPEED LIMIT SIGNS,(LEFT: SPEED LIMIT ON THE PROJECTED SIGN. RIGHT: THE DETECTED SPEED LIMIT, AS SHOWN ON THE MOBILEYE DISPLAY, X MEANS NO DETECTION)

Projected Speed limit	Detected Speed limit
0	X
1	X
2	X
3	X
4	X
5	5
6	X
7	X
8	X
9	X
27	X
43	X
69	60
71	70
88	80
150	X
160	X
170	X
180	110
190	110
200	X

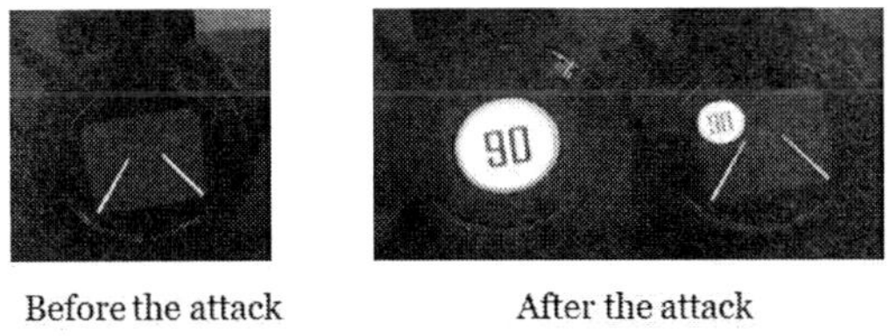

Fig. 5. Mobileye display before and during the attack.

2) Results: We managed to fool Mobileye so it classified the speed limit as 90 km/h when the speed limit for a city road is only 30 km/h.

VI. FUTURE WORK

As future work, we suggest to test whether camera spoofing can be applied by embedding a traffic sign to an advertisement presented on a digital billboard in an invisible manner (e.g., by flashing the traffic sign for a split second) [11]. We also suggest examining whether the attack can be applied using infrared projection, exploiting the fact that a narrow spectrum of frequencies, the near infrared, is also captured by some CMOS sensors (this fact was exploited to establish an optical covert channel [12] and to break the confidentiality of FPV channel of commercial drones [13], [14]). We also suggest to test whether attackers can project a fake lane in order to fool Mobileye 630's lane detection functionality [15].

REFERENCES

[1] Wikipedia contributors, "Advanced driver-assistance systems — Wikipedia, the free encyclopedia," 2019, [Online; accessed 27-May-2019]. [Online]. Available: https://en.wikipedia.org/w/index.php?title=Advanced_driver-assistance_systems&oldid=898181591

[2] N. Akhtar and A. Mian, "Threat of adversarial attacks on deep learning in computer vision: A survey," *IEEE Access*, vol. 6, pp. 14410–14430, 2018.

[3] J. Lu, H. Sibai, E. Fabry, and D. Forsyth, "Standard detectors aren't (currently) fooled by physical adversarial stop signs," *arXiv preprint arXiv:1710.03337*, 2017.

[4] J. Petit, B. Stottelaar, M. Feiri, and F. Kargl, "Remote attacks on automated vehicles sensors: Experiments on camera and lidar," *Black Hat Europe*, vol. 11, p. 2015, 2015.

[5] T. K. S. Lab, "Experimental security research of tesla autopilot," https://keenlab.tencent.com/en/whitepapers/Experimental_Security_Research_of_Tesla_Autopilot.pdf, 2019.

[6] C. Sitawarin, A. N. Bhagoji, A. Mosenia, M. Chiang, and P. Mittal, "Darts: Deceiving autonomous cars with toxic signs," *arXiv preprint arXiv:1802.06430*, 2018.

[7] K. Eykholt, I. Evtimov, E. Fernandes, B. Li, A. Rahmati, C. Xiao, A. Prakash, T. Kohno, and D. Song, "Robust physical-world attacks on deep learning models," *arXiv preprint arXiv:1707.08945*, 2017.

[8] C. Yan, W. Xu, and J. Liu, "Can you trust autonomous vehicles: Contactless attacks against sensors of self-driving vehicle," *DEF CON*, vol. 24, 2016.

[9] A. Greenberg, "Hackers remotely kill a jeep on the highway-with me in it (2015)," *URL https://www.wired.com/2015/07/hackers-remotely-kill-jeep-highway*, 2017.

[10] S. Checkoway, D. McCoy, B. Kantor, D. Anderson, H. Shacham, S. Savage, K. Koscher, A. Czeskis, F. Roesner, T. Kohno *et al.*, "Comprehensive experimental analyses of automotive attack surfaces." in *USENIX Security Symposium*, vol. 4. San Francisco, 2011, pp. 447–462.

[11] B. Nassi, Y. Mirsky, D. Nassi, R. Ben-Netanel, O. Drokin, and Y. Elovici, "Phantom of the adas: Securing advanced driver-assistance systems from split-second phantom attacks," in *Proceedings of the 2020 ACM SIGSAC Conference on Computer and Communications Security*, ser. CCS '20. New York, NY, USA: Association for Computing Machinery, 2020, p. 293âĂŞ308. [Online]. Available: https://doi.org/10.1145/3372297.3423359

[12] B. Nassi, A. Shamir, and Y. Elovici, "Xerox day vulnerability," *IEEE Transactions on Information Forensics and Security*, vol. 14, no. 2, pp. 415–430, 2018.

[13] B. Nassi, R. Ben-Netanel, A. Shamir, and Y. Elovici, "Drones' cryptanalysis-smashing cryptography with a flicker," in *2019 IEEE Symposium on Security and Privacy (SP)*. IEEE, 2019, pp. 1397–1414.

[14] R. Ben Netanel, B. Nassi, A. Shamir, and Y. Elovici, "Detecting spying drones," *IEEE Security Privacy*, vol. 19, no. 1, pp. 65–73, 2021.

[15] B. Nassi, D. Nassi, R. Ben-Netanel, Y. Mirsky, O. Drokin, and Y. Elovici, "Phantom of the adas: Phantom attacks on driver-assistance systems."

Fooling Perception via Location: A Case of Region-of-Interest Attacks on Traffic Light Detection in Autonomous Driving

Kanglan Tang, Junjie Shen, Qi Alfred Chen
University of California, Irvine

Abstract—**The perception module is the key to the security of Autonomous Driving systems. It perceives the environment through sensors to help make safe and correct driving decisions on the road. The localization module is usually considered to be independent of the perception module. However, we discover that the correctness of perception output highly depends on localization due to the widely used Region-of-Interest design adopted in perception. Leveraging this insight, we propose an ROI attack and perform a case study in the traffic light detection in Autonomous Driving systems. We evaluate the ROI attack on a production-grade Autonomous Driving system, named Baidu Apollo, under end-to-end simulation environments. We found our attack is able to make the victim a red light runner or cause denial-of-service with a 100% success rate.**

I. Introduction

In the automotive industry, a revolution is taking place: the rise of Autonomous Vehicles (AVs). AVs have been demonstrated to lower transportation costs and energy consumption, improve travel convenience and comfort, and reduce traffic accidents and congestion [1]. However, the Autonomous Driving (AD) system, which serves as the "brain" of an AV to make driving decisions, may have vulnerabilities that could lead to severe security threats to road safety. For example, vulnerabilities in the localization module, whose outputs are critical for route planning and navigation, can be exploited by attackers to manipulate the routes of AVs [2]. In fact, attacks on the localization will not only affect AVs' route planning and navigation but also have direct effects in other modules such as the perception module to cause false detection.

The perception module processes sensor inputs to perceive the surrounding obstacles and traffic lights, which are necessary for planning a safe driving path and making the correct driving decision. Typically, the perception sensors (i.e., camera, LiDAR, radar, ultrasonic sensor) in the AD system [3], [4] have wide ranges of views. For example, AVs are usually equipped with high-resolution cameras that are capable of detecting obstacles as far as 100 meters or more [3]. However, in this work, we discover an interesting design consideration, which is common in AD systems, that enables an attacker to *blind or misguide the perception without tampering the perception sensor inputs themselves*.

The root cause for such a vulnerability is the design of Region-of-Interests (ROIs). ROI is a strategy commonly employed in AD perception that utilizes information from the localization to *narrow* the detection scope in the sensor inputs [3], [4]. It can effectively reduce the computation overhead by running detection algorithms on smaller input dimensions and filter detection noises by preventing ambiguous detection, e.g., when multiple traffic lights exist in the camera view. Despite the benefits in improving the detection efficiency and accuracy, the accuracy of ROI mainly depends on the localization results–a wrong localization would result into a wrong ROI, which in turn causes the perception module to look at a wrong area in the sensor input.

For AD systems, cameras are especially critical for traffic light (TL) detection since they are the only sensors that are able to accurately detect TL colors. Thus, as the first study, we start from the TL detection and leverage the existing GPS spoofing attacks [5], [6] on localization to demonstrate attack consequences of such ROI attacks in an end-to-end AD system. Attack demos showing the end-to-end attack consequences are at **https://sites.google.com/view/roiattack**.

Considering the severity of the attack, we hope this work can bring immediate attention to the AD system developers for more robust ROI designs. In summary, while this work is still work-in-progress, it makes the following contributions:

- We perform the first security analysis on the ROI design in the perception module in AD systems and identify a design-level vulnerability that allows the attacker to fool AD perception using GPS spoofing.
- We design a concrete ROI attack targeting the TL detection in AD perception. Results show that our attack is able to achieve a 100% success rate in causing the victim AV to run red lights or denial-of-service.

II. Background

A. AD Systems and TL Detection

Baidu Apollo overview. Baidu Apollo [3] is a production-grade open-source AD system for Level-4 AVs [7], which has already been deployed for RoboTaxi services in China [8]. It follows a typical Level-4 AD system design, which mainly consists of localization, perception, prediction, planning, and control modules [3]: the localization module localizes the AV on a map; the perception module uses perception sensors to detect obstacles and TLs; the prediction module predicts the future trajectories of the obstacles; the planning module incorporates maps, localization outputs, and predicted obstacle trajectories to calculate a safe driving trajectory; the control module executes the planned trajectory by actuating the steering, throttle, and brake on the AV. In this work, we focus on two of these modules: localization and perception.

The localization module takes inputs from sensors such as GPS and LiDAR to estimate the real-time position of the AV.

Workshop on Automotive and Autonomous Vehicle Security (AutoSec) 2021
25 February 2021, Virtual

https://dx.doi.org/10.14722/autosec.2021.23029
www.ndss-symposium.org

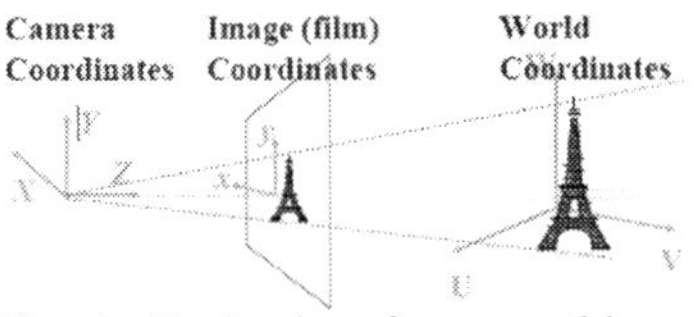

Fig. 1: Projection from world coordinates to image coordinates.

Fig. 2: Illustration of the ROI in TL detection.

Depending on the sensor availability, the localization module can be configured in GPS mode or Multi-Sensor Fusion (MSF) mode [9]. The GPS mode directly takes positioning from GPS, while the MSF mode combines GPS and LiDAR for more accurate and robust positioning. For example, Baidu Apollo, by default, uses MSF in the localization; however, it also provides a GPS mode when there is no LiDAR installed on the AV. Tesla Autopilot, as a Level-2 AD system [7], also do not use LiDARs and thus relies on GPS for localization [10].

The perception module incorporates sensors such as cameras, radars, LiDARs, and ultrasonic sensors to recognize vehicles and pedestrians surrounding the AV. In addition, it also performs important tasks such as TL detection.

TL detection and ROI design. TL detection is an essential feature for Level-4 AVs. If an AV cannot detect and recognize TLs, it may violate traffic rules resulting in some catastrophic consequences, such as running red lights and causing car accidents. Recently, as Level-2 AV companies aiming to achieve higher level driving autonomy, companies such as Tesla starts to add TL detection into their AD systems [11]. TL detection leverages Deep Neural Networks (DNNs) to detect and classify TLs in the camera images [3], [4]. For example, Baidu Apollo applies two DNNs for TL detection; one for the object detection to recognize the TL object in the image, and the other for the classification to recognize the light color [3].

Since the camera image may contain multiple TLs, it is thus necessary to identify the correct TL for the current intersection. To address this, AD systems commonly adopt an ROI design [3], [4], which projects the current TL in the world coordinates obtained from the High-Definition (HD) map to image coordinates based on the localization outputs (Fig. 1). To compensate for any localization or HD map inaccuracies, an ROI area with an empirically determined radius or height/width centered at the projected image coordinates is selected for TL detection. Such an ROI design not only helps prevent ambiguous TL detection but also reduces the computation overhead. Fig. 2 show an example of the ROI in Baidu Apollo. As shown, the ROI anchor box is the projected position of the TL. However, due to inaccuracies in localization and HD map, the projected position is not perfectly aligned with the actual TL. Thus, Baidu Apollo defines a larger rectangle as the ROI for TL detection (② in Fig. 2). After that, it crops the ROI area from the image and applies DNNs to recognize all TL bounding boxes and their colors in the ROI. Finally, the TL bounding box (③ in Fig. 2), which is the closest to the ROI anchor box, is selected as the TL detection result.

B. GPS spoofing attacks to AD localization

Civilian GPS systems are known to be vulnerable to spoofing attacks due to the lack of signal authentication in the infrastructure. In the spoofing attack, the attacker broadcasts fake satellite signals to the victim GPS receiver to deceive it into resolving false positions specified by the attacker [5]. So far, GPS spoofing has been demonstrated to be feasible on various systems, including smartphones [12], drones [5], and vehicles such as Tesla [10].

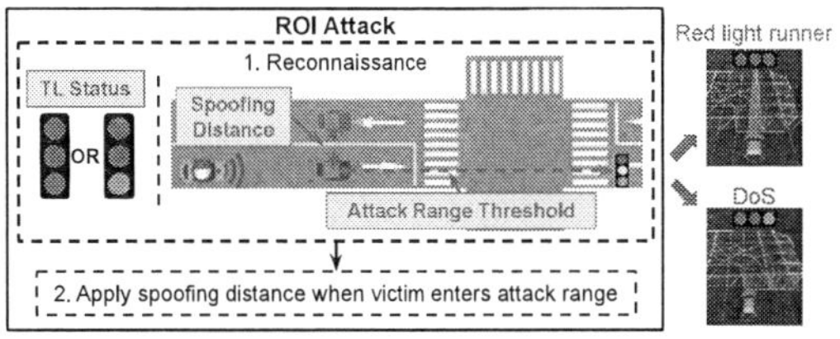

Fig. 3: Illustration of the ROI attack for TL detection.

The attack capabilities of GPS spoofing are different in GPS-based localization and MSF-based localization. In GPS mode, GPS inputs are the only positioning source for localization, and thus GPS spoofing can directly control the localization outputs in the AD system. In MSF mode, since the positioning from GPS will be fused with LiDAR, GPS spoofing cannot set an arbitrary position in the localization output. Nevertheless, Shen et al. [6] have demonstrated that they can inject a large deviation in the MSF-based localization outputs using GPS spoofing.

III. Threat Model and Attack Goal

Threat model. Similar to the threat model used in prior works [6], [12], we assume a car-following model where the attacker launches GPS spoofing attack while tailgating the victim AV. We assume the attacker can arbitrarily manipulate the victim's localization outputs under GPS spoofing, which is valid for AVs using only GPS for localization, such as Baidu Apollo in GPS mode and Tesla. We also assume the attacker can track the physical position of the victim AV, which is feasible if the attacker's vehicle is also an AV [6].

Attack goal. The goal of our attack is to influence the position of ROI in the perception module via GPS spoofing, and thus cause the victim AV to detect a wrong TL to run the red light or fail to detect any TLs to stop at the green light (i.e., denial-of-service or DoS).

IV. Attack Insight and Design

Attack insight. Although from high-level design, the localization and perception modules appear to be independent of each other, the perception module in fact heavily relies on the localization, especially for the ROI logic in TL detection as mentioned in §II-A. Since the localization output directly determines the ROI that the TL detection pipeline will be performed on, any errors in the localization would result in a wrong ROI and may cause incorrect TL detection.

Attack design. To perform the ROI attack on TL detection, the attacker launches GPS spoofing when the victim AV is in front of an intersection. When the victim AV drives towards the intersection, a longitudinal error in the localization would naturally have a smaller effect on the ROI position compared to a lateral deviation. Thus, to maximize the effect on the ROI, we design the attack as spoofing a *lateral* distance away from the physical position of the victim AV, e.g., the spoofing distance shown on the Fig. 3.

Fig. 3 illustrates the ROI attack for TL detection, which is composed of a reconnaissance stage and a spoofing stage. In the reconnaissance stage, the attacker examines the current TL status and determines the best attack parameters to be applied. Depending on the TL status, the attacker will use different spoofing distances to achieve the desired attack goals. For example, when the TL is red, the attacker needs to spoof a distance such that the ROI includes another green TL in the camera view to cause false detection. Alternatively, if the TL is green, the attacker can simply spoof a distance large enough such that the ROI contains no TLs, which would trigger a safe stop in the planning since the AV knows from the HD map that there is a TL in the front but fails to detect one. In addition, we set an *attack range threshold* for determining the timing to launch the spoofing. If the attacker starts spoofing when the victim is too far or too close to the intersection, the victim might have already been deviated out of the road boundary that prevented it from reaching the intersection or have already detected the correct TL color and committed the correct driving decision. After that, the attacker closely monitors the victim's position and spoofs the corresponding lateral distance when the victim enters the attack range.

V. Evaluation

Experimental setup. Due to the high cost of evaluating self-driving algorithms on real AVs, we follow the common practice for AV testing and perform a simulation-based evaluation, in which we run Baidu Apollo in an industry-grade AV simulator, LGSVL [13]. To facilitate AV simulation, LGSVL provides photo-realistic simulation environments with diverse road structures and a wide range of vehicle models. In our evaluation, we use the Shalun map and Lincoln MKZ vehicle. The Shalun map models a common two-lane road with multiple intersections along the road. We use Lincoln MKZ since it contains the compatible sensor configurations for Baidu Apollo. We simulate our attack on Baidu Apollo version 5.0, which is the latest version fully supported by LGSVL.

To simulate the attack consequences, we create two concrete attack scenarios: *red light detection* and *green light detection*. Specifically, for red light detection, we set the front TL in the first intersection to red and the back TL in the second intersection to green; for green light detection, we set the front TL to green and the back TL to red. We have confirmed that in benign driving, the AV will always correctly detect the front TLs, and make the correct driving decisions, i.e., stop before the intersection or drive through the intersection.

Evaluation metric. In our evaluation, we explore the attack effectiveness of the ROI attack under different attack range thresholds and spoofing distances, aiming to find the parameters that can achieve the highest attack effectiveness. We define a successful attack case as the victim AV mis-detects the front TL and commits the wrong driving decisions, i.e., running the red light or stopping in front of the green light. Since both Baidu Apollo and LGSVL involve random factors such as messaging delays, we calculate a success rate by repeating the simulation for 5 times for each attack parameter.

Attack construction. For the ease of evaluation, we implement the attack logic as an independent module in Baidu Apollo to receive original GPS inputs from LGSVL. If the victim AV is within the attack range threshold, we apply the spoofing distance to the original GPS positions. After that, we publish the spoofed GPS inputs to the localization module.

Results. As mentioned in §IV, the red light detection scenario has a more restricted spoofing distance requirement since the attacker needs to spoof the GPS such that the ROI covers the back green TL but not the front red TL. Thus, we start by exploring the attack parameters for this scenario. The left figure in Fig. 4 shows the attack success rates when using different attack range thresholds, i.e., the distance from the AV to the TL that triggers the attack. During the experiments, a spoofing distance of 3 meters is applied to the victim's GPS inputs. As shown, the best attack range threshold falls between 24 and 28 meters. When using a small attack range threshold (e.g., 22 meters), the attack fails because the victim is too close to the intersection, and it already executed the stop decision based on the TL detection prior to the attack. On the other hand, if the attack range threshold is too large (e.g., over 28 meters), the victim might already be deviated out of road boundary since the AD system is constantly correcting any deviation between the localization and the planned trajectory [6].

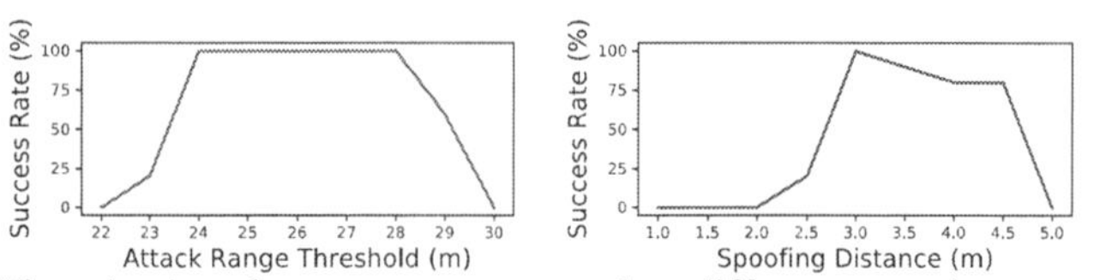

Fig. 4: Attack success rates under different attack range thresholds (left) and spoofing distances (right).

The right figure in Fig. 4 shows the attack success rates when using different spoofing distances. Based on the previous experiments on the attack range threshold, we launch the attack when the victim AV is 26 meters away from the TL. As shown in Fig. 4, a spoofing distance of smaller than or equal to 2 meters is too small to move the red TL out of the ROI, so the victim can still detect it. On the other hand, when the spoofing distance is larger than 4.5 meters, both front and back TLs are moved out of the ROI, causing the victim to fail to detect any TL and simply stop in front of the intersection. When the spoofing distance is 3–4.5 meters, the attack success rate is at least 80%, where the front red TL is moved out of the ROI, but the back green TL is still in and thus detected by the victim AV, causing it to continue driving forward to run the red light. In particular, a 100% attack success rate is achieved when using a spoofing distance of 3 meters.

In the green light detection scenario, instead of controlling the ROI to be at a particular position, the attacker can simply spoof the ROI to the area without any TLs. In such a case, the TL detector will report "unknown" as no TLs exist in the ROI. Consequently, the planning module in the AD system issues a stop decision conservatively. This results in a DoS attack since the victim stops at the green TL. Similarly, we evaluate this scenario and found that our ROI attack can achieve a 100% success rate when using a spoofing distance of 5 meters.

Attack demos. We create two attack demos to illustrate the severe consequences of the ROI attack. Fig. 5 and Fig. 6 show the snapshots when attacking the red and green light detections, respectively. The left sub-figures show the camera images with the ROI annotations, and the right sub-figures show the corresponding driving decisions in Baidu Apollo. As shown, our attack can successfully fool the victim AV to detect a wrong TL or fail to detect any TLs due to the ROI position shifts caused by GPS spoofing. Such an attack poses great dangers to road safety since it can cause the AV to violate traffic rules and may even lead to car crashing consequences, e.g.,

Fig. 5: Snapshot of attacking the red light detection. The green TL at the next intersection is falsely detected by the AV due to the incorrect ROI.

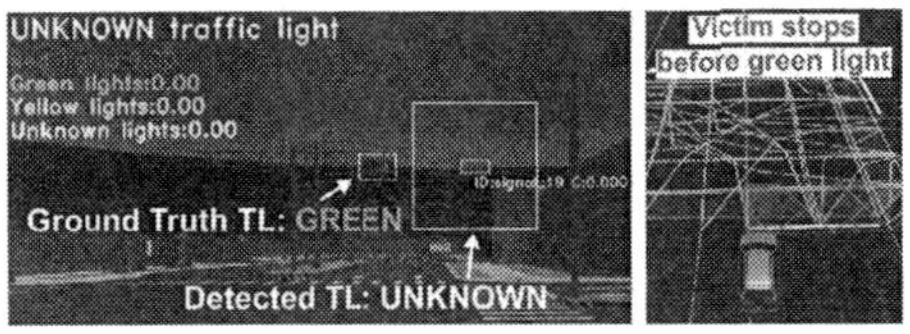

Fig. 6: Snapshot of attacking the green light detection. The TL detector failed to detect any light in the ROI, causing the victim to stop at the stop line despite the light is green.

when another vehicle fails to yield in time when the victim AV is running the red light. Demo videos with and without attacks are available at **https://sites.google.com/view/roiattack**.

VI. Related Work, Limitations, and Future Work

Related work. To the best of our knowledge, we are the first to attack ROI and TL detection in AD systems. Since TL detection relies on DNNs and camera inputs, thus attacks to these two are direct threats to TL detection. Prior work used physical-world perturbations to fool the DNNs. For example, Eykholt et al. [14] uses stickers with carefully devised patterns to fool the stop sign detection. However, TLs are not as accessible as stop signs since they are usually installed at a high place and thus it is unclear how the attacker can put the stickers without alerting other drivers and law enforcement. Another line of research explored physical sensor attacks to blind the camera by shooting strong lights to it [15]. However, such attacks cannot cause the victim to be a red light runner and can only lead to denial-of-service. In this work, the ROI attack does not require any physical perturbations to the TLs and can achieve both attack goals.

Limitations and future work. As the first study of ROI attacks in AD perception using GPS spoofing, we start by attacking AD system with a GPS-based localization, where GPS is the only positioning resource. Indeed, for GPS-based localization, it is possible to simply spoof the GPS to a road without any TLs, such that the victim is not in a state where it realizes that it should sense a TL, resulting in red light running. However, this is not the case for MSF-based localization, which is predominantly adopt in today's Level-4 AVs, since GPS alone can no longer dictate the localization output. Although MSF is considered to be more robust against GPS spoofing, prior work has demonstrated that MSF-based localization can be deviated by as large as 10 meters using GPS spoofing [6]. In the future, we plan to incorporate the MSF attack to improve the practicality of the ROI attack. Another limitation is that we only evaluate the attack on one AD system, i.e., Baidu Apollo [3]. Although Baidu Apollo implements a representative TL ROI design and is already in production, it is necessary to also evaluate on other TL ROI implementations (e.g., Autoware [4]) to show the generality of our attack. We leave this as a future work. Besides, since the attack parameters are highly dependent on factors such as victim's speed and road shape, more diverse driving scenarios are needed to evaluate the applicability of our attack. In addition, currently the best attack parameters are found via exhaustive search. In the next step, we plan to use the victim AV/TL positions and camera configurations to calculate the best spoofing distances to be applied in different scenarios.

VII. Conclusion

In this paper, we perform the first security analysis on perception ROI design and take the TL detection as a case study. We discover that using GPS spoofing can cause the AV to recognize a wrong TL or fail to detect any TLs. Our study shows that strategic GPS spoofing can achieve a 100% success rate to fool TL detection in the AV, leading to red-light running or denial-of-service consequences, which can be detrimental to road safety. The future of AVs is bright, but more security investigations are still needed in the AD systems. We hope our research can bring more attention to the security threats to AVs, improving AD systems for safer AVs for the public.

Acknowledgements

This research was supported in part by the National Science Foundation under grants CNS-1850533, CNS-1929771, and USDOT UTC Grant 69A3552047138.

References

[1] S. A. Bagloee, M. Tavana, M. Asadi, and T. Oliver, "Autonomous Vehicles: Challenges, Opportunities, and Future Implications for Transportation Policies," *Journal of modern transportation*, 2016.

[2] Q. Luo, Y. Cao, J. Liu, and A. Benslimane, "Localization and Navigation in Autonomous Driving: Threats and Countermeasures," *IEEE Wireless Communications*, vol. 26, no. 4, pp. 38–45, 2019.

[3] "Baidu Apollo." https://github.com/ApolloAuto/apollo.

[4] S. Kato, S. Tokunaga, Y. Maruyama, S. Maeda, M. Hirabayashi, Y. Kitsukawa, A. Monrroy, T. Ando, Y. Fujii, and T. Azumi, "Autoware On Board: Enabling Autonomous Vehicles with Embedded Systems," in *ICCPS'18*, pp. 287–296, IEEE Press, 2018.

[5] A. J. Kerns, D. P. Shepard, J. A. Bhatti, and T. E. Humphreys, "Unmanned Aircraft Capture and Control via GPS Spoofing," *Journal of Field Robotics*, 2014.

[6] J. Shen, J. Y. Won, Z. Chen, and Q. A. Chen, "Drift with Devil: Security of Multi-Sensor Fusion based Localization in High-Level Autonomous Driving under GPS Spoofing," in *USENIX Security*, 2020.

[7] SAE On-Road Automated Vehicle Standards Committee and others, "Taxonomy and Definitions for Terms Related to Driving Automation Systems for On-Road Motor Vehicles," *SAE International*, 2018.

[8] "Baidu debuts Robotaxi ride hailing service in China, using self-driving electric taxis." https://www.marketwatch.com/story/baidu-debuts-robotaxi-ride-hailing-service-in-china-using-self-driving-electric-taxis-2019-09-26.

[9] G. Wan, X. Yang, R. Cai, H. Li, Y. Zhou, H. Wang, and S. Song, "Robust and Precise Vehicle Localization based on Multi-Sensor Fusion in Diverse City Scenes," in *ICRA*, pp. 4670–4677, IEEE, 2018.

[10] "Tesla Model S and Model 3 Vulnerable to GNSS Spoofing Attacks." https://www.gpsworld.com/tesla-model-s-and-model-3-vulnerable-to-gnss-spoofing-attacks/.

[11] "Tesla releases new, highly anticipated Traffic Light and Stop Sign Control feature." https://electrek.co/2020/04/24/tesla-autopilot-traffic-light-and-stop-sign-control-feature/.

[12] K. C. Zeng, S. Liu, Y. Shu, D. Wang, H. Li, Y. Dou, G. Wang, and Y. Yang, "All Your GPS Are Belong To Us: Towards Stealthy Manipulation of Road Navigation Systems," in *USENIX Security*, 2018.

[13] "LGSVL Simulator." https://github.com/lgsvl/simulator.

[14] K. Eykholt, I. Evtimov, E. Fernandes, B. Li, A. Rahmati, C. Xiao, A. Prakash, T. Kohno, and D. Song, "Robust Physical-World Attacks on Deep Learning Visual Classification," in *CVPR*, 2018.

[15] J. Petit, B. Stottelaar, M. Feiri, and F. Kargl, "Remote Attacks on Automated Vehicles Sensors: Experiments on Camera and Lidar," *Black Hat Europe*, vol. 11, p. 2015, 2015.

Demo: Attacking Multi-Sensor Fusion based Localization in High-Level Autonomous Driving

Junjie Shen, Jun Yeon Won, Zeyuan Chen, Qi Alfred Chen
University of California, Irvine

I. Introduction

To enable high-level driving automation [1], the Autonomous Driving (AD) system in an Autonomous Vehicle (AV) needs to perform *centimeter-level localization* of its own global positions on the map [2]. Such localization function is highly security and safety critical in the AV context, since positioning errors can directly cause an AV to drive off road or onto a wrong way. For outdoor localization in general, GPS is the *de facto* location source, and thus a direct threat to it is GPS spoofing, a long-existing but still unsolved security problem with practicality proven on a wide range of end systems. Fortunately, AV systems today predominantly use Multi-Sensor Fusion (MSF) algorithms [3] that are generally believed to have the potential to practically defeat GPS spoofing [4]. However, no prior work has studied whether today's MSF algorithms are indeed sufficiently secure under GPS spoofing, especially in AV settings. In this work, we perform the first study to fill this critical gap. We consider the attack goal as using GPS spoofing to cause large *lateral* deviations in the MSF output, i.e., deviating to the left or right. This can cause the AV to drive off road or onto a wrong way.

To systematically understand the security property, we first analyze the upper-bound attack effectiveness and find that in the real-world trace, the majority of such upper-bound attack can only cause less than 50 cm deviation, which is far from causing the AV to drive off road. This shows that MSF can indeed generally enhance the security against GPS spoofing. Interestingly, we also observe that there still exist a few upper-bound attack results that can cause *exponential growths* of deviations. This allows the spoofed GPS to become the dominating input source in the fusion process and eventually cause the MSF to reject other input sources, which thus *fundamentally defeats the design principle of MSF*. In this work, we call it a *take-over effect*. We perform a cause analysis and find that such vulnerability only appears dynamically and non-deterministically. Leveraging this insight, we design *FusionRipper*, a novel and general attack that opportunistically captures and exploits take-over vulnerabilities with 2 stages: (1) *vulnerability profiling*, which measures when vulnerable periods appear, and (2) *aggressive spoofing*, which performs exponential spoofing to exploit the take-over opportunity.

II. Demonstration Plan

In the demo, we will show the end-to-end attack consequences of FusionRipper on Baidu Apollo [5], a production-grade Level-4 AD system, running in LGSVL [6], an industry-grade AV simulator. Specifically, the LGSVL accepts the control inputs from Baidu Apollo and produces real-time sensor inputs as the AV drives in the simulation environment. In the demo, we will run the simulation on the complete Baidu Apollo AD system with all functional modules enabled, i.e., localization, transform, perception, prediction, planning, routing, and control. We implement the attack logic as an independent component in Baidu Apollo, which intercepts GPS inputs from LGSVL and replaces them with the corresponding spoofed ones. In the demo, we will show two attack scenarios with one attacking to the left of the road and another to the right, where both have concrete safety consequences such as causing the AV to hit the road barrier or traffic sign.

Scenario 1: Attack to the left. In this scenario, the AV is driving on a road with a concrete barrier separating the opposite lanes. During the attack, the MSF localization results is taken over by the spoofed GPS inputs, causing the AV to deviate to the left and hit into the barrier.

Scenario 2: Attack to the right. In this scenario, the simulation environment has a stop sign installed on the roadside and the AV is driving on the lane next to the road curb. In the demo, we will show that the AV is deviated by the attack to drive over the road curb and finally crash into the stop sign.

In both scenarios, we will show the AV driving behaviors with and without attack to demonstrate the severity of the FusionRipper attack. To better show the take-over effect of FusionRipper, we will also visualize the real-time MSF localization outputs when the sensor inputs arrive. Attendees will be able to clearly see the two attack stages in FusionRipper as well as the immediate effect of the attack on the MSF outputs. The previews of the demo videos are available on our project website: **https://sites.google.com/view/cav-sec/fusionripper**.

Workshop on Automotive and Autonomous Vehicle Security (AutoSec) 2021
25 February 2021, Virtual

https://dx.doi.org/10.14722/autosec.2021.23010
www.ndss-symposium.org

Acknowledgements

This research was supported in part by the National Science Foundation under grants CNS-1850533, CNS-1929771, and USDOT UTC Grant 69A3552047138.

References

[1] SAE On-Road Automated Vehicle Standards Committee and others, "Taxonomy and Definitions for Terms Related to Driving Automation Systems for On-Road Motor Vehicles," *SAE International*, 2018.

[2] T. G. Reid, S. E. Houts, R. Cammarata, G. Mills, S. Agarwal, A. Vora, and G. Pandey, "Localization Requirements for Autonomous Vehicles," *arXiv preprint arXiv:1906.01061*, 2019.

[3] G. Wan, X. Yang, R. Cai, H. Li, Y. Zhou, H. Wang, and S. Song, "Robust and Precise Vehicle Localization based on Multi-Sensor Fusion in Diverse City Scenes," in *ICRA*, pp. 4670–4677, IEEE, 2018.

[4] J. Bhatti and T. E. Humphreys, "Hostile Control of Ships via False GPS Signals: Demonstration and Detection," *NAVIGATION: Journal of the Institute of Navigation*, 2017.

[5] "Baidu Apollo." https://github.com/ApolloAuto/apollo.

[6] "LGSVL Simulator." https://github.com/lgsvl/simulator.

Demo: Security of Deep Learning based Automated Lane Centering under Physical-World Attack

Takami Sato*, Junjie Shen*, Ningfei Wang, Yunhan Jack Jia†, Xue Lin‡, and Qi Alfred Chen
Univesity of California, Irvine; †ByteDance; ‡Northeastern University

Abstract—**Automated Lane Centering (ALC) systems are convenient and widely deployed today, but also highly security and safety critical. Recently, Dirty Road Patch (DRP) attack is proposed as a state-of-the-art adversarial attack against ALC systems. We will show interactive demonstrations for the malicious road patch generation and the serious consequences.**

I. Introduction

Automated Lane Centering (ALC) is a Level 2 driving automation technology that automatically steers a vehicle to keep it centered in the traffic lane. So far, Deep Neural Network (DNN) based lane detection achieves the highest accuracy and is adopted in the most performant production ALC systems today such as Tesla Autopilot. Recent works show that DNNs are vulnerable to physical-world adversarial attacks.However, these methods cannot be directly applied to attack ALC systems due to three domain-specific design challenges: lack of legitimately-deployable attack vector, camera frame inter dependencies, lack of the optimization objective function designs for lane detection. To overcome the challenges, *Dirty Road Patch* (DRP) attack [1] is recently proposed as a domain-specific adversarial attack to ALC systems.

We will demonstrate the malicious road patch generation and the serious consequences of the DRP attack with a production-grade Autonomous Driving (AD) simulator LGSVL and a production ALC system in OpenPilot [2], which is reported to have close performance to Tesla Autopilot.

II. Threat Model and Attack Goal

Threat Model. We assume that the attacker can obtain a full (white-box) knowledge of the victim ALC.

Attack Goal. We consider an attack goal that directly breaks the design goal of ALC systems. The attack goals are to hit the concrete barrier or the truck under the average driver reaction time is 2.5 sec.

III. Attack Design: Dirty Road Patch Attack

We identify *dirty road patches* as a novel and domain-specific attack vector for physical-world adversarial attacks on ALC systems because road patches with dirt or white stains can appear to be legitimately deployed on the physical-world. We then design systematic malicious road patch generation with 2 major novel and domain specific designs: motion model based input generation, and lane-bending objective function. Motion model based input generation combines vehicle motion model and perspective transformation to dynamically synthesize camera frame updates according to attack-influenced vehicle control. Lane-bending objective function allow us to adopt the optimization-based attack generation, which has shown both high efficiency and effectiveness in previous works. More details are in [1].

*The first two authors contributed equally.

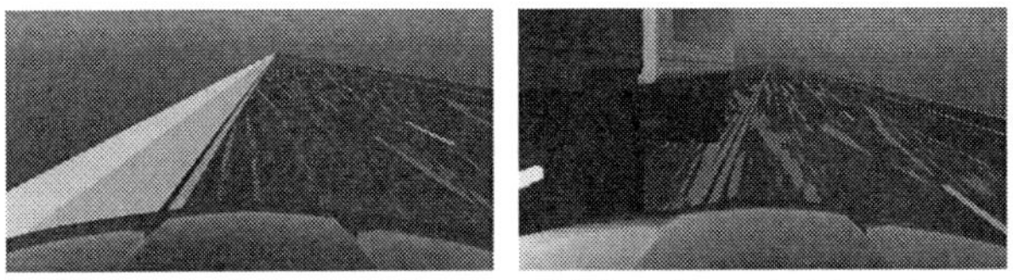

(a) Highway: hit concrete barrier. (b) Local: crash into a truck.

Fig. 1: Snapshots of the attack demo videos.

IV. Demonstration Plan

Demonstration of the malicious road patch generation. We will demonstrate how the road patch is generated by displaying intermediate and final patches, and camera inputs.

Demonstration of the attack in AD simulator. We will show two videos [1] of end-to-end attack scenarios for highway and local road settings respectively. The snapshots of the demo are shown in Fig 1. We deploy our malicious road patches in the production-grade the AD simulator, LGSVL. The target ALC system is the production ALC system OpenPilot [2]. For the highway scenario, we place a concrete barrier on the left, and for the local road scenarios, we place an NPC truck driving on an opposite direction lane. These videos demonstrate that our attacks cause the victim vehicle to hit the concrete barrier and the truck respectively.

Acknowledgements

This research was supported in part by the National Science Foundation under grants CNS-1850533, CNS-1929771, CNS-1932464, and USDOT UTC Grant 69A3552047138.

References

[1] T. Sato, J. Shen, N. Wang, Y. J. Jia, X. Lin, and Q. A. Chen, "Hold tight and never let go: Security of deep learning based automated lane centering under physical-world attack," *arXiv:2009.06701*, 2020.
[2] "OpenPilot," https://github.com/commaai/openpilot, 2018.

[1] https://youtu.be/y_5spn0Kxt8, https://youtu.be/TpipXnIvVhA

Workshop on Automotive and Autonomous Vehicle Security (AutoSec) 2021
25 February 2021, Virtual
https://dx.doi.org/10.14722/autosec.2021.23026
www.ndss-symposium.org

Impact Evaluation of Falsified Data Attacks on Connected Vehicle Based Traffic Signal Control Systems

Shihong Ed Huang
University of Michigan, Ann Arbor
edhuang@umich.edu

Yiheng Feng
Purdue University, West Lafayette
feng333@purdue.edu

Wai Wong
University of Michigan, Ann Arbor
waiwong1012@connect.hku.hk

Qi Alfred Chen
University of California, Irvine
alfchen@uci.edu

Z. Morley Mao
University of Michigan, Ann Arbor
zmao@umich.edu

Henry X. Liu
University of Michigan, Ann Arbor
henryliu@umich.edu

***Abstract*—Connected vehicle (CV) technologies enable data exchange between vehicles and transportation infrastructure. In a CV environment, traffic signal control systems receive CV trajectory data through vehicle-to-infrastructure (V2I) communications to make control decisions. Comparing with existing data collection methods (e.g., from loop-detectors), the CV trajectory data provide much richer information, and therefore have great potentials to improve the system performance by reducing total vehicle delay at signalized intersections. However, this connectivity might also bring cyber security concerns.**

In this paper, we aim to investigate the security problem of CV-based traffic signal control (CV-TSC) systems. Specifically, we focus on evaluating the impact of falsified data attacks on the system performance. A black-box attack scenario, in which the control logic of a CV-TSC system is unavailable to attackers, is considered. A two-step attack model is constructed. In the first step, the attacker tries to learn the control logic using a surrogate model. Based on the surrogate model, in the second step, the attacker launches falsified data attacks to influence the control systems to make sub-optimal control decisions. In the case study, we apply the attack model to an existing CV-TSC system (i.e., I-SIG) and find intersection delay can be significantly increased. Finally, we discuss some promising defense directions.

I. Introduction

Advanced communication technologies such as Dedicated Short Range Communication (DSRC) and cellular LTE/5G enable vehicles and transportation infrastructure to communicate with each other in real-time. Vehicles that have communication capabilities are referred as connected vehicles (CVs). The communication mechanism greatly enhances information exchange between CVs and transportation infrastructure and therefore has great potential to improve various mobility applications, including traffic signal control (TSC), a critical component in urban traffic operation. Different from conventional traffic control systems that depends on infrastructure-based sensor data, a CV-based traffic control system (CV-TSC) utilizes CV trajectory data as input to make control decisions. A typical CV-TSC system is illustrated in Figure 1. Each CV is equipped with an On-Board Unit (OBU), which broadcasts Basic Safety Messages (BSMs). A BSM records a CV's information including its location, speed, heading, and acceleration. Consecutive BSMs represent the vehicle trajectory. On the infrastructure side, an intersection is equipped with a Roadside Unit (RSU), a signal controller, and traffic signals. The RSU receives BSMs (i.e., CV trajectories), which are used to optimize traffic signal timing plans. The signal controller executes the optimal signal timing plans and controls traffic signals to display corresponding colors. The signal controller is usually connected to a transportation management center (TMC), which sends commands remotely to the signal controller (e.g., time-of-day signal timing plans). Meanwhile, the RSU continuously broadcasts Signal Phase and Timing (SPaT) messages, which record current signal status (i.e., green/yellow/red) and remaining time. Based on continuously received BSMs, the CV-TSC system responds to real-time traffic demands by updating the signal timing plans dynamically. Over the past decade, various CV-TSC models have been proposed and significant mobility

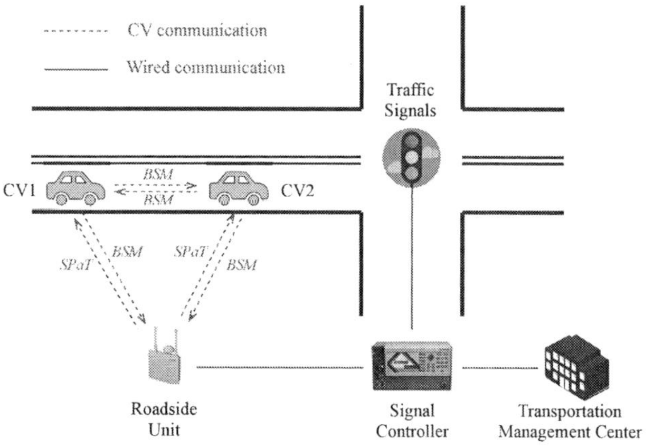

Fig. 1. Illustration of a connected vehicle based traffic signal control system

Workshop on Automotive and Autonomous Vehicle Security (AutoSec) 2021
25 February 2021, Virtual

https://dx.doi.org/10.14722/autosec.2021.23005
www.ndss-symposium.org

improvements are observed [10]. Because of this benefit, it is envisioned that CV-TSC systems may gradually replace the conventional TSC systems in the future [23].

Despite great improvements in system performance, the new trait, connectivity between vehicles and infrastructure, might open a new door to cyber attacks. The benefit of CV-TSC systems can be achieved only if the systems are secure in cyberspace. Therefore, cyber security is a crucial component when developing CV-TSC systems. However, most of the existing CV-TSC models are designed without considering cyber security issues and thus may be vulnerable to cyber attacks. Before developing defense strategies, it is important to identify potential cyber threats and investigate the impact of cyber attacks. Existing studies on this topic usually consider a "white-box" attack scenario, which assumes that attackers have full access to the traffic control system and/or control logic so that they can manipulate the traffic signal phasing and timing freely [4], [7]–[9], [15], [19], [24]. For example, Perrine et al. [19] assumes that the traffic signals can be selectively disabled to flashing-red status (equivalent to a four-way stop-sign intersection) without explaining how the attack is conducted. Chen et al. [4] assumes that the source code of the signal control model is known to the attacker so a comprehensive analysis can be performed. "Manipulating signal phasing and timing freely" is a very strong and unrealistic assumption. For most of the commercial traffic control systems, various levels of protection from hardware (e.g., Malfunction Monitoring Unit) to software (e.g., controller firmware) are designed to prevent such manipulations, no mentioning access to the source code. Thus, it is necessary to build an attack model and evaluate the impact of cyber attacks under real-world scenarios where the controller hardware and control logic are inaccessible.

In this paper, we aim to evaluate the impact of falsified data attacks on CV-TSC systems by considering a "black-box" attack scenario, in which the attackers do not know the details of the signal control system and do not have physical access to the system (e.g., signal cabinet). Attackers first need to learn the signal control logic using a surrogate model that includes critical traffic features. With the learned model, the optimal signal timing plan generated from the control system can be predicted by the attackers using received CV trajectories. Then the attackers alter the critical traffic features and subsequently the signal timing plan by injecting falsified CV data into the system. The impact of attacks is measured by comparing the total vehicle delay before and after attack. In the case study, we apply the proposed attack model on I-SIG, an existing CV-TSC system. Results show that falsified data attacks can create excessive delay at the intersection and degrade the performance of the CV-TSC system. We also briefly discuss two defense strategies as future research directions.

The remainder of this paper is organized as follows. Background knowledge on traffic signal control is introduced in Section II. Section III presents the attack model, including how attackers may learn the signal control logic and how attackers may generate falsified data to launch attacks. Section IV presents a comprehensive case study, which realistically evaluates the impact of falsified data attacks on I-SIG. In Section V, we discuss two defense strategies. Related studies regarding cyber attacks on CV-TSC systems are introduced in Section VI. Finally, conclusions are drawn in Section VII.

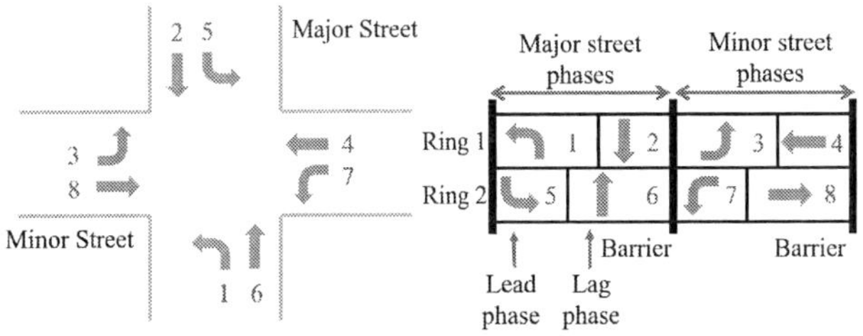

Fig. 2. Ring-barrier structure

II. Background

A. *Traffic Signal Control*

This study assumes that the CV-TSC system uses a ring-barrier phasing. The ring-barrier structure [13] illustrated in Figure 2 is the standard traffic signal phasing setting in North America. Starting from the major street and moving clockwise, the through phases are labeled as phases 2, 4, 6, and 8. Starting from the left-turn phase that is next to phase 6 and moving clockwise, the left-turn phases are labeled as phases 1, 3, 5, and 7. Ring 1 includes phases 1 to 4 and ring 2 includes phases 5 to 8. A barrier separates major street phases (phases 1, 2, 5, and 6) from minor street phases (phases 3, 4, 7, and 8). The phases that operate first within a barrier in each ring are called lead phase (e.g., phases 1 and 5) and the other phase (e.g., phases 2 and 6) is called lag phase. Therefore a barrier includes two lead phases and two lag phases. A signal optimization algorithm changes phase sequence and allocates green time of each phase to minimize/maximize predefined performance indexes, based on collected traffic data (e.g., CV trajectories).

B. *I-SIG*

In this study, I-SIG system from the Multi-Modal Intelligent Traffic Signal System (MMITSS) project is selected as the targeted CV-TSC system [23] for case study. Both simulation and field experiments have demonstrated the effectiveness of I-SIG in terms of delay reduction and mobility improvement [6]. The reason for choosing I-SIG is that it is one of the most cited work related to CV-TSC and the proposed framework has been adopted by many other studies. The control logic of I-SIG system is briefly introduced. At the beginning of each barrier, I-SIG takes a snapshot of the trajectories received from all the CVs within the RSU's communication range. Each trajectory is converted to an ETA (estimated time of arrival), which is calculated as the CV's distance to stop bar divided by its speed. Based on the ETAs of each signal phase, an arrival table is constructed. Then I-SIG solves an dynamic programming (DP) based optimization problem with the objective to minimize total vehicle delay or total queue length. Each barrier is considered as one stage in the DP formulation. Ideally, I-SIG should plan as many stages as needed so that all the vehicles can be properly served. For real-world implementations, however, I-SIG plans only two stages (i.e., one signal cycle) because of computational limitations in the edge computing device and real-time performance requirement. I-SIG then executes the timing plan of the first stage (the four phases in the current barrier) and arranges the phase sequence of the second stage (the four phases in the

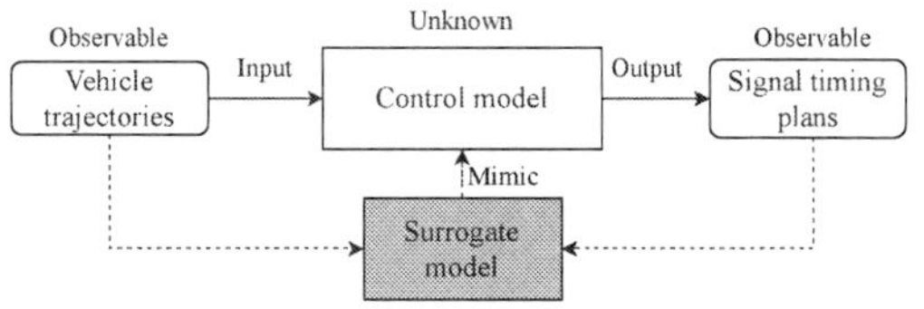

Fig. 3. The process of learning control logic

next barrier). When a new barrier starts, I-SIG repeats this optimization process. For more details, please refer to [6].

III. Attack Model

The proposed attack model includes two steps. In the first step, the attacker tries to learn the control logic using a surrogate model. Based on the surrogate model, in the second step, the attacker launches falsified data attacks to influence the control system to make sub-optimal decisions.

A. Learning Control Logic

In a real-world implementation, a CV-TSC system utilizes vehicle trajectories (i.e., BSMs) as the input and generates optimal signal timing plans. Both vehicle trajectories and signal timing plans are observable to the attacker in the forms of BSMs and SPaT messages respectively, because all messages are transmitted in a broadcast mode. The actual signal control logic, however, is unknown to the attacker. In order to launch effective attacks, the attacker needs to learn the control logic first using a surrogate model. The surrogate model takes the same trajectories as the input and outputs predicted signal timing plans. Historical BSM and SPaT data can be used to train the surrogate model. The attacker uses the surrogate model as the replacement of the real control logic when launching attacks. The whole learning process is illustrated in Figure 3.

1) Surrogate Model: A signal timing plan includes two parts, green time of each phase and phase sequence. The prediction of green time can be considered as a regression problem because green time is continuous. In contrast, the prediction of phase sequence is a classification problem since there is a finite number of possibilities for phase sequences. In this study, decision tree regression/classification [2] is adopted to be the surrogate model. Decision tree models are chosen because they are easy to implement and their output always falls within the feasible ranges, i.e., minimum and maximum green time. Most importantly, decision tree models possess inherent "if-then-else" structures and can effectively map nonlinear relationships, making signal control algorithms particularly easy to fit into programmatic structures. The input features to the surrogate model are critical traffic features extracted from observed CV trajectories.

2) Critical Traffic Features: Different CV-TSC systems use different objectives and performance indexes to optimize the signal timing plan. Since the objectives are typically functions of one or more traffic features, the signal timing plan should be closely related to these associated traffic features. For example, a signal controller may allocate green time based on the queue length of each phase, or a signal controller may terminate a green phase when there is a large headway. A list of common traffic features applied in existing studies include queue length (QL), number of approaching vehicles (NAV), headway (HW), estimated time of arrival (ETA), vehicle delay (VD), and flow rate (FR). These traffic features will be used in the case study in Section IV.

For a particular CV-TSC system, usually not all traffic features are utilized to optimize the signal timing. We define the traffic features that determine the signal timing plan as critical features. When falsified data alter the values of these critical features, signal control decisions are changed accordingly. As a result, the attacker needs to identify the critical features that have a significant impact on the signal timing plan before launching attacks. Identifying critical features from the list of features is a feature selection problem. In this study, a sequential forward selection algorithm (SFS) is applied [1]. Starting from an empty feature set, SFS greedily searches for the best features that can improve the prediction performance. John et al. [12] suggests using SFS for identifying useful features and shows that SFS can improve the performance of decision tree models. The output of SFS is a set of critical features. Note that in Section III-A1, only critical features are used as the input features of the decision tree models.

B. Falsified Data Generation

In the previous section, the attacker has obtained the surrogate model $f(\cdot)$ by training the decision tree models. Then the attacker launches attacks by broadcasting falsified trajectories using the compromised communication device (i.e., OBU). Based on received real CV trajectories, the attacker can compute critical traffic features $\boldsymbol{X_o}$ (e.g., queue length) identified in the previous step, and use the trained surrogate model to predict the signal timing plan, i.e., $f(\boldsymbol{X_o})$. $f(\boldsymbol{X_o})$ is referred to as the pseudo-optimal timing plan because it is not the exact timing plan generated from the actual control system, but a plan predicted by the trained surrogate model. By injecting falsified trajectories, the attacker tries to alter the values of the critical features from $\boldsymbol{X_o}$ to $\boldsymbol{X_a}$. Similarly, the attacker can predict the signal timing plan with the altered critical feature, i.e., $f(\boldsymbol{X_a})$. The dissimilarity between the pseudo-optimal timing plan and the timing plan under attack are computed using the L2 norm. The attacker's objective is to maximize the dissimilarity by generating falsified trajectories that can alter the values of the critical features, as shown in the following problem (**P1**):

$$\max_{\boldsymbol{X_a}} \quad \|f(\boldsymbol{X_o}) - f(\boldsymbol{X_a})\|_2 \tag{1}$$

$$\text{s.t.} \quad \boldsymbol{X_a} \in \Omega_{\boldsymbol{X_a}|\boldsymbol{X_o}} \tag{2}$$

In **P1**, the feasible region $\Omega_{\boldsymbol{X_a}|\boldsymbol{X_o}}$ is dependent on $\boldsymbol{X_o}$. For example, after injecting a falsified stopped vehicle (a falsified vehicle has a legitimate trajectory in the form of BSMs but is not physically on road), the new queue length cannot be smaller than the originally observed queue length.

When broadcast by the attacker's OBU, the falsified trajectory is mixed with regular CV trajectories. The RSU collects all the trajectories and uses them as input data for traffic signal optimization. Thus, the generated signal timing plans are influenced by the falsified trajectory, and thus are no longer optimal. As a result, vehicles may spend extra time passing the intersection and hence the total travel time is increased.

This attack model aligns with a recent study on black-box attacks against unknown machine learning models [18]. By using a surrogate model, the attacker crafts adversarial images to fool a target model so that the target model would output erroneous predictions.

IV. Attack Evaluation

In this section, a case study is presented to evaluate the impact of the proposed attack model on the I-SIG system.

A. Simulation Setup

A simulation environment is built using Matlab. A typical 4-leg intersection with eight phases is modeled. Each approach has one left-turn lane and one through lane. Right-turn lanes are not explicitly modeled since their phase allocations are usually the same as adjacent through lanes. The car-following model from the NGSIM project is used to model vehicle motions [25]. The minimum green time and the maximum green time are set to be 5 seconds and 30 seconds for each phase, respectively. The transition time between phases (i.e., yellow and red clearance time) is 4 seconds. The traffic demand for each movement is 400 veh/h. The communication range is set to be 300 meters. The free flow speed is 15.65 m/s. The resolution of the simulation is 10 Hz, which is consistent with the frequency of CV communication [21]. Attacks are launched every time I-SIG optimizes the signal timing plan.

B. Applying the Proposed Attack Model

1) Learning Control Logic: Because I-SIG executes optimized signal timing for one barrier each time, the surrogate model only needs to predict the green time of the four phases in the current barrier. The surrogate model consists of two decision tree regression models. The output of the first decision tree model (labeled as Tree 1) is the barrier length (i.e., lead phase plus lag phase). The second decision tree model (labeled as Tree 2) outputs the green time of the lead phase. Then the green time of the lag phase can be calculated by subtracting that of the corresponding lead phase from the barrier.

A 30-hour simulation is run to generate a data set needed for both training and validation. Totally, 2206 optimizations are conducted. 80% of the data are randomly chosen for training, while the remaining 20% are used for validation. Mean absolute error (MAE), mean absolute percentage error (MAPE), and root mean square error (RMSE) are utilized to quantify errors for a given set of traffic features. The errors are defined as the differences between predicted phase (barrier) duration and the phase (barrier) duration generated by original I-SIG. The SFS is applied to the list of common features and the results are shown in Table I. In the first round, only one feature is used for fitting the decision tree models. The model with NAV has the least error for both trees. Therefore, NAV is added to the critical feature set. In the second round, two features are used for fitting the decision tree models, with one feature fixed to be NAV. The model with NAV and ETA has the least error. Thus, ETA is chosen as the second feature and added to the critical feature set. This process is repeated to find the third feature. However, the models with three features are all worse than the best model in the second round. Thus, NAV and ETA are identified as critical features. We note that the two identified critical features are consistent with the findings from a previous vulnerability analysis on I-SIG [4].

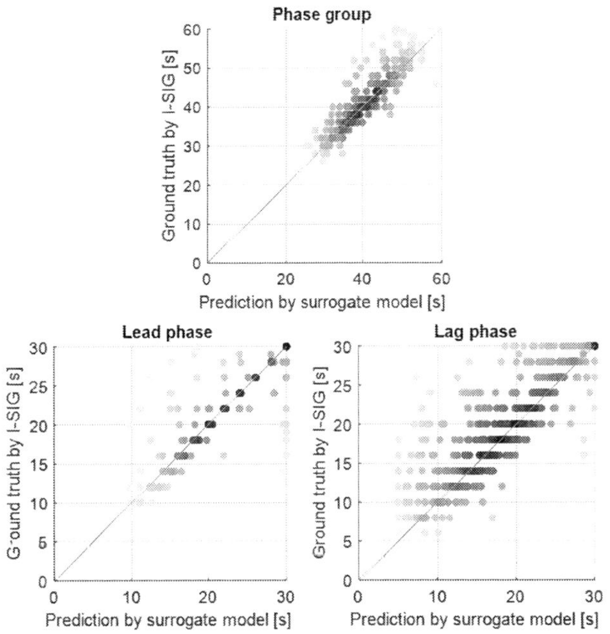

Fig. 4. Comparison between I-SIG and the trained surrogate model

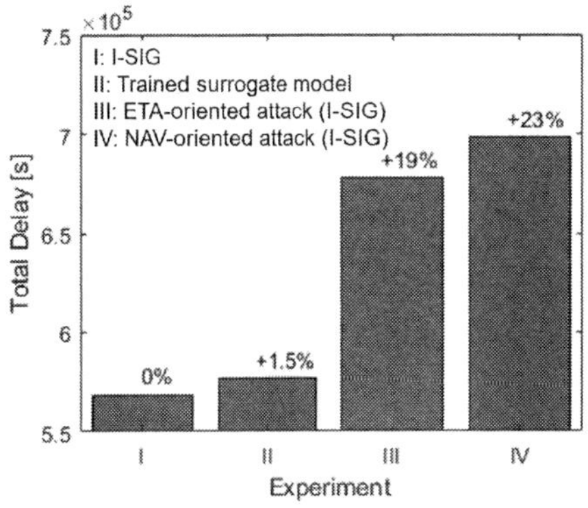

Fig. 5. Total delay for each experiment

Figure 4 shows the effectiveness of the trained surrogate model, in which the prediction by the trained surrogate model and the ground truth generated by I-SIG are compared. The color depth represents the density of the data. The majority of the data lie on or near the 45-degree line, indicating that the surrogate model has a good prediction accuracy. The MAE for lead phase and barrier duration prediction are only 0.52s and 1.33s respectively (Table I). The prediction of the lag phase has a relatively greater error because it is estimated indirectly from the barrier and the lead phase.

2) Evaluating the Impact of Attacks: Four simulation experiments are conducted to assess the impact of the proposed attack model. Each experiment lasts for 5 hours, with the exact same traffic demand and vehicle arrival patterns. The total delay for each experiment is shown in Figure 5.

In Experiment I, the original I-SIG system operates normally without attacks. This experiment serves as the bench-

TABLE I. APPLYING SFS FOR IDENTIFYING CRITICAL TRAFFIC FEATURES

	Tree 1 (Barrier)				Tree 2 (Lead Phase)			
	Feature set	MAE[s]	MAPE	RMSE[s]	Feature set	MAE[s]	MAPE	RMSE[s]
Round 1	QL	3.6771	9.32%	4.6842	QL	2.6690	14.34%	3.6185
	NAV	1.3967	3.46%	2.3786	NAV	1.1888	6.82%	2.2235
	HW	6.0618	15.53%	7.5209	HW	3.3484	17.76%	4.4968
	ETA	5.4608	14.04%	6.7911	ETA	3.8290	19.84%	4.6471
	VD	6.4353	16.45%	8.0939	VD	4.8858	25.85%	6.0647
	FR	4.6341	11.76%	5.7694	FR	3.4285	17.85%	4.2815
Round 2	NAV+QL	1.6386	4.06%	3.0106	NAV+QL	1.2375	7.01%	2.6973
	NAV+HW	1.5842	3.89%	2.8640	NAV+HW	1.1151	6.29%	2.3574
	NAV+ETA	1.3287	3.26%	2.3469	NAV+ETA	0.5205	2.95%	1.5097
	NAV+VD	1.6177	3.97%	2.9335	NAV+VD	1.3257	7.64%	2.8670
	NAV+FR	1.5162	3.74%	2.5721	NAV+FR	1.1948	6.86%	2.2860
Round 3	NAV+ETA+QL	1.3959	3.46%	2.5778	NAV+ETA+QL	0.5513	3.10%	1.7964
	NAV+ETA+HW	1.4065	3.48%	2.5982	NAV+ETA+HW	0.5398	3.07%	1.7040
	NAV+ETA+VD	1.3977	3.44%	2.5750	NAV+ETA+VD	0.5404	3.02%	1.7978
	NAV+ETA+FR	1.4059	3.49%	2.4968	NAV+ETA+FR	0.5398	3.04%	1.6367

mark for all the other experiments. In Experiment II, the trained surrogate model is used to generate signal timing plans and control the traffic signals. However, no falsified CV data are injected to the system. As evidenced by a small increase of 1.5%, the total delay is very close to the benchmark. This indicates that the trained surrogate model could effectively mimic the actual signal control logic. In Experiment III, the attacker is assumed to attack I-SIG based on the feature ETA. To achieve this, the attacker alters ETA by manipulating the location and speed data in the falsified BSMs. It is worth noting that only one falsified trajectory is injected into the system per attack. The total delay increases by 19%. In Experiment IV, the attacker is assumed to attack I-SIG based on the feature NAV. The attacker alters NAV by injecting multiple falsified trajectories to different phases per attack. The total delay increases by 23%. Results indicate that the ETA attack (only one falsified trajectory) is more effective than the NAV attack (multiple falsified trajectories) because it can trigger a vulnerability called "last vehicle advantage" in the I-SIG's logic. When under ETA attack, the I-SIG algorithm extends the green time to the maximum value to serve the fake vehicle. However, the NAV attack only adds fake vehicles into the arrival table, which only marginally increase the green time allocation. More details about the ETA attack can be found in our previous study [4]. These experiment results show that the proposed "black-box" attack model is effective in increasing intersection delay, even with a limited budget. In the original study, the maximum delay decrease brought by I-SIG is 16.33% [6]. It means that our proposed attack model can completely reverse the benefit brought by the CV technology.

V. DEFENSE STRATEGY

Although the focus of this study is on the impact evaluation of falsified data attacks, defense strategies are briefly discussed. Because the attacker needs to learn the control logic before attack, one natural defense strategy is to interfere with the learning process. For example, we may add noise to the optimized signal timing plans. This may increase the difficulty in learning the surrogate model. However, when the environment is benign (i.e., no attacks), adding noise makes the system operate under sub-optimal conditions. Thus, a trade-off needs to be made between security and efficiency.

Another defense strategy is to proactively identify falsified trajectories before they are utilized by the control system. The falsified trajectories are generated to alter the values of the critical features, which does not represent true traffic conditions. For example, in our case study, to alter ETA to a large value, the attacker needs to generate a falsified trajectory which shows that the falsified vehicle approaches the intersection with a low speed. Such falsified trajectories are behaviorally different from normal trajectories. By applying methods from the area of misbehavior detection, we may be able to identify abnormal (falsified) trajectories. We will investigate this defense strategy in our future research.

VI. RELATED WORK

Based on the general structure of a CV-TSC system in Figure 1, three attack surfaces can be identified at a connected intersection: the transportation infrastructure (RSU, signal controller, and traffic signals), the TMC, and the CVs. Usually, the transportation infrastructure is deployed in an agency's local network with firewall protection. It is difficult to access the infrastructure devices remotely from the public domain. In order to initiate an attack, attackers have to open up the signal control cabinet and establish a wired connection to the devices. Once attackers gain access to the system, they can directly manipulate the signal timing. Alternatively, attackers may trespass into the TMC and send control commands to the signal controller directly. These attacks are referred to as direct attacks, which have been investigated by previous studies [5], [9], [15], [19], [20]. These studies mainly focus on conventional traffic control systems, for instances, fixed-timing signal control [15] and ramp metering control [20].

The other type of attack towards the traffic control system is indirect attacks, in which attackers try to influence signal control decisions by injecting falsified data. Indirect attacks can be launched from the vehicle side. By exploiting software vulnerabilities, it is practically feasible that attackers hack into the communication devices in their own CVs and broadcast falsified messages. This is similar to compromising other Electronic Control Units as demonstrated in the literature [3], [14]. Alternatively, attackers may hack into their vehicles' internal networks. This can be achieved in many ways. For example, attackers may hack into the infotainment system of the vehicle [16]. Once attackers are in the vehicle's internal network, they would be able to take control of a wide range of vehicle functions [14], including sending malicious BSMs that contain falsified data elements. Because attackers have arbitrary access to their own vehicles, indirect attacks are much more achievable. Recent studies have shown that falsified input data can indeed influence system control decisions and significantly downgrade the system performance. For example, influencing routing decisions in social navigation systems by generating virtual traffic jams (e.g., Google map, Waze) [11], [22], or increasing total travel delay by affecting signal control decisions [4], [7], [8], [17], [24].

VII. Conclusion

In this paper, we aim to investigate the security problem of CV-TSC systems. Compared to the literature, this study considers a more realistic attack scenario in which the control logic of CV-TSC systems is unavailable to the attacker. We assume that the attacker may learn the signal control logic using a surrogate model and identify critical traffic features. With the learned model, the signal timing plan generated by the control system can be predicted by the attacker. Falsified BSMs then can be constructed to alter the values of the critical traffic features. Consequently, the signal control decisions are influenced. The attacker is assumed to find the "best" value of the critical features by maximizing the dissimilarity between the pseudo-optimal timing plan and the resultant signal timing plan under attack. A comprehensive case study is conducted with I-SIG as the selected CV-TSC system. We find that the surrogate model can effectively mimic the actual control logic of I-SIG, which is sensitive to two critical traffic features: ETA (estimated time of arrival) and NAV (number of approaching vehicles). Two types of attacks are launched based on these two features. Simulation experiments show that the total delay increases by 19% and 23% respectively under these two attacks. This indicates that even though the control logic is unknown, an attacker is still able to cause severe damage to the CV-TSC system. To protect the system, two defense strategies are briefly discussed. Based on the findings of this paper, future work will focus on the proactive defense strategy to safeguard CV-TSC systems from falsified data attacks. The goal of the defense strategy is to detect anomaly in BSMs and filter out falsified trajectories before applying them in the CV-based applications.

Acknowledgment

This research is supported in part by NSF through Grant SaTC #1930041, CNS #1850533, CNS #1929771, USDOT UTC Grant 69A3552047138 and Mcity at the University of Michigan for financial support. The views presented in this paper are those of the authors alone.

References

[1] S.-T. Bow, *Pattern recognition and image preprocessing.* Marcel Dekker New York, 2002.

[2] L. Breiman, *Classification and regression trees.* Routledge, 2017.

[3] S. Checkoway, D. McCoy, B. Kantor, D. Anderson, H. Shacham, S. Savage, K. Koscher, A. Czeskis, F. Roesner, T. Kohno *et al.*, "Comprehensive experimental analyses of automotive attack surfaces." in *USENIX Security Symposium*, vol. 4. San Francisco, 2011.

[4] Q. A. Chen, Y. Yin, Y. Feng, Z. M. Mao, and H. X. Liu, "Exposing congestion attack on emerging connected vehicle based traffic signal control," in *Network and Distributed Systems Security (NDSS) Symposium*, 2018.

[5] J. M. Ernst and A. J. Michaels, "Framework for evaluating the severity of cybervulnerability of a traffic cabinet," *Transportation Research Record*, vol. 2619, no. 1, pp. 55–63, 2017.

[6] Y. Feng, K. L. Head, S. Khoshmagham, and M. Zamanipour, "A real-time adaptive signal control in a connected vehicle environment," *Transportation Research Part C: Emerging Technologies*, vol. 55, pp. 460–473, 2015.

[7] Y. Feng, S. Huang, Q. A. Chen, H. X. Liu, and Z. M. Mao, "Vulnerability of traffic control system under cyberattacks with falsified data," *Transportation research record*, vol. 2672, no. 1, pp. 1–11, 2018.

[8] A. Ghafouri, W. Abbas, Y. Vorobeychik, and X. Koutsoukos, "Vulnerability of fixed-time control of signalized intersections to cyber-tampering," in *2016 Resilience Week (RWS).* IEEE, 2016, pp. 130–135.

[9] B. Ghena, W. Beyer, A. Hillaker, J. Pevarnek, and J. A. Halderman, "Green lights forever: Analyzing the security of traffic infrastructure," in *8th {USENIX} Workshop on Offensive Technologies ({WOOT} 14)*, 2014.

[10] Q. Guo, L. Li, and X. J. Ban, "Urban traffic signal control with connected and automated vehicles: A survey," *Transportation research part C: emerging technologies*, vol. 101, pp. 313–334, 2019.

[11] T. Jeske, "Floating car data from smartphones: What google and waze know about you and how hackers can control traffic," *Proc. of the BlackHat Europe*, pp. 1–12, 2013.

[12] G. H. John, R. Kohavi, and K. Pfleger, "Irrelevant features and the subset selection problem," in *Machine Learning Proceedings 1994.* Elsevier, 1994, pp. 121–129.

[13] P. Koonce and L. Rodegerdts, "Traffic signal timing manual," United States Federal Highway Administration, Tech. Rep., 2008.

[14] K. Koscher, A. Czeskis, F. Roesner, S. Patel, T. Kohno, S. Checkoway, D. McCoy, B. Kantor, D. Anderson, H. Shacham *et al.*, "Experimental security analysis of a modern automobile," in *2010 IEEE Symposium on Security and Privacy.* IEEE, 2010, pp. 447–462.

[15] A. Laszka, B. Potteiger, Y. Vorobeychik, S. Amin, and X. Koutsoukos, "Vulnerability of transportation networks to traffic-signal tampering," in *2016 ACM/IEEE 7th International conference on Cyber-Physical Systems (ICCPS).* IEEE, 2016, pp. 1–10.

[16] S. Mazloom, M. Rezaeirad, A. Hunter, and D. McCoy, "A security analysis of an in-vehicle infotainment and app platform," in *10th {USENIX} Workshop on Offensive Technologies ({WOOT} 16)*, 2016.

[17] P. Oza, M. Foruhandeh, R. Gerdes, and T. Chantem, "Secure traffic lights: Replay attack detection for model-based smart traffic controllers," in *Proceedings of the Second ACM Workshop on Automotive and Aerial Vehicle Security*, 2020, pp. 5–10.

[18] N. Papernot, P. McDaniel, I. Goodfellow, S. Jha, Z. B. Celik, and A. Swami, "Practical black-box attacks against machine learning," in *Proceedings of the 2017 ACM on Asia conference on computer and communications security*, 2017, pp. 506–519.

[19] K. A. Perrine, M. W. Levin, C. N. Yahia, M. Duell, and S. D. Boyles, "Implications of traffic signal cybersecurity on potential deliberate traffic disruptions," *Transportation research part A: policy and practice*, vol. 120, pp. 58–70, 2019.

[20] J. Reilly, S. Martin, M. Payer, and A. M. Bayen, "Creating complex congestion patterns via multi-objective optimal freeway traffic control with application to cyber-security," *Transportation Research Part B: Methodological*, vol. 91, pp. 366–382, 2016.

[21] D. SAE, "J2735 dedicated short range communications (dsrc) message set dictionary," *Society of Automotive Engineers, DSRC Committee*, 2009.

[22] M. B. Sinai, N. Partush, S. Yadid, and E. Yahav, "Exploiting social navigation," *arXiv preprint arXiv:1410.0151*, 2014.

[23] USDOT, "Multi-modal intelligent traffic safety system," https://www.its.dot.gov/research_archives/dma/bundle/mmitss_plan.htm, 2019, online; Accessed: 2019-05-21.

[24] C.-C. Yen, D. Ghosal, M. Zhang, C.-N. Chuah, and H. Chen, "Falsified data attack on backpressure-based traffic signal control algorithms," in *2018 IEEE Vehicular Networking Conference (VNC).* IEEE, 2018, pp. 1–8.

[25] H. Yeo, A. Skabardonis, J. Halkias, J. Colyar, and V. Alexiadis, "Oversaturated freeway flow algorithm for use in next generation simulation," *Transportation Research Record*, vol. 2088, no. 1, pp. 68–79, 2008.

Denial-of-Service Attacks on C-V2X Networks

Nataša Trkulja
ECE Department
Boston University
Boston, MA, USA
ntrkulja@bu.edu

David Starobinski
ECE Department
Boston University
Boston, MA, USA
staro@bu.edu

Randall A. Berry
ECE Department
Nothwestern University
Evanston, IL, USA
rberry@northwestern.edu

***Abstract*—Cellular Vehicle-to-Everything (C-V2X) has been adopted by the FCC as the technology standard for safety-related transportation and vehicular communications in the US. C-V2X allows vehicles to self-manage the network in absence of a cellular base-station. Since C-V2X networks convey safety-critical messages, it is crucial to assess their security posture. This work contributes a novel set of Denial-of-Service (DoS) attacks on C-V2X networks. The attacks are caused by adversarial resource block selection and vary in sophistication and efficiency. In particular, we consider "oblivious" adversaries that ignore recent transmission activity on resource blocks, "smart" adversaries that do monitor activity on each resource block, and "cooperative" adversaries that work together to ensure they attack different targets. We analyze and simulate these attacks to showcase their effectiveness. Assuming a fixed number of attackers, we show that at low vehicle density, smart and cooperative attacks can significantly impact network performance, while at high vehicle density, oblivious attacks are almost as effective as the more sophisticated attacks.**

I. Introduction

Cellular Vehicle-to-Everything (C-V2X) is an LTE-based technology that enables communications between automotive vehicles (V2V), vehicles and pedestrians (V2P), vehicles and infrastructure (V2I), and vehicles and the network (V2N). Specifications for C-V2X communications started from release 14 of the 3rd Generation Partnership Project (3GPP) [1], [2]. This release defined two new modes of LTE operation (Mode 3 and Mode 4) whose major difference is resource allocation: where Mode 3 relies on the cellular base-station to perform resource allocation, Mode 4 has been designed to allow vehicles to allocate resources on their own. Operating in Mode 4, vehicles utilize their own radio user equipment (UE) to communicate without having access to the cellular network.

To operate in Mode 4, vehicles select appropriate resource blocks (RBs) that will be used to transmit their Basic Safety Messages (BSMs). A resource block is a set of OFDM sub-carriers within a given time-slot. Vehicles operating in Mode 4 sense and process incoming signals to select resource blocks from the 20% of those available with the lowest Received Signal Strength Indicator (RSSI) [2]. When a vehicle selects a resource block, it periodically transmits BSMs on that resource block for a certain duration called the "semi-persistent period". Once the semi-persistent period expires, the vehicle selects a new resource block with a probability p^1. As vehicles go through this process, they may randomly end up choosing the same resource block for a period of time which results in packet collisions. It is these types of collisions that serve as the basis for the Denial-of-Service (DoS) attacks on C-V2X networks that we are envisioning.

The purpose of this paper is to investigate if and how the resource block selection process can be abused by a malicious party. Specifically, we consider one or more adversaries, each equipped with a C-V2X device, that aim to launch a DoS attack on the network by inducing packet collisions and hence lowering the packet reception ratio (PRR). We consider adversaries with different levels of sophistication. Thus, we consider "oblivious" adversaries, which ignore recent transmission activity on resource blocks and just select a new resource block with probability $p' \neq p$, versus "smart" adversaries that monitor activity on each resource block before deciding on which one to transmit next. We also consider "cooperative" adversaries that work together to ensure they attack different targets. Our goal is to assess the potency of these attacks as a function of the vehicle density and the number of attackers.

Our main contributions are as follows:

1) We show that C-V2X networks are vulnerable to DoS attacks caused by adversarial resource block selection.
2) We introduce attack types of increasing level of sophistication, and investigate their effect through analysis and simulation based on the specifications of the C-V2X protocol.
3) We show that the most effective oblivious attack is one where the attacker selects a new resource block with probability $p' = 1$. This result is formally proven for a special case and shown to hold in general through simulation.
4) We show that collaborative attacks are more potent than smart attacks, which in turn are more potent than oblivious attacks, especially at low vehicle density. Yet, at

[1]In general p can be set anywhere in the range between 0.2 and 1. In our simulations, we use $p = 0.2$ as in [3], while in some of our theoretical results we allow p to take any value in $[0, 1]$.

Workshop on Automotive and Autonomous Vehicle Security (AutoSec) 2021
25 February 2021, Virtual

https://dx.doi.org/10.14722/autosec.2021.23006
www.ndss-symposium.org

high vehicle density, oblivious attacks become almost as effective as the more sophisticated attacks.

To the best of our knowledge, the attacks presented in this paper have not been studied before. The goal of the paper is to provide insight into these attacks, and hence we start by evaluating them in simple network configurations. In the paper's conclusion, we discuss potential areas for future work.

This paper is organized as follows. Section II discusses existing work regarding DoS attacks on vehicular networks and C-V2X security in general. Section III introduces the different attack types. Section IV presents analysis that sheds light on the effectiveness of the attacks. Section V showcases the results we obtained by simulation to investigate the effectiveness of the different attack types under a variety of conditions. Section VI concludes the paper.

II. Related Work

Denial-of-Service attacks have long been recognized as a significant threat to vehicular networks [4]. Their ability to congest the RF spectrum and prevent vehicles from accessing necessary RF resources, their ability to impede the flow of safety-critical information between vehicles, as well as their ability to deny vehicles access to road-side units (RSUs) have rendered them one of the most dangerous attacks against vehicular networks. DoS attacks have been studied to a great extent within the context of Dedicated Short Range Communication (DSRC). For instance, [5], [6] evaluate the performance of DSRC-based vehicular networks under jamming attacks and [7]–[9] focus on developing DoS detection mechanisms and antijamming techniques.

Being more recent than DSRC, research on C-V2X has mostly focused on performance aspects, e.g., [3], [10]. There is a limited pool of work that investigates the security aspect of C-V2X networks. The work in [11] reviews potential threats to C-V2X networks, including Denial-of-Service attacks, recognizing that such attacks could compromise the reliability of C-V2X service. The work in [12] evaluates the security of the C-V2X protocol, as outlined in [2], and proposes a privacy-preserving scheme. Additional work develops a mechanism for detecting DoS attacks while operating in Mode 3 of the C-V2X protocol [13]. That work identifies a DoS attack that maliciously reserves the resources at an evolved NodeB (eNB) node with the goal of denying service to honest vehicles. To the best of our knowledge, our work is the first to explore the impact of DoS attacks in Mode 4 of C-V2X networks.

III. Attack Types

In this section, we introduce different types of DoS attacks based on adversarial resource block selection. These attacks increase the likelihood of packet collisions. Under the assumption that all resource blocks are orthogonal, packet collisions happen when two or more vehicles in the system choose the same resource block at the same time. Here, we assume that all vehicles are within a close enough range of each other so that when such a collision occurs, this results in neither of the two vehicles' messages being received by the remaining vehicles. Note that such collisions may occur even in the absence of attacks due to the random nature of resource block selection. There simply will be instances when two or more vehicles happen to randomly choose the same resource block even without any malicious vehicles in the system. This scenario, without malicious vehicles, represents the **baseline** case against which we will be comparing the different attack types.

Before describing the attack types, we need to define several important system parameters. We assume that BSMs are sent by each vehicle every T_{tr} seconds, which we refer to as the *transmission period.* Each vehicle v_i uses a resource block r_i to transmit its BSM, where i represents a specific resource block. T_s is the number of transmission periods within a semi-persistent period, that is vehicle i transmits BSMs on resource block r_i for T_s times. Upon the expiration of the semi-persistent period, an honest vehicle changes its resource block with a probability p as mentioned earlier.

Attacker goal. The attacker's goal is to minimize the packet reception ratio (PRR) in the network, which is the fraction of correctly received packets to the total number of transmitted packets.

Attacker capabilities. We assume each attacker to be a vehicle with the same C-V2X capabilities as the target vehicles (e.g., they receive and transmit valid BSMs). In particular, each attacker can only use one resource block at a time and switch its selected resource block after a semi-persistent period. We use the following characteristics to further classify the attacks:

- **Oblivious**: An attack is oblivious if attacker vehicles do not have to listen in on target vehicles' communication (i.e., which resource blocks they are transmitting on).
- **Cooperation**: An attack type is cooperative if attackers cooperate to deliver a more efficient attack.

A. Attack Type 1: Oblivious Attack

In **attack type 1**, attacker vehicles select a resource block with a probability p' choosing from the entire pool of RBs. There are a couple of special cases of this attack type:

- $p' = 0$. This implies that the attacker vehicles never change the resource block they originally and randomly selected. As the attacker resource block selection is random, it may or may not select a resource block that is in use by a target vehicle at the start of the attack. Attacker vehicles may also choose the same resource block, even if it is an idle resource block. Therefore, the collisions are solely dependent on the pure chance that the attacker vehicle selects a resource block already in use at the start of the attack.
- $p' = 1$. This implies that the attacker vehicles change the resource block upon expiration of every semi-persistent period. They randomly select a new resource block among all possible blocks. The attacker vehicles may or may not choose a resource block that is already in use; this is again dependent on chance. We anticipate this special case to be more effective than when $p' = 0$.

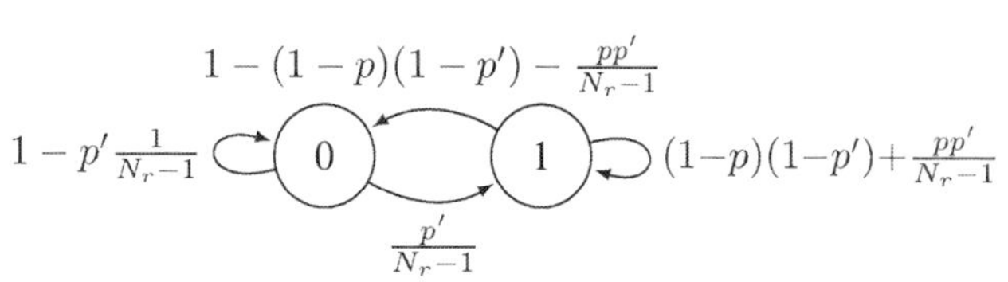

Fig. 1. Markov chain state diagram for two vehicles (one attacker, one target). State 0 represents the state in which the target vehicle and the attacker vehicle use different resource blocks. State 1 represents the state in which the target and the attacker use the same resource block, resulting in packet collision.

B. Attack Type 2: Smart Attack

In **attack type 2**, attacker vehicles look for resource blocks that are being used by only one vehicle (which we refer to as a *loner vehicle*) and select one of such resource blocks. The adversaries have to spend a period of time listening to messages sent by target vehicles to establish a list of loner vehicles' resource blocks from which they randomly choose their own. Attacker vehicles do not cooperate implying that they may choose the same loner vehicle to attack during one attack period, reducing the effectiveness of attack.

C. Attack Type 3: Cooperative Attack

In **attack type 3**, attacker vehicles look for all resource blocks that are being used by loner vehicles and each selects one of those resource blocks while ensuring no two attackers choose the same block. They have to spend a period of time listening to messages sent by target vehicles to establish a list of loner vehicles' resource blocks from which they choose their own RBs. Additionally, they have to communicate between themselves to ensure that they select different resource blocks from this list. This attack type is cooperative making it more efficient in theory, but also more challenging to implement in practice.

IV. Analysis

In this section, we analyze the potency of oblivious attacks. Lemmas 1 and 2 assume that the vehicles are synchronized implying that their semi-persistent periods are aligned.

Lemma 1. *Consider attack type 1 (oblivious attack), with one attacker and one target. Then, for any $0 < p \leq 1$, PRR is minimized with $p' = 1$.*

Proof. If there are two vehicles in the system, a single target and a single attacker, then we can model these vehicles as a Markov chain with two possible states:

- State 0: The two vehicles use different resource blocks.
- State 1: The two vehicles use the same resource block.

To minimize the PRR, the best strategy for the attacker is to maximize the fraction of time spent in state 1 because collisions take place in that state. The packet collision probability corresponds to the probability of finding the Markov chain in state 1. A Markov chain state diagram for this system is depicted in Figure 1.

Next, we explain the transition probabilities shown in Figure 1. Recall that N_r denotes the total number of resource blocks. A transition from state 0 to state 1 occurs when the attacker moves to a resource block used by the target vehicle. Note that the target vehicle will never switch to the resource block currently used by the attacker (because the channel is perceived as busy and the target won't select it as per the protocol). The transition probability from state 1 to state 0 is the complement of the transition probability from state 1 to itself. Such a self-transition occurs either if both the attacker and the target continue to use their current mutual resource block or if they both choose the same new resource block.

Let π_0 and π_i respectively represent the stationary probabilities to find the Markov chain in state 0 and in state 1. These probabilities can be computed using the balance equation:

$$\pi_0 \frac{p'}{N_r-1} = \pi_1 \left(1-(1-p)(1-p')\frac{pp'}{N_r-1}\right). \quad (1)$$

Combining Eq. (1) with the normalization equation $\pi_0 + \pi_1 = 1$, we obtain

$$\pi_1 = \frac{p'}{(N_r-1)[p+p'(1-p)+\frac{p'}{N_r-1}(1-p)]}. \quad (2)$$

We next take the derivative of π_1 with respect to p'. If it is positive for all $p' \in [0,1]$, it means that π_1 is maximized when $p' = 1$.

Taking the derivative of the expression given in Eq. (2) we obtain

$$\frac{d\pi_1}{dp'} = \frac{p}{(N_r-1)(p+p'(1-p)+\frac{p'}{N_r-1}(1-p))^2} > 0, \quad (3)$$

for all $0 \leq p' \leq 1$ and $0 < p \leq 1$.

Therefore, we conclude that π_1 increases with p' and achieves its maximum when $p' = 1$. Conversely, the PRR decreases with p' and is minimized when $p' = 1$. □

From the proof, we note that the derivative of the packet collision probability π_1 decreases with p' (while staying positive), i.e., increasing p' leads to a diminishing return. That is, increasing p' has a much greater effect in reducing the PRR while p' is low compared to when p' is already on the higher end of its range from 0 to 1. Our simulations in Section V show that the same effect holds true in the general case of many attackers and many targets.

From the proof, we further note that the derivative of the packet collision probability converges to 0 as p tends to 0, that is the effect of p' becomes negligible as p tends to 0. The next lemma shows that this result holds in the general case.

Lemma 2. *Consider attack type 1 (oblivious attack), with an arbitrary number of attackers N_a and an arbitrary number of target vehicles N_v. If $p = 0$, then PRR is unaffected by p' for any $0 < p' \leq 1$.*

Proof. If $p = 0$, then each target vehicle always stays on the same resource block (RB). Because the attackers choose their RBs randomly, in steady-state, each attacker is equally likely to be transmitting on any RB, independently of p' (assuming $p' > 0$, so that the initial state of each attacker does not have an effect in steady-state). Therefore, if there are N_r RBs, the probability that a given attacker transmits on RB r_i is $1/N_r$, for any $i \in \{1, 2, \ldots, N_r\}$. Assume RB r_i is used by a target vehicle, then the steady-state probability that RB r_i is jammed by one or more attackers is $1-(1-1/N_r)^{N_a}$, which is independent of p' and i. □

V. Simulation Results

In this section, we present Monte-Carlo simulation results to measure the potency of each attack type. Specifically, we aim to answer the following questions:

1) What impact does the number of attackers have on the potency of each type?
2) What impact does the value of p' have on the potency of attack type 1?
3) Which attack types are the most and the least potent, and under what conditions?

We measure the potency of the different attack types using the packet reception ratio (PRR) metric, which is the ratio of the number of packets that were successfully received to the total number of packets sent (BSMs in our case). We explore how PRR changes as a function of the total number of vehicles in the network, where *the total number of vehicles* is defined as the sum of the target vehicles and the attacker vehicles.

Simulation Setup

To simulate the attack types, we adapt a Monte-Carlo simulation model in Matlab of C-V2X networks that was introduced in [3]. The simulations are run under the following assumptions and conditions unless otherwise noted in the figures' captions:

- The vehicular network is fully-connected, implying that all vehicles are within the range of one another.
- There is no signal fading and packet losses are only due to collisions.
- Simulation time is 300 s.
- Number of simulation trials is 10.
- Transmission period, T_{tr}, is 100 ms.
- The length of the semi-persistent period is $T_s T_{tr} = 1$ s.
- There are 200 resource blocks ($N_r = 200$).
- The probability that a target vehicle changes its resource block is $p = 0.2$.

Note that the initial offsets of the semi-persistent periods for different vehicles are chosen at random, and hence the semi-persistent periods are not synchronized. Simulation parameters are representative of real-world C-V2X configurations [14], though actual deployments may implement a random semi-persistent period with a mean time of 1 s.

A. Attack Type 1: Oblivious Attack

In this attack type, attacker vehicles choose random resource blocks with the probability p'. We focus on two special cases: $p' = 0$ and $p' = 1$. For the PRR performance plots, we vary the total number of vehicles N_v and the number of attackers N_a. The results are shown in Figure 2 and Figure 3 for $p' = 0$ and $p' = 1$, respectively. The black curve is the PRR of the baseline representing the case when there are no attackers. As can be seen, the PRR drops with the increase of the total number of vehicles in both special cases. The special case of $p' = 0$ appears to have very little to no effect irrespective of the number of attackers. The special case of $p' = 1$ drops the PRR for a single attacker and five attackers by approximately 0.5% and 2% on average, respectively. This matches the analysis provided by Lemma 1 that showed that PRR is minimized when $p' = 1$ in attack type 1, but to further confirm that, we next investigate the effect of varying p' in attack type 1.

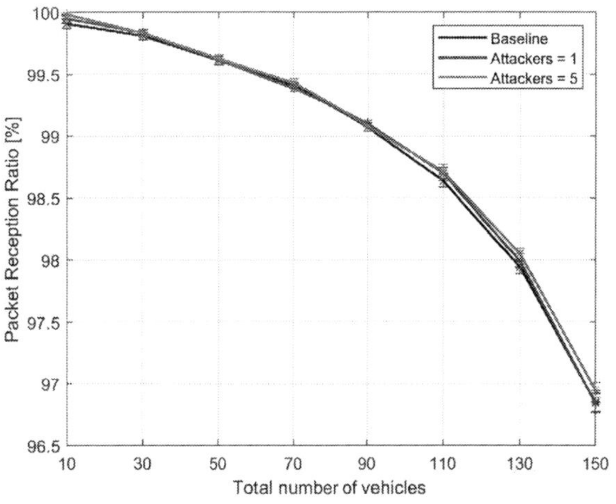

Fig. 2. PRR versus the total number of vehicles in **attack type 1,** $p' = 0$ with 95% confidence intervals. Simulation time is 3000 s.

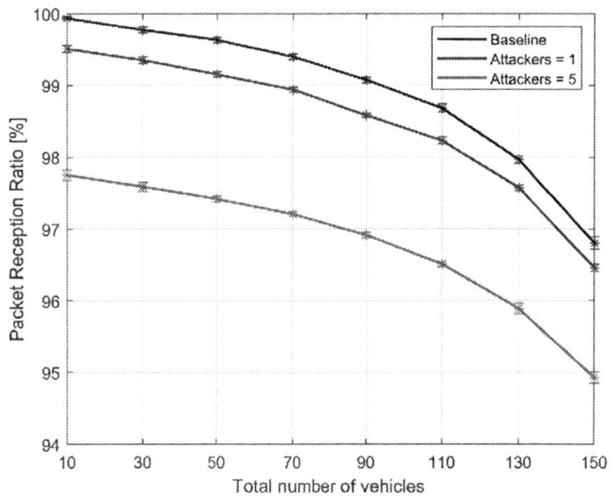

Fig. 3. PRR versus the total number of vehicles in **attack type 1,** $p' = 1$ with 95% confidence intervals. Simulation time is 3000 s.

Varying p' in Attack Type 1: To answer our second research question regarding the impact of the value of p' on the potency of attack type 1, we evaluate the PRR against the total number of vehicles. We compare the performance of the attack type at $p' = 0$, $p' = 0.5$, and $p' = 1$ while the number of attackers

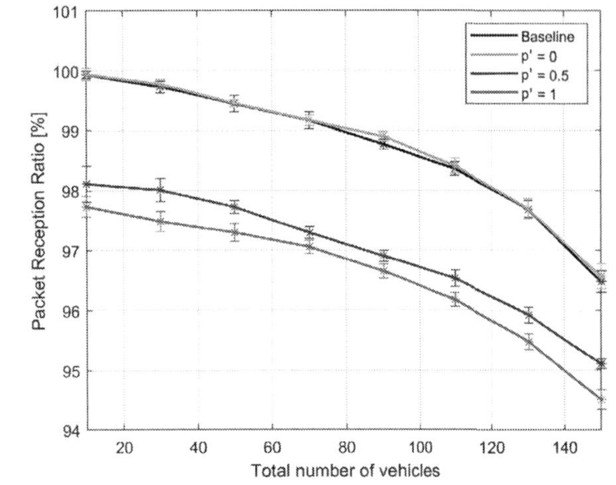

Fig. 4. PRR versus the total number of vehicles in **attack type 1** with 95% confidence intervals. We vary the value of p' to explore its effect on the potency of attack type 1. When p' is equal to 0, the attack has almost no effect. The PRR drops as the p' is increased.

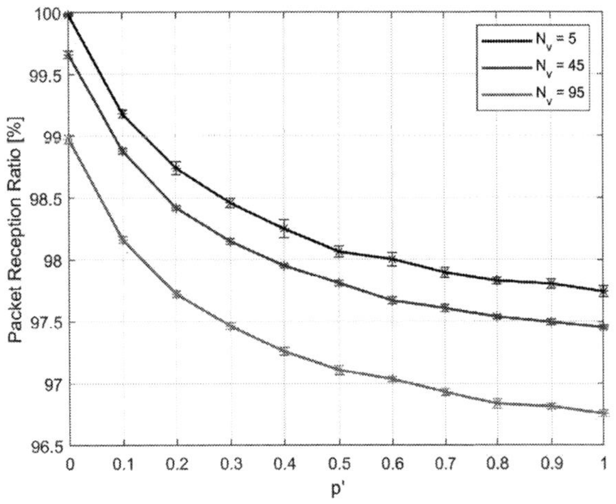

Fig. 5. PRR versus p' in **attack type 1** with 95% confidence intervals and different values of the target vehicles, N_v. The number of attackers, N_a, is fixed at 5. As p' increases, the PRR drops, with $p' = 1$ having the lowest PRR for any number of target vehicles. Simulation time is 30000 s.

N_a is fixed at 5. As shown by the resulting Figure 4, the PRR drops with the increase of p' and $p' = 1$ has the lowest PRR, in line with Lemma 1. This is perhaps the most obvious in Figure 5 where we fixed the number of attackers, N_a, to five and observed the behavior of PRR as p' is varied. The three resulting curves represent different number of target vehicles N_v. As observed from our analysis in Section IV, the effect of increasing p' becomes less pronounced as p' gets larger.

B. Attack Type 2: Smart Attack

In this attack type, attacker vehicles look for resource blocks that are used by loner vehicles and randomly select one of those resource blocks. Attackers do not cooperate implying that they may target the same loner vehicle during one attack period. The results of this attack type are shown in Figure 6. The black curve is the baseline representing PRR when there are no attackers. When the total number of vehicles is 10, this attack type significantly lowers the PRR, down to 90% for a single attacker and to 55% for 5 attackers. Figure 6 shows an interesting phenomenon: as the total number of vehicles varies, with a fixed number of attackers, the PRR increases up to a certain point and then starts decreasing. Indeed, a fixed number of attackers N_a can collide with at most N_a RBs at a time. Initially, when the number of target vehicles is low, many of them are successfully jammed. However, when the number of target vehicles grows and they use different RBs, then only a subset can be affected. At high vehicle density, the PRR starts decreasing due to channel congestion.

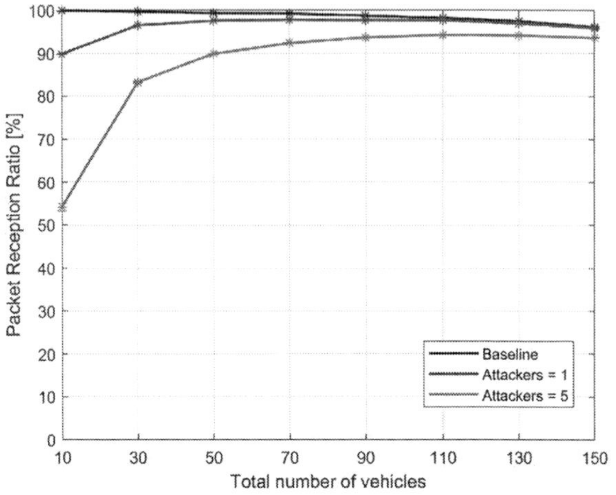

Fig. 6. PRR versus the total number of vehicles in **attack type 2** with 95% confidence intervals.

C. Attack Type 3: Cooperative Attack

In this attack type, just like in attack type 2, attacker vehicles look for resource blocks that are being used by loner vehicles. In this type, however, attacker vehicles cooperate and ensure that they all choose a different target. The results of this attack type are shown in Figure 7. The blue curve is the baseline representing PRR when there are no attackers. As can be seen from the figure, this attack is highly efficient (PRR = 10%) when there are 5 attackers and the total number of vehicles is 10. This is because there are 5 targets and 5 attackers that collaborate, which results in collisions on all 5 targets. The PRR at that point is not 0 because the attacks occur every semi-persistent period and the target vehicles are not synchronized with respect to it. Hence, there will be target vehicles that will change their resource blocks during an attack period and before the attackers have a chance to react.

D. Comparison between Attack Types

To answer our third research question, we plot the PRR versus the total number of vehicles for $N_a = 5$ for all the

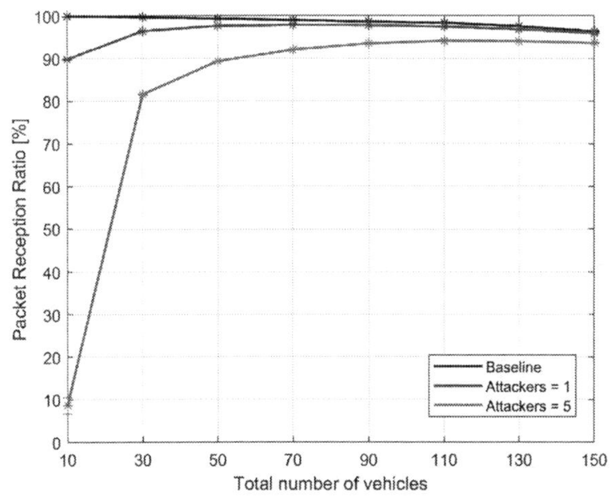

Fig. 7. PRR versus the total number of vehicles in **attack type 3** with 95% confidence intervals.

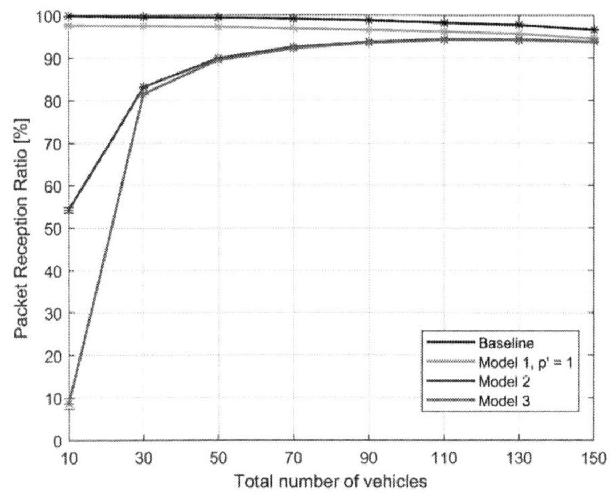

Fig. 8. Comparison of the attack types. PRR versus the total number of vehicles with 95% confidence intervals, $N_a = 5$.

attack types on the same graph (see Figure 8). As can be seen from the figure, attack type 3 is the most effective at minimizing the PRR when the vehicle density is low. Its effect is reduced as the total number of vehicles increases. This is because there will be a relatively smaller fraction of packet collisions caused by the attackers. Attack type 1 is the least effective in minimizing the PRR of the three, but the other two attack types perform only slightly better at high vehicle density.

VI. Conclusion

We introduced three types of denial-of-service attacks on C-V2X networks operating in Mode 4: oblivious, smart, and cooperative attacks. We performed extensive Monte-Carlo simulation, complemented with theoretical analysis, to investigate the potency of the various attack types. We gained the following insights from our investigation: (1) the oblivious attack is most effective when $p' = 1$; (2) for a fixed number of attackers, the smart and cooperative attacks are most effective at low vehicle density and have a significant impact; (3) when the number of target vehicles grows, oblivious attacks become almost as effective as the smart and cooperative attacks.

Our work opens several directions for further research, including modeling vehicular mobility and limited communication range, evaluating other attack objectives that are different from minimizing PRR, and incorporating channel impairments. On the theoretical side, formally proving that $p' = 1$ is optimal for an oblivious attacker in the general case is an interesting open question.

Acknowledgment

This research was supported in part by NSF under grants CNS-1908087, CNS-1908807, and CCF-2006628.

References

[1] A. Mansouri, V. Martinez, and J. Härri, "A First Investigation of Congestion Control for LTE-V2X Mode 4," in *2019 15th Annual Conference on Wireless On-demand Network Systems and Services, WONS 2019 - Proceedings*, 2019, pp. 56–63.

[2] TSGR, "TS 136 213 - V14.2.0 - LTE; Evolved Universal Terrestrial Radio Access (E-UTRA); Physical layer procedures (3GPP TS 36.213 version 14.2.0 Release 14)," Tech. Rep., 2017. [Online]. Available: https://portal.etsi.org/TB/ETSIDeliverableStatus.aspx

[3] X. Wang, R. A. Berry, I. Vukovic, and J. Rao, "A Fixed-Point Model for Semi-Persistent Scheduling of Vehicular Safety Messages," *IEEE Vehicular Technology Conference*, vol. 2018-August, pp. 1–5, 2018.

[4] H. Hasbullah, I. A. Soomro, and J. L. Ab Manan, "Denial of service (DOS) attack and its possible solutions in VANET," *World Academy of Science, Engineering and Technology*, vol. 65, no. 5, pp. 411–415, 2010.

[5] Ó. Puñal, C. Pereira, A. Aguiar, and J. Gross, "Experimental characterization and modeling of RF jamming attacks on VANETs," *IEEE Transactions on Vehicular Technology*, vol. 64, no. 2, pp. 524–540, feb 2015.

[6] Y. O. Basciftci, F. Chen, J. Weston, R. Burton, and C. E. Koksal, "How vulnerable is vehicular communication to physical layer jamming attacks?" in *2015 IEEE 82nd Vehicular Technology Conference, VTC Fall 2015 - Proceedings*. Institute of Electrical and Electronics Engineers Inc., jan 2016.

[7] A. Benslimane and H. Nguyen-Minh, "Jamming Attack Model and Detection Method for Beacons under Multichannel Operation in Vehicular Networks," *IEEE Transactions on Vehicular Technology*, vol. 66, no. 7, pp. 6475–6488, jul 2017.

[8] P. Gu, C. Hua, R. Khatoun, Y. Wu, and A. Serhrouchni, "Cooperative Antijamming Relaying for Control Channel Jamming in Vehicular Networks," *IEEE Transactions on Vehicular Technology*, vol. 67, no. 8, pp. 7033–7046, aug 2018.

[9] N. Lyamin, D. Kleyko, Q. Delooz, and A. Vinel, "Real-Time Jamming DoS Detection in Safety-Critical V2V C-ITS Using Data Mining," *IEEE Communications Letters*, vol. 23, no. 3, pp. 442–445, mar 2019.

[10] A. Nabil, K. Kaur, C. Dietrich, and V. Marojevic, "Performance Analysis of Sensing-Based Semi-Persistent Scheduling in C-V2X Networks," in *IEEE Vehicular Technology Conference*, vol. 2018-August. Institute of Electrical and Electronics Engineers Inc., jul 2018.

[11] V. Marojevic, "C-V2X Security Requirements and Procedures: Survey and Research Directions," jul 2018. [Online]. Available: http://arxiv.org/abs/1807.09338

[12] K. J. Ahmed and M. J. Lee, "Secure LTE-Based V2X Service," *IEEE Internet of Things Journal*, vol. 5, no. 5, pp. 3724–3732, oct 2018.

[13] Y. Li, R. Hou, K. S. Lui, and H. Li, "An MEC-Based DoS Attack Detection Mechanism for C-V2X Networks," in *2018 IEEE Global Communications Conference, GLOBECOM 2018 - Proceedings*. Institute of Electrical and Electronics Engineers Inc., 2018.

[14] T. Shimizu, B. Cheng, H. Lu, and J. Kenney, "Comparative analysis of dsrc and lte-v2x pc5 mode 4 with sae congestion control," in *2020 IEEE Vehicular Networking Conference (VNC)*.

Vision-Based Two-Factor Authentication & Localization Scheme for Autonomous Vehicles

Anas Alsoliman
University of California, Irvine
aalsolim@uci.edu

Marco Levorato
University of California, Irvine
levorato@uci.edu

Qi Alfred Chen
University of California, Irvine
alfchen@uci.edu

***Abstract*—In autonomous vehicle systems – whether ground or aerial – vehicles and infrastructure-level units communicate among each other continually to ensure safe and efficient autonomous operations. However, different attack scenarios might arise in such environments when a device in the network cannot physically pinpoint the actual transmitter of a certain message. For example, a compromised or a malicious vehicle could send a message with a fabricated location to appear as if it is in the location of another legitimate vehicle, or fabricate multiple messages with fake identities to alter the behavior of other vehicles/infrastructure units and cause traffic congestion or accidents. In this paper, we propose a Vision-Based Two-Factor Authentication and Localization Scheme for Autonomous Vehicles. The scheme leverages the vehicles' light sources and cameras to establish an "Optical Camera Communication (OCC)" channel providing an auxiliary channel between vehicles to visually authenticate and localize the transmitter of messages that are sent over Radio Frequency (RF) channels. Additionally, we identify possible attacks against the proposed scheme as well as mitigation strategies.**

I. Introduction

Autonomous vehicles such as self-operated drones and cars will soon enable new applications in different domains, such as autonomous transportation and drone delivery. However, safety-critical operations, such as object-detection and avoidance, are integral components of these applications and it would make them appealing targets for cybercriminals [1]. In the United States, various efforts from government agencies have been directed to set up the rules, regulations, and policies for managing the secure operations of future autonomous systems (i.e., vehicles and Roadside Units, or RSUs). For connected and self-driving cars, the U.S. Department of Transportation (USDOT) has adopted the Security Credential Management System (SCMS) [2] for handling secure vehicle-to-vehicle (V2V) and vehicle-to-infrastructure (V2I) communications. For Unmanned Aerial Vehicles (UAVs), the Federal Aviation Administration (FAA) and National Aeronautics and Space Administration (NASA) have jointly developed the Remote ID framework [3] which would set the foundation for the anticipated Unmanned Aircraft System (UAS) Traffic Management System (UTM) [4]. Unfortunately, these systems still lack effective security measures to defend against existing attacks [5][6].

Acknowledgement:
This work was partially supported by *CNS-1850533, CNS-1929771, and USDOT UTC Grant 69A3552047138.*
This work was partially supported by the *NSF grant IIS-1724331.*

Network and Distributed Systems Security (NDSS) Symposium 2021
25 February 2021, Virtual

https://dx.doi.org/10.14722/autosec.2021.23021
www.ndss-symposium.org

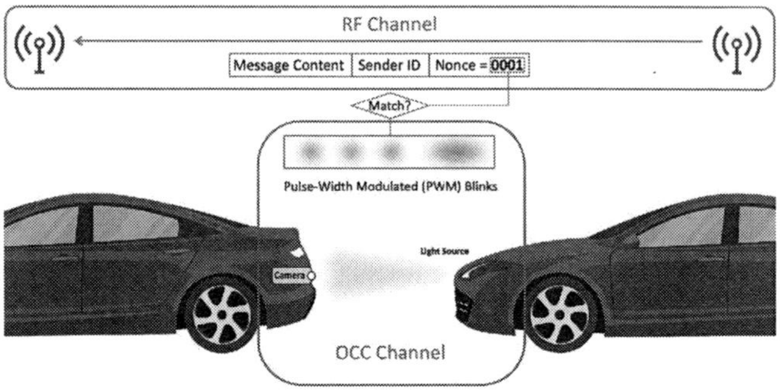

Fig. 1: Scheme Overview: a vehicle sends an RF message and a visual nonce as optical Pulse-Width Modulated (PWM) symbols using its headlights

In the academic community, several attacks have been demonstrated against autonomous systems such as GPS spoofing attacks [7], V2I attacks [8], and Sybil (vehicle ID duplication) attacks [9]. These attacks have different threat models and attack methodologies, and find different mitigation approaches. However, we contend that all these attacks stem from the same root: *the decoupling between the sender of a message and its transmitting location*. In other words, if receiver of a message cannot locate its transmitter, multiple threats are exposed.

In this paper, we propose a Vision-Based Two-Factor Authentication & Localization Scheme for Autonomous Vehicles to pinpoint and authenticate the location of a message transmitter. In this scheme, we leverage the lighting source of the vehicle to create an Optical Camera Communication (OCC) channel to send a random *nonce* – a randomly generated number that to be used only once – encoded as flashing blinks from the light source, while at the same time the sending vehicle includes the same nonce into the message to be sent over the Radio Frequency (RF) channel (figure 1). In this scheme, the receiver is equipped with an RF interface and a camera, so that it can receive the message via the RF channel while simultaneously use its camera to record the sender's blinks and decode the visually modulated nonce using computer-vision algorithms. The receiver then matches the

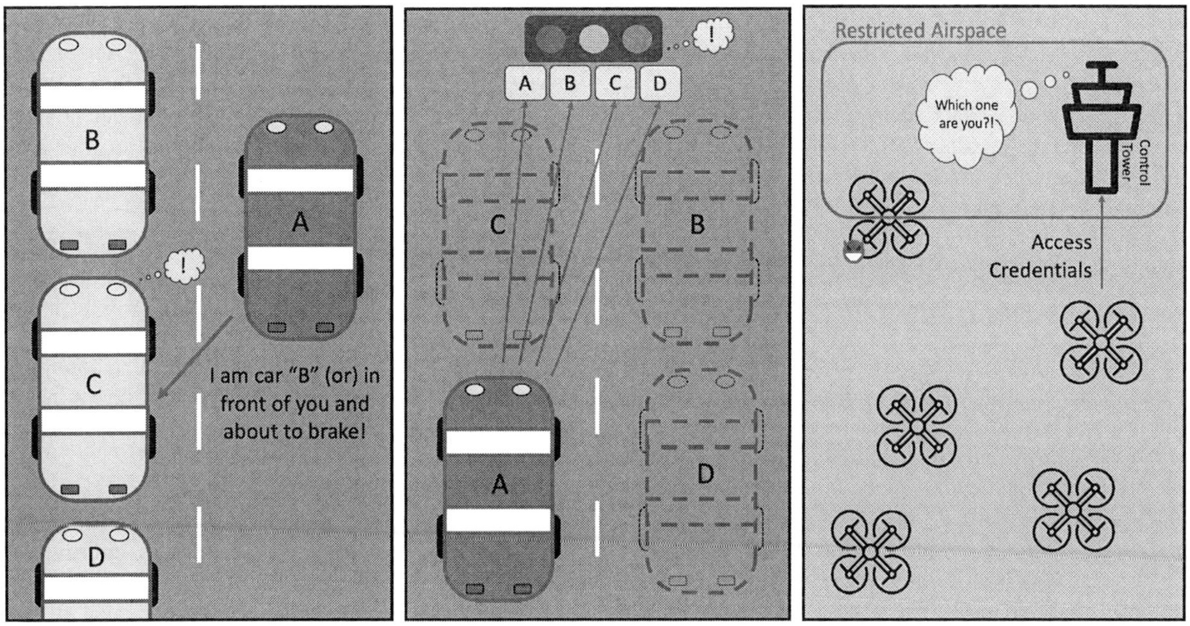

(a) C cannot tell if the message came from A or B (b) RSU cannot tell who actually sent the four messages (c) Control tower cannot tell which one is the legitimate UAV

Fig. 2: Aerial view of three different attack scenarios

nonces received on the two channels (RF and OCC). If the nonces match, then the vehicle is visually authenticated and localized and is indeed identified as the transmitter of the message. Note that our scheme can be used to authenticate each RF message as well as it can be used as a bootstrap to authenticate a vehicle's location once then establish a secure channel with the localized vehicle.

We summarize our contributions as follows:

- We propose a vision-based authentication scheme that pinpoints (authenticates and localizes) the actual transmitter of a message sent over the RF channel by utilizing cameras and light sources to create an OCC channel.
- We identify a possible attack (named a Copycat Attack) with different variants against the proposed scheme, where a malicious party mimics another legitimate transmitter's visual blinks to spoof its identity or location.
- We present mitigation approaches that circumvent all variants of the copycat attack.

In the next section, we present our threat model with three different attack scenarios. In section III, we give a brief background about wireless communications that utilize optical techniques. In section IV, we provide an overview of our proposed scheme. In section V, we evaluate the attack scenarios discussed in section II against our scheme presented in section IV. Section VI demonstrates a new adaptive attack (named Copycat Attack) under multiple scenarios as well as mitigation approaches for each scenario. Related work is discussed in section VII and section VIII concludes the paper.

II. Threat Model

In our threat model (figure 2), a malicious party exploits the decoupling of a sent message from the location of its transmitter. Therefore, our main objective in this threat model is to identify and authenticate the physical location of a message's transmitter, whether the transmitter is an attacker or a legitimate vehicle. To illustrate further, three different attack scenarios are demonstrated as examples:

Location Spoofing: In this scenario, a compromised or a malicious vehicle fabricates fake GPS coordinates about its current location to cause accidents, alter a system's behavior, or earn unlawful privileges. For example in figure 2a, a platoon of vehicles (cars $\mathcal{B}$, $\mathcal{C}$, and $\mathcal{D}$) is already formed and a malicious adversarial vehicle $\mathcal{A}$ sends an emergency-braking message to vehicle $\mathcal{C}$ while pretending to be in the location of vehicle $\mathcal{B}$. Or if vehicle $\mathcal{A}$ is capable of compromising the identity of vehicle $\mathcal{B}$, $\mathcal{A}$ can pretend to be $\mathcal{B}$ itself without the need of fabricating any coordinates. Vehicle $\mathcal{C}$ would react to $\mathcal{A}$'s fabricated message and apply its brakes to avoid crashing into $\mathcal{B}$ but also it would cause $\mathcal{D}$ to crash into $\mathcal{C}$ if there are no implemented precautions against this scenario. In this scenario, the malicious vehicle does not need to wait for an opening to physically drive up in front of the targeted vehicle. Instead, the attack can be launched from faraway.

Identity Duplication: Identity Duplication attack, also known as Sybil Attack, is an attack carried out when a single malicious vehicle sends out multiple messages with multiple identities to give an impression of a congested road and alter the behavior of the infrastructure and/or other vehicles. For example, in figure 2b, the additional fake vehicles (ghost cars

$\mathcal{B}$, $\mathcal{C}$, and $\mathcal{D}$) generated by $\mathcal{A}$ would cause the traffic light to turn green sooner in the attacker's lane and longer for other lanes in order to clear the congested lane.

Identity Confusion: In this scenario (figure 2c), a swarm of unmanned aerial vehicles (UAVs) are flying in close-proximity of each other. A legitimate UAV is supplementing its credentials to the control tower for accessing the nearby restricted airspace. During that time, another intruding UAV enters the restricted airspace. Here the control tower cannot enforce the given access (e.g., take down the intruding UAV) since it cannot physically differentiate between the legitimate and the intruding UAV.

We can observe that each scenario represents different attacking capabilities. In the first scenario, the attacker has the ability to either *fabricate the content of its messages or use the identity of another legitimate vehicle*. In the second scenario, the attacker has the ability to *generate multiple identities of non-existing vehicles*. In the third scenario, the attacker is able to *passively listen to messages* in order to make an opportunistic attack (e.g. invasive access towards a restricted airspace). However, all three scenarios can be exploited due to the same reason; *the inability of the receiver to localize the transmitter of the messages.*

III. Background on Optical Wireless Communication

A. Overview

Optical Wireless Communication (OWC) is any communication channel that utilizes the terahertz band of the electromagnetic spectrum which includes the infrared and ultraviolet frequencies. Furthermore, an OWC channel utilizing the visible-light portion of the terahertz band is referred to as Visible Light Communication (VLC).

Optical communications require an imaging sensor for receiving the incoming light photons. That sensor is commonly known as a photodetector. A camera sensor such as Complementary Metal Oxide Semiconductor (CMOS) consists of a matrix of photodetectors, each represents a pixel which gets its color by measuring the intensity and frequency of the recorded photon by its corresponding photodetector. The main objective of a camera sensor is to create an image out of the CMOS output as a grid of colored pixels, and the rate of images created by the sensor is known as frame per second (FPS). However, since cameras have become a commodity hardware, their sensors have been repurposed for various applications such as decoding messages that are digitally modulated into images. This type of optical communication technique is commonly known as Optical Camera Communication (OCC).

B. OCC Channel Model

Our channel model is based on two assumptions: **(i)** The modulation scheme used over the OCC channel is assumed to be optical On-Off Keying (OOK) since it only requires a single narrowband frequency (i.e., single color) which makes it applicable to any light sources. Note that visual symbols in figure 1 and 3 are pulse-width modulated (PWM) for ease of illustration only. **(ii)** We assumes the use of cameras that are operated using the global shutter mode where all camera pixels are scanned simultaneously. The rolling shutter mode (its counterpart) scans rows of pixel independently one after another. However, the security intuitions in this paper still holds true for both assumptions and should be applicable to different imaging techniques.

In OCC systems, a communication channel using OOK modulation can be modeled as a rectangular waveform. Let T_e denote to the camera exposure time which defines how long a camera shutter stays open to capture a single frame. Therefore, T_e is the inverse of the camera sampling rate FPS such that $T_e = \frac{1}{FPS}$. Let PW_s denote the symbol pulse-width which defines how long a light source stays on during the T_e time frame. Intuitively, we have $PW_s < T_e$. However, there is a minimum duty cycle $DC_{min} = \frac{PW_s}{T_e}$ for a given OCC system under certain conditions and SINR requirements. Furthermore, a guard width PW_g must be left unoccupied at the beginning and the end of the T_e time frame to prevent symbols from leaking into adjacent frames (similar to the guard bands that are added between RF channels to prevent inter-symbol interference). Finally, in our scheme, the OCC can be modeled as $PW_s + PW_g < T_e$ for $PW_s \geq DC_{min} \times T_e$. Note that the propagation delay is omitted from the channel model since it has a negligible effect especially for close-range communications such as in V2V and V2I. Furthermore, the guard band PW_g should mitigate the effects of propagation delay whenever it becomes critically high.

C. Challenges

There are several challenges when working with OCC systems such as: **(i)** unidirectional link - a lighting source can only be used for transmitting while a camera is only for receiving, **(ii)** highly directional communications - the camera and the lighting source need to face each other in a clear line-of-sight (LOS), and **(iii)** low bitrate - common camera sensors can sample up to 30 FPS (stand-alone photodetectors are capable of higher sampling rates with more complex modulation schemes, but cannot construct an image out of the received photons).

The requirements of our scheme are not affected by these shortcomings. For instance, the receiver in our scheme does not require a feedback channel for locating the sender, and whenever a feedback is required (e.g. loss in clock synchronization) the RF channel can be used. Also based on the threat model discussed in Section II, the sender is expected to be in a clear view of the receiver which means that clear LOS is an inherent requirement for all the three attack scenarios explained in Section II. Concerning the bitrate, the sender encodes only a short nonce into the OCC channel whereas the main message is sent over the RF channel. Therefore, a low OCC bitrate is sufficient to execute the authentication scheme. Furthermore, lower bitrates can be modulated using longer symbol periods which inherently make it cover larger distances in the optical domain.

IV. Scheme Overview

As discussed in section I, our scheme utilizes two different communication channels, an RF channel and an OCC channel. Both the sender and the receiver are equipped with an RF interface to implement an RF channel while the OCC channel requires the sender to be equipped with lighting source such as a light-emitting diode (LED), and the receiver to be equipped with a camera. We assume that these equipment are already available in most autonomous vehicles since we expect modern autonomous systems to have the minimum set of requirements to carry out safe and secure autonomous operations, which include: an RF interface (for wireless communications), a camera (for object detection and navigation), and a lighting source (for safety, illumination, and identification purposes) such as car's headlights/taillights and drone's anti-collision strobe lights.

Authentication & Localization Process: When a sender transmits a message over the RF channel, it includes a nonce in the message, while at the same time it encodes the same nonce as modulated blinks into the OCC channel using its light source. On the other hand, the receiver will continuously scan every captured camera frame for possible OOK modulated symbols. Here the receiver employs computer-vision algorithms and look at every two consecutive frames for a sudden change in pixel intensity. When a pixel intensity change is found, the algorithm locks on the object emitting the light source that caused the intensity change and extract the symbols encoded into each subsequent frame. The area of the locked object is called Region of Interest (ROI). Now whenever the receiver receives a message over the RF channel, it cross-references its nonce with the demodulated nonces emitted by the current ROI over the OCC channel at the time of message reception. To illustrate, to transmit bit_i = "1" as an OOK modulated symbol, the sender sets its light source on high for PW_s seconds during the camera exposure time frame T_{e_i}. To transmit the next bit_{i+1} = "0", the sender sets its light source to off-state during the next transmission window $T_{e_{i+1}}$. The receiver would detect a transition period from T_{e_i} to $T_{e_{i+1}}$ time frames as a change in pixel intensity caused by bit_i and bit_{i+1} respectively. As a result, the receiver will lock on the ROI region of the captured picture that has a pixel intensity change. This process will be triggered from the very first transmitted bit_1 where a timer T_{OCC} will be set starting from the beginning of T_{e_1}. When the receiver receives a message from the RF channel that has the same nonce which is received from the OCC channel, the time difference between the two messages must satisfy the following condition: $|T_{OCC} - T_{RF}| < \theta$ where T_{RF} denote to the time where the first bit of the message was received over the RF channel and θ denote to a minimum threshold that can be used as an attack window. More details on the aforementioned attack will be discussed in Section VI-A.

Technical Considerations: To prevent accidental ROI locks that are caused by pixel intensity change due to random environmental factors (such as a vehicle turning on its headlights or an object moving in front of a light source which would be interpreted as an OOK modulated symbol), OCC systems would use a preamble with an alternating 0s and 1s to synchronize the sender with the receiver before locking on the ROI and recording the nonce. Another point to consider is that during an OCC transmission, the nonce encoded by the sender might include long runs of 0s or 1s (continuous repetitions of 0s or 1s) which would cause multiple consecutive frames to not have any intensity change across their transitions which in turn cause a loss in clock synchronization on receiver side (cannot distinguish whether the transmission has ended or a long run is being transmitted). Therefore, the sender would use Run Length Limited (RLL) codes such as Manchester encoding where a "1" is represented as "01" and "0" is represented as "10". In this case, the receiver would have at most two consecutive frames with the same modulated symbol (maximum possible run is two frames). Finally, the change in OCC channel state (i.e. blinking) should be *faster than the perception of the human eye* to prevent causing confusions to surrounding human drivers/pedestrians and also physiological effects such as nausea. The IEEE 802.15.7 standard [10] for Short-Range Optical Wireless Communications recommends the use of at least 200 Hz in light flickering frequency.

V. Scheme Defense Analysis

In this section, we evaluate our scheme (section IV) against the threat model (section II).

Scenario A: in figure 2a, the malicious vehicle $\mathcal{A}$ attempts to deceive vehicle $\mathcal{C}$ by pretending to be vehicle $\mathcal{B}$ or by fabricating its location to appear as if $\mathcal{A}$ is in front of $\mathcal{C}$. With our scheme, whenever $\mathcal{C}$ receives a message pretending to be from $\mathcal{B}$, it checks the message's nonce with the visual nonce emitted by $\mathcal{B}$ which is physically in front of $\mathcal{C}$. If the two nonces from the two channels (RF and OCC) match, the message is indeed from $\mathcal{B}$. Otherwise, the message will be flagged as a spoofing attempt.

Scenario B: in figure 2b, the malicious vehicle attempts to deceive the traffic light into believing that the lane is crowded by broadcasting multiple messages with different IDs. Here the traffic light will use the OCC channel to match each message with its sender. Since the attacker is the sender of all the messages, all message IDs will be mapped to the same vehicle which will trigger a spoofing attempt.

Scenario C: in figure 2c, a malicious unmanned aerial vehicle (UAV) attempts to access a restricted airspace by opportunistically waiting for a legitimate UAV to present its access credentials to the control tower. When the credentials are broadcasted, the malicious UAV flies to the restricted airspace knowing that the control tower cannot physically distinguish between the legitimate UAV from the malicious one. With our scheme, the legitimate UAV can physically present itself using OCC channel to distinguish itself from all other nearby UAVs.

VI. Copycat Attack & Mitigation Methods

The threat model presented in section II represents three different attack scenarios that an attacker might attempt under

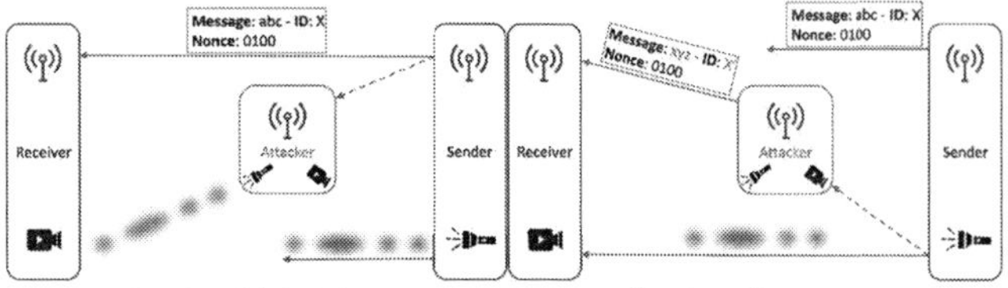

(a) Receiver thinks the attacker is the sender of the RF message

(b) Receiver thinks the sender has sent the fabricated RF message

Fig. 3: RF/OCC Channel Synchronization Problem

different capabilities. However, we identified a possible attack against our authentication and localization scheme where the attacker adapts to our authentication strategy by recording visual nonces using its own camera then plays them back to mimic the legitimate sender (hence, the name Copycat), or fabricate new messages with someone else's OCC nonce.

Copycat attack can be executed under different scenarios. To mitigate its impact, we present the scenarios where this vulnerability might exist and discuss how to overcome it.

A. RF/OCC Channel Synchronization

In this scenario, the attacker attempts to exploit the time difference between the transmission time over the RF channel and the transmission time over the OCC channel in order to inject a spoofed message/nonce. To illustrate, let us consider the scenario in figure 3a. The legitimate vehicle transmits a message over the RF channel then shortly later transmits the nonce over the OCC channel. Assuming the attacker is capable of reading the RF message, the attacker extracts the nonce from the message then reproduces it over the OCC channel using its own lighting source. Now the receiver will believe that the RF message was actually sent by the attacker since the receiver correctly received the attacker's OCC nonce first.

Similarly, in the scenario demonstrated in figure 3b, the legitimate vehicle first transmits the nonce over the OCC channel then afterwards it transmits the message over the RF channel. By assuming the attacker is capable of fabricating the legitimate vehicle's identity, the attacker can read the legitimate vehicle's visual nonce and then fabricate an RF message using that nonce. Now any receiver would believe the attacker's message was actually transmitted by the legitimate vehicle since the two nonces match (attacker's RF nonce and legitimate vehicle's OCC nonce).

To understand how to mitigate this attack, we need first to define the notion of "attacker response time". Let $AttRes$ denote to the attacker response time which defines the minimum time the attacker needs to react to a message transmission. In other words, $AttRes$ is the elapsed time from the moment the attacker detects a transmitted message to the time the attacker reacts to that message by sending a spoofed message on the opposite channel. By knowing or estimating the $AttRes$ time, we can formulate a minimum acceptable RF/OCC transmission time difference such that: $|T_{OCC} - T_{RF}| < AttRes$. In other words, when one of the channels (either RF or OCC) starts transmitting, the other channel should start transmitting no later than $AttRes$ seconds. Note that since we omitted the propagation delay in section III-B, we re-used T_{RF} and T_{OCC} from section IV to denote to transmitting time instead of receiving time.

B. Sender/Receiver Channel Synchronization

In the previous scenario, the attacker either listen to the RF channel then transmit over the OCC channel, or listen to the OCC channel then transmit over the RF channel. In this scenario, the attacker listen to the OCC channel then transmit over the OCC channel as well to mimic the legitimate vehicle's visual nonce and cause confusion at the receiver side. In other words, the receiver would receive a single RF message from the legitimate vehicle but at the same time it will receive the same visual nonce from two different vehicles. Therefore, the receiver cannot distinguish who is the actual transmitter since there are two different vehicles emitting the same visual nonce.

To mitigate the impact of this attack scenario, the camera frame captured by the receiver must only include the OCC symbol produced by the sender. To achieve this property, the sender needs to delay its OCC transmission to the end of the receiver's frame exposure time window T_e. This would cause the attacker's symbol to appear in the subsequent/different frame at the receiver side. To accomplish this, the sender needs to know the sampling rate of the receiver's camera (i.e. its FPS) as well as the receiver's clock time at which the camera starts and ends its shutter exposure period for each frame. Let st_i and st_{i+1} denote to the the start time of $frame_i$ and $frame_{i+1}$ respectively. If the sender knows st_i, then it can synchronize its clock with the receiver for all subsequent frame start times such that $st_{i+1} = st_i + T_e$. Now for the sender to transmit an OCC $symbol_i$ to be captured during $frame_i$, the time to transmit $symbol_i$ is at time $T_i = st_{i+1} - (PW_s + PW_g)$. This would cause $symbol_i$ to be transmitted as close as possible to the end of $frame_i$ but not too close to risk an inter-symbol interference. Furthermore, in section III-B we discussed that the symbol pulse-width must satisfy $PW_s \geq DC_{min} \times T_e$. In this section after defining the Sender/Receiver Channel Synchronization problem, we set $PW_s = DC_{min} \times T_e$ to minimize the attack window as much as possible. Therefore, for the OCC symbol transmission to be safely and successfully captured, the transmission time for $symbol_i$ is $T_i = st_{i+1} - (PW_s + PW_g)$ and the total pulse-width is $AttRes > (PW_s + PW_g) < T_e$ for $PW_s = DC_{min} \times T_e$.

VII. Related Work

Most previous efforts related to vehicle authentication are directed toward authenticating their identities (e.g. through the use of digital certificates) [2]. However, such conventional authentication cannot be directly applied to many threat models as we have seen in section II where authenticating the location (i.e. "where you are") factor is also required. Mainly there are two localization techniques in the literature, RF-based and optical-based. Note that since we are interested in locating transmitters, techniques for localizing passive devices/objects such as computer-vision object detection and radar will not be discussed.

RF-Based Localization has abundant number publications. It mainly relies on Time/Difference of Arrival (ToA/TDoA), Angle of Arrival (AoA) and RSSI measurements techniques. For example [9] proposed an RSSI-based localization algorithm that depends on vehicles or RSUs as observers to triangulate the target vehicle. However, the dependence on other trusted vehicles sets a limitation to the threat model. Furthermore, the location of a target vehicle is approximated as an area (a common limitation for most RF-based localization schemes). That means a group of vehicles in close-proximity with each other (a typical road scenario) would have very similar RF transmissions in terms of timing and angle which makes it a challenging task to localize one of the vehicles among the other group members. Even a single attacker can manipulate its transmission power and timing to deviate the observers. In general, RF-based localization schemes tend to be complex, require special antenna designs, and suffer from multipath and interference phenomena [11].

Vision-Based Localization is a well studied research field but mostly in the context of using visual cues as beacons for enabling devices to localize themselves. For example, [11] uses projectors and photodetectors while [12] uses LEDs and cameras as indoor localization solutions. However, such solutions cannot be repurposed to our threat model since it either require the cooperation of the localized device or require a map reconstruction phase (also found in RF-based techniques) prior to rolling out the localization system. In vehicle network, the use of VLC channels is gaining a great attention lately but mainly in the context of communication rather than localization which might make it inapplicable to our threat model. For example to increase the bitrate of the VLC channel, [13] sampled each row of a rolling shutter independently while [14] suggested the use of a standalone photodiode but both techniques make it impossible (or at least extremely difficult) to construct an image from the received VLC signal. [15] and [16] attempted to increase the VLC bitrate with a fully constructed image by utilizing visual-MIMO (Multiple Input Multiple Output) where multiple light sources act as multiple output and the individual pixels of the receiver's camera are considered the multiple inputs. However, visual-MIMO via OCC requires additional hardware and its bit error rate drastically increases with increased distances [17]. In an alternative approach, [18] implemented a visual localization scheme for drone swarms where a locator commands the target drone that need to be localized to perform a short flight maneuver such as a quick turn which would act as a visual cue for the locator who is equipped with a camera to distinguish the target drone among the other swarm members. However, the maneuver command cannot be performed until a safe distance from all surrounding objects is established. Furthermore, it is difficult for stationary vehicles to perform maneuvers such as cars stopped at a red light. Finally, accepting maneuver requests from other devices adds an additional attack surface to the autonomous system.

VIII. Conclusion & Future Work

We proposed a vision-based authentication and localization scheme for autonomous vehicles that employ localization as a form of authentication where we use visual nonces as a proof of RF message transmission. We also introduced a Copycat Attack that exploits our scheme's synchronization vulnerabilities as well as mitigation approaches for each vulnerability. In future work, we will design testbed to **(i)** numerically define $AttRes$ and PW_g then evaluate if $AttRes > (DC_{min} \times T_e) + PW_g$ can be applied using commodity cameras with an acceptable SINR, **(ii)** implement an encoding scheme that utilizes a low frame rate (e.g. 30FPS) as a receiver and high flickering frequency (e.g. 200Hz) as a transmitter without introducing the sender/receiver sync problem, and **(iii)** demonstrate a dual-channel protocol that sync between the low bitrate of the OCC channel and high bitrate of the RF channel without introducing the OCC/RF sync problem.

References

[1] Y. Cao *et al.*, "Adversarial sensor attack on lidar-based perception in autonomous driving," in *Proceedings of the 2019 ACM SIGSAC Conference on Computer and Communications Security*, 2019.

[2] USDOT, *Security Credential Management System (SCMS)*, 2021 (accessed January 5, 2020). https://www.its.dot.gov/resources/scms.htm.

[3] FAA, *UAS Remote Identification*, 2021 (accessed January 5, 2020). https://www.faa.gov/uas/research$_{d}evelopment/remote_{i}d/$.

[4] FAA, *Unmanned Aircraft System Traffic Management (UTM)'*, 2021 (accessed January 5, 2020). https://www.faa.gov/uas/research$_{d}evelopment/traffic_{m}anagement/$.

[5] M. D. Furtado *et al.*, "Threat analysis of the security credential management system for vehicular communications," in *2018 IEEE International Symposium on Technologies for Homeland Security (HST)*, IEEE, 2018.

[6] A. Alsoliman *et al.*, "Privacy-preserving authentication framework for uas traffic management systems," in *2020 4th Cyber Security in Networking Conference (CSNet)*, pp. 1–8, IEEE, 2020.

[7] X. Huang *et al.*, "Exposing spoofing attack on flocking-based unmanned aerial vehicle cluster: A threat to swarm intelligence," *Security and Communication Networks*, vol. 2020, 2020.

[8] S. E. Huang *et al.*, "Impact evaluation of falsified data attacks on connected vehicle based traffic signal control," *arXiv preprint arXiv:2010.04753*, 2020.

[9] M. T. Garip *et al.*, "Interloc: An interference-aware rssi-based localization and sybil attack detection mechanism for vehicular ad hoc networks," in *2017 14th IEEE Annual Consumer Communications & Networking Conference (CCNC)*, pp. 1–6, IEEE, 2017.

[10] *IEEE Standard for Local and metropolitan area networks.* IEEE 802.15.7-2018.

[11] S. Ma *et al.*, "Foglight: Visible light-enabled indoor localization system for low-power iot devices," *IEEE Internet of Things Journal*, vol. 5, no. 1, pp. 175–185, 2017.

[12] P. Chavez-Burbano *et al.*, "Optical camera communication system for three-dimensional indoor localization," *Optik*, vol. 192, p. 162870, 2019.

[13] T. Nguyen *et al.*, "High-speed asynchronous optical camera communication using led and rolling shutter camera," in *2015 Seventh International Conference on Ubiquitous and Future Networks*, IEEE, 2015.

[14] P. H. Pathak *et al.*, "Visible light communication, networking, and sensing: A survey, potential and challenges," *IEEE communications surveys & tutorials*, vol. 17, no. 4, pp. 2047–2077, 2015.

[15] J.-E. Kim *et al.*, "Color-space-based visual-mimo for v2x communication," *sensors*, vol. 16, no. 4, p. 591, 2016.

[16] W. Yuan *et al.*, "Computer vision methods for visual mimo optical system," in *CVPR 2011 workshops*, pp. 37–43, IEEE, 2011.

[17] N. T. Le *et al.*, "A survey of design and implementation for optical camera communication," *Signal Processing: Image Communication*, vol. 53, pp. 95–109, 2017.

[18] C. Ruiz *et al.*, "Idrone: Robust drone identification through motion actuation feedback," *Proceedings of the ACM on Interactive, Mobile, Wearable and Ubiquitous Technologies*, vol. 2, no. 2, pp. 1–22, 2018.

Low-risk Privacy-preserving Electric Vehicle Charging with Payments

Andreas Unterweger, Fabian Knirsch, Clemens Brunner and, Dominik Engel
Center for Secure Energy Informatics, Salzburg University of Applied Sciences, Puch bei Hallein, Austria

***Abstract*—The increasing amount of electric vehicles and a growing electric vehicle ecosystem is becoming a highly heterogeneous environment with a large number of participants that interact and communicate. Finding a charging station, performing vehicle-to-vehicle charging or processing payments poses privacy threats to customers as their location and habits can be traced. In this paper, we present a privacy-preserving solution for grid-to-vehicle charging, vehicle-to-grid charging and vehicle-to-vehicle charging, that allows for finding the right charging option in a competitive market environment and that allows for built-in payments with adjustable and limited risk for both, producers and consumers of electricity. The proposed approach builds on blockchain technology and extends a state-of-the-art protocol with payments, while still preserving the privacy of the users. The protocol is evaluated with respect to privacy, risk and scalability. It is shown that pseudonymity and location privacy (against third parties) is guaranteed throughout the protocol, even beyond a single protocol session. In addition, both, risk and scalability can be adjusted based on the used blockchain.**

I. Introduction

Electric vehicles (EVs) are gaining widespread attention in both, academia and real-world implementation, see e.g., [7], [13], [14]. In order to meet the increasing demand, the widespread roll out of EVs also requires to establish a massive charging infrastructure, which also impacts the electricity grid in terms of demand and supply. In the context of heterogeneous market participants in *smart grids* and *local energy communities*, the finding of suitable charging stations and the payment processes are of particular importance. These processes are executed in an environment that is shaped by a large number of players and participants that do not necessarily trust each other to full extent and where the privacy of customers is crucial. Customer privacy can be impacted severely by allowing charging stations or other EVs to track the customer, to establish movement profiles and to learn customer habits [12].

EVs can either use the (public) electricity grid for charging and approach one of the charging stations available or EVs use another EV to charge. This leads to a dynamic and competitive market situation with volatile demand and supply. In order to simplify and optimize the process of finding a charging station, a number of protocols have been proposed [2], [11], [24]. These protocols often build on blockchain technology in order to have a public and immutable record for managing and ordering requests and offers. Furthermore, some protocols propose blockchain technology for handling the payment.

Workshop on Automotive and Autonomous Vehicle Security (AutoSec) 2021
25 February 2021, Virtual
https://dx.doi.org/10.14722/autosec.2021.23001
www.ndss-symposium.org

However, the proposed protocols often (i) do not cover customer privacy to a full extent; (ii) do not allow for combined bidding and payment transfer with limited risk for both, the EV and the charging station; and (iii) do not cover both, grid-to-vehicle and vehicle-to-vehicle charging.

Due to limited trust and anonymity in privacy-preserving systems, there is also a substantial financial risk for both, the EV (or the consumer in general) and the charging station (or the producer in general). While the EV runs the risk of paying without receiving a sufficient amount of energy (or any energy at all), the charging station runs the risk of providing energy and not receiving sufficient compensation. This is largely unaddressed in prior work.

Following a privacy-preserving protocol for grid-to-vehicle charging presented in [11], in this paper, we present a comprehensive protocol for EV charging with payments. The protocol preserves the privacy of all participants and the location privacy of the EVs during the exploration and bidding phase. Furthermore, pseudonymity is preserved during the charging phase and the payment phase, and a parameter is proposed which allows for controlling risk. Two different implementations for transferring installments in exchange for energy are described and evaluated. These implementations are compared in terms of risk, scalability, performance and privacy.

The rest of this paper is structured as follows: Section II describes EV charging, blockchain technology, hash time-locked contracts and state channels. Section III describes the proposed privacy-preserving protocol. Section IV evaluates the protocol with respect to risk, privacy and scalability. Section V provides an overview of related work. Section VI summarizes this paper.

II. Background

This section summarizes the relevant background for EV charging and blockchain technology.

A. Electric Vehicle Charging

One of the most common types of EVs relies on batteries which need to be recharged from an electric power source [15]. Depending on their capacity and usage, these batteries may retain significant portions of their initial charge over longer periods of time. Three different types of charging can be distinguished [15], [20]: (i) *G2V (Grid-to-Vehicle) Charging*: The EV is charged by the power grid. This is the most common case and is usually done via a charging station, see e.g., [15]

(ii) *V2V (Vehicle-to-Vehicle) Charging*: As described in [20], EVs may also rely on other EV's batteries instead of charging stations to recharge; and (iii) *V2G (Vehicle-to-Grid) Charging*: Reversing the G2V process, the EV may also provide power to the power grid during peak hours [15]. Due to its properties, the EV can act as both, a consumer (G2V, V2V) and a producer (V2V, V2G). In this paper, all three types of charging are supported, despite existing standards, e.g., ISO 15118 [9] and OCPP [17], focusing on the V2G case. To the best of our knowledge, at the time of writing, no finalized standards for V2G and V2V exist.

B. Blockchain

A blockchain is a decentralized append-only database, initially presented by Bitcoin [16], to enable a chronologically ordered and practically tamper-proof log of financial transactions.

To interact with the decentralized database, signed transactions are used as write requests. *Blockchain nodes*, which are responsible to find a consensus [1] for the global state, group multiple transactions together and create a new block, which is cryptographically linked to the previous block. The index of the block is denoted as block height. Users in a blockchain are represented by public-private key pairs. The ID of a user is the public key or the hash of the public key and it is possible to use a new ID for each transaction. Blockchains are often used as a decentralized programmable service. Additionally, blockchains enable programmable and conditional payments, which require that predefined constrains are met before the payment is considered valid. Conditional payments in Bitcoin are enabled by a scripting language [1] with limited functionality. In contrast to Ethereum, [22], where a Turing complete language, e.g., Solidity, [2] allows for the creation of smart contracts where any condition for payments can be implemented.

1) HTLCs: Hash Time Locked Contracts (HTLCs) are conditional payments, supported by both, the Bitcoin scripting language and by smart contracts. They consist of a hash and a time lock and are mostly used to allow for off-chain payments over multiple untrusted hops [8], [18] as well as other applications [6]. A transaction that transfers x coins from A to B, secured with a HTLC can be represented by the function $HTLC(A, B, x, y, t)$ [5]. To create this HTLC, A needs to create a random number r with $y = H(r)$ and specify t, which is the time (maximum block number) where the transaction can be spent by B. To unlock the $HTLC$, B need to publicly disclose (cryptographically proof) the knowledge of r via a blockchain transaction within the period defined in t. If B does not provide the necessary information to unlock the transaction, A gets back the control over x coins and can spend them again. $HTLC$ can also be time-bounded commitment schemes with additional payment functionalities. The random value r used to open the hash lock can be replaced by a commitment value of A.

2) State-Channels: An alternative to HTLCs is the use of state channels. They can be implemented in blockchains with support for Turing complete smart contracts, such as Ethereum [22]. The purpose of a state-channels is to reduce the number of on-chain transactions by enabling an off-chain negotiation of a locked portion of a global blockchain state. For this, a state-channel uses three steps: (i) opening; (ii) off-chain state modifications; and (iii) closing. In the opening step, a predefined set of participants p lock a collateral by sending a single on-chain transaction to a previously deployed smart contract. Once all participants locked a state, the off-chain state modification starts. In this step, all participants need to exchange signed off-chain messages, in which the new distribution of the locked state is defined. The new off-chain state is considered valid if signatures of all participants have been collected. The negotiation can be repeated as often as needed. In the last step, the state channel will be closed by using an signed off-chain state and the new distribution of the locked collateral will be send back to the participants. A detailed description of state-channels and off-chain solutions can be found in [8] and a comparison of use cases for state-channels in the energy domain is summarized in [4].

In order to create and use a state-channel with n participants, n on-chain transactions are needed to lock the collateral for all participants. In addition, for deploying the smart contract and for closing the state channel two additional transactions are required.

For the protocol proposed in this paper, we use the blockchain to publicly store and timestamp small amounts of data and to enable conditional payments for the consumed electricity.

III. Electric Vehicle Charging with Payments

This section describes the proposed EV charging protocol and its separate phases. The protocol builds upon [11], but includes a built-in payment phase. Furthermore, it generalizes the role of the EV as it can act as both, a producer and a consumer, as described in Section II-A. Thus, as opposed to [11], where the EV is always assumed to be a consumer, the proposed protocol uses the notion of *producers* for entities who offer electrical power and *consumers* for entities who require it. The EV may be either or both, at the same time, depending on the use case.

For the description of the phases of the protocol the structure and notation of [11] are retained. Figure 1 provides an overview of the phases in the protocol and shows the operations by the actors and the exchanged messages.

ζ denotes the unique ID of a consumer looking to acquire (charge) an energy amount $e \in \mathbb{Q}^+ \backslash \{0\}$, e.g., 20 kWh, within a specified time interval $T \in \mathcal{P}(\mathbb{T})$, e.g., between 12 p.m. and 2 p.m., within a certain geographical (world) region $R \in \mathcal{P}(\mathbb{W})$, e.g., the city of Salzburg, Austria. Similarly, i denotes the unique ID of a producer at a location $w_i \in \mathbb{W}$. Both, the unique ID of a consumer and a producer are represented by blockchain ID. While the protocol is expressed from the point of view of one consumer ζ, there can be arbitrarily many producers, each denoted with an index i equal to its ID.

A. Exploration

In order to find producers who can offer the required energy amount e within the time interval T in the region

[1] https://en.bitcoin.it/wiki/Script [Last access: April, 2020]

[2] https://solidity.readthedocs.io/en/latest/ [Last access: April,2020]

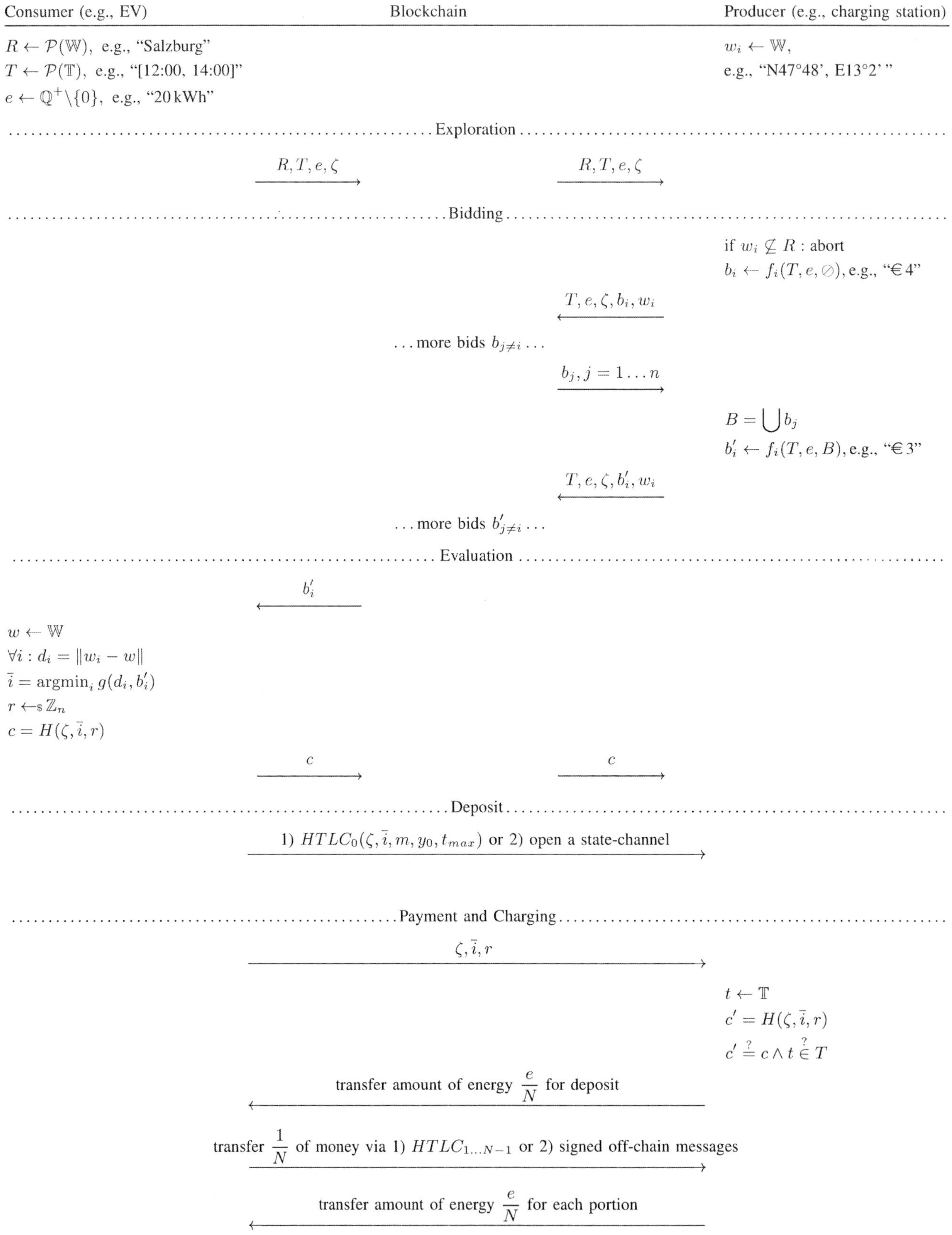

Fig. 1. This diagram shows the phases of our proposed protocol and the protocol presented in [11]. In the deposit phase either 1) HTLCs or 2 state channels can be used. Messages are exchanged between a consumer, a blockchain and a producer.

R, a consumer posts its ID ζ, together with the aforementioned required parameters on the blockchain. The request (R, T, e, ζ) is visible to all actors in the network and allows all producers to subsequently prepare bids.

B. Bidding

After a request has been placed, all actors who can provide energy within the specified region R (producers) can post prices for the desired time interval T and energy amount e on the blockchain, considering an actor-specific price-computing function $f_i(T, e, \oslash)$. The bid $b_i = f_i(T, e, \oslash)$ is the initial offer of producer i, which may also be an EV. Producers may act upon observing other actors' bids b_j and, in turn, update their own bid, b_i to b'_i. To do so, they consider the other bids in their actor-specific price-computing function f_i so that the new bid $b'_i = f_i(T, e, \cup_j b_j)$ considers the existing parameters as well as the other actors' bids b_j.

C. Evaluation

After either a certain number of bids has been observed or a time limit has passed, the consumer collects all bids and computes the best one using its decision function $g(d, b)$ that is based on the distance d to each producer and the bidding price b that this producer offers, i.e., the consumer chooses the desired producer $\bar{i} = \operatorname{argmin}_i g(d_i, b'_i)$, where $d_i := ||w_i - w||$ is the geographical distance between the consumer and the producer i and b'_i is the most recent bid of producer i. Once the consumer has decided to use the producer $\bar{i}$, it commits to this producer, its bid $b'_{\bar{i}}$ and the time interval.

D. Deposit

In order to communicate the decision for producer i and time interval T, the consumer creates a commitment for a payment in N installments in order to reduce the risk on both sides. In order to implement the installments on a blockchain, the payment can either be split up into a total of N HTLCs or alternatively a state channel is created. Instead of submitting the full payment of $b'_{\bar{i}}$ at once, one N-th is used as a deposit in both cases.

1) HTLCs: For HTLCS, initially, an $HTLC_0(\zeta, \bar{i}, m, y_0, t_{max})$ is created, where the sender is ζ, the receiver is $\bar{i}$, m is the amount of money to be locked and $y_0 = H(r_0)$ is created with a fresh random number r_0. t_{max} is chosen by the consumer with respect to the charging time interval so that this value lies before the beginning of the charging period, i.e., $t_{max} < \min(T)$. The monetary amount $m := \frac{b'_{\bar{i}}}{N}$ is one N-th of the agreed-upon price. The HTLC guarantees that only the consumer ζ (who knows r_0) can reveal itself and the payment, at the producer. To activate the initial payment and to unlock the deposit from $HTLC_0$, the producer needs to know r_0, the pre-image of y_0, which is communicated from the consumer to the producer before the charging process can start. If r_0 is not revealed or if it is revealed too late, the charging process cannot begin.

2) State Channel: Alternatively, for state channels, the total amount $\bar{i}$ is locked as collateral by the consumer. The initial state of the channel is defined, so that one N-th of the amount belongs to the producer and the remaining amount is used for off-chain transfers during the payment and charging phase.

E. Payment and Charging

During payment and charging the risk for both, consumer and producer is minimized by continuously transferring fractions of the payment for exchange of energy. More precisely, after each transfer one N-th of the total energy e, one N-th of the payment is released. If either the consumer or the producer violate the protocol, e.g., by not confirming the charge and withholding the next installment, the charging process can be aborted with a maximum remaining loss of $\frac{e}{N}$ in energy and m in funds.

1) HTLCs: When using HTLCs, once the producer has received r_0 and thus the deposit, the charging process can start. After having received $\frac{e}{N}$, i.e., one N-th of the agreed-upon charge, the consumer confirms the receipt and reveals r_1 to unlock the next fraction of the payment through $HTLC_1$. This process continues for every fraction of energy $\frac{e}{N}$ received until charging is completed, i.e., the N-th HTLC, $HTLC_{N-1}$, is opened and the full amount e has been charged.

2) State Channel: When using state channels, all intermediate states are handled off-chain. After having received $\frac{e}{N}$, i.e., one N-th of the agreed-upon charge, the state is updated, so that another N-th of the collateral is assigned to the producer. Both, the producer and the consumer need to sign this state change off-chain. After exchanging the last N-th of energy, one final on-chain transaction is required to lock the last agreed-upon state on the blockchain.

IV. Evaluation

In this section, we evaluate our proposed protocol with respect to risk, scalability, performance and privacy.

A. Risk

Since this protocol is about a financial transaction in exchange for a good, i.e., electricity, there is a risk of not receiving either the good or the money. In different phases of the protocol the risk is with different entities.

If the full amount of money is paid upon reserving a charging slot at the producer, the risk of not receiving energy is with the consumer. Conversely, if the payment happens after receiving the energy, the risk of not receiving any money for the provided energy is with the producer. In order to minimize the risk for both, the producer and the consumer, the payment is split into a total of N fragments. A fraction of $\frac{1}{N}$ of the total amount $b'_{\bar{i}}$ is reserved as a deposit upon reservation via either an HTLC or a state channel. If the producer ceases communication fraudulently, the loss is limited to $\frac{1}{N}$ on the consumer side. While the producer suffers no damage, a scoring system can be used to mark the producer as non-trustworthy for future consumers [2]. If, on the other hand, the consumer does not show up for charging, the lost time of the producer is compensated by the deposit of $\frac{1}{N}$.

After the charging process is started successfully and a fraction of $\frac{1}{N}$ of the total amount to be charged e has been transferred from the producer to the consumer, the risk on both sides is zero. The consumer has received what he paid for and the producer has provided not more than he has been paid. For the next fraction $\frac{1}{N}$ of the payment and energy, the same risk distribution applies: While there is a maximum risk of $\frac{1}{N}$ of the total amount with the consumer directly after payment, the risk goes to zero for the producer and the consumer after the corresponding fraction of energy has been transferred. This repeats for the remaining fractions, but limits the risk with $\frac{1}{N}$ at any time. For small values of N, the risk is relatively large, while higher values of N reduce and limit the risk. However, in case of HTLCs, a larger number of N requires more HTLCs and therefore more transactions, which impact scalability.

B. *Scalability*

In case of HTLCs, the number of blockchain transactions is proportional to N, and the charging process is limited by the reserved time interval T. Thus, the number of transactions per second is proportional to $\frac{N}{||T||}$ (where $||T||$ denotes the length of the time interval). For example, a charging time of 10 minutes in two installments requires less than one transaction per minute. Conversely, a charging time of one hour in 100 installments, more than 3 transactions per second are required. The number of transactions per second is limited by the blockchain design and varies greatly [1]. It is thus crucial to select a blockchain with sufficient throughput, especially considering that multiple charging sessions may be ongoing at the same time. Any practical implementation of the protocol must therefore find reasonable bounds for (i) the number of installments N; (ii) the length of charging intervals T; and (iii) the number of concurrent charging sessions in a given blockchain.

However, when using state channels instead of HTLCs, only four on-chain transactions are required, one for deploying, two for opening the state channel and one for closing it. Since all other transactions are performed off-chain, the number of transaction on-chain are independent of the number of installments N.

C. *Performance*

From a producer and consumer perspective, the guarantees and results of both, HTLCs and state channels, are the same. However, in terms of performance, the two implementations vary significantly.

Table I summarizes the key performance metrics of the proposed protocol as described in the sections above. First, the risk for producer and consumer is the same for both, HTLCs and state channels (see Section IV-A). Second, the required number of on-chain transactions is dependent on N for HTLCs and limited to four for state channels (see IV-B). Conversely, HTLCs do not require off-chain transactions, whereas a state channel requires $N-1$ updates off-chain until the full deposit belongs to the producer. Third, the scalability of the blockchain in terms of transactions per second, is proportional to the number of on-chain transactions. Note that the costs for on-chain transactions are proportional to the number and speed in which they need to be processes. Thus, for high values of N and the corresponding low risk, HTLC transactions are expected to be impracticably expensive (e.g., splitting a ten Dollar payment into $N = 10$ installments with transaction costs of one Dollar each, would incur transaction costs as high as the energy costs [21]). In contrast, state channels avoid this issue and require a constant amount and therefore constant costs.

TABLE I. PERFORMANCE COMPARISON OF HTLCS AND STATE CHANNELS.

	HTLC	**State Channel**
Number of on-chain transactions	N	4
Number of off-chain transactions	0	$N-1$
Required blockchain scalability	$\frac{N}{\lVert T \rVert}$	$\frac{4}{\lVert T \rVert}$
Maximum consumer risk	$\frac{b'_i}{N}$	$\frac{b'_i}{N}$
Maximum producer risk	0	0

D. *Privacy*

The proposed protocol is designed to preserve the privacy of both, the consumer and the producer. The location privacy of the consumer and producer is preserved during the bidding phase and pseudonymity is preserved during the charging phase and the payment phase. While, for the charging process itself, the consumer has to approach a producer, the location of either participant is neither revealed to each other nor to third parties before the charging process and as long as no contract is established. Within the blockchain, each participant is identified with a unique ID. This ID can be changed after each protocol run to preserve privacy. Each new ID is a pseudonym of the participant. Thus, pseudonymity is preserved [19].

V. RELATED WORK

Related work in the area of e-mobility is roughly clustered in the following areas: (i) blockchain-based approaches, having the focus on a decentralized approach for finding charging stations or for handling payments; (ii) approaches that primarily focus on privacy-preservation; and (iii) protocols that discuss similar use cases, such as ride sharing, but attempt to provide comparable guarantees for privacy.

In [2], a privacy-preserving ride sharing protocol based on a blockchain is presented. The proposed protocol uses zero knowledge proofs and is evaluated in an Ethereum test net. This protocol provides similar privacy guarantees with respect to location privacy and the protocol implements a pay-as-you-go service where the driver proofs the elapsed distance in order to get paid. In contrast, our approach uses HTLCs in order to spread payments over a longer period of time and we propose a risk-limiting variable for balancing risk and costs. This allows for high flexibility in various practical settings and is widely blockchain independent.

While our proposed protocol allows individual consumers, e.g., EVs, to find a producer, e.g., a charging station, individually, approaches exist in literature which aim at optimizing more globally given multiple charging requests [3], [23]. However, these protocols do not allow for individual decisions and introduce a waiting time until the optimized solution is computed. [23] supports V2V charging with these limitations via a distributed optimization process. [3] uses such a process – on the basis of a blockchain – not for EV charging, but for the use case of privacy-preserving energy storage unit charging.

In [10], an approach similar to ours is proposed, but privacy aspects are not considered as they remain future work. In contrast, the protocol in our paper is designed with strong guarantees for location privacy and identity. Furthermore, the risk for the producer and the consumer is fixed in [10], i.e., it cannot be changed. In contrast, our proposed approach allows for flexible distribution of risk with a risk parameter.

In [24], privacy additions to ISO 15118 and other common standards for EV charging are analyzed and it is found that this is not possible in a fully privacy-preserving way. The authors propose their own protocol to mitigate this, but they require pre-installed trusted platform modules (TPMs) in the EVs, which puts the required trust to the entities manufacturing these TPMs. In contrast, our approach is blockchain based, which means that the trust is distributed among all actors, minimizing single points of failure in a security sense.

VI. Conclusion

In this paper we present a protocol for privacy-preserving charging of EVs with payments, supporting vehicle-to-grid, grid-to-vehicle and vehicle-to-vehicle configurations. It has been demonstrated that the proposed protocol preserves pseudonymity and location privacy. Furthermore, the scalability and risk of both, the producer and the consumer, have been evaluated. A novel risk parameter has been shown to allow for adjusting the trade-off between risk and scalability. The performance has been evaluated for two implementation variations, HTLCs and state channels. It is found that state channels are better-suited to implement risk-minimized charging due to its lower number of on-chain transactions and thus practical costs.

VII. Acknowledgment

The financial support by the Federal State of Salzburg is gratefully acknowledged.

References

[1] S. Bano, A. Sonnino, M. Al-Bassam, S. Azouvi, P. McCorry, S. Meiklejohn, and G. Danezis, "Consensus in the Age of Blockchains," in *Proceedings of the 1st ACM Conference on Advances in Financial Technologies*. New York, NY, USA: ACM, 2019, pp. 183–198. [Online]. Available: http://arxiv.org/abs/1711.03936

[2] M. Baza, N. Lasla, M. M. Mahmoud, G. Srivastava, and M. Abdallah, "B-Ride: Ride Sharing with Privacy-preservation, Trust and Fair Payment atop Public Blockchain," *IEEE Transactions on Network Science and Engineering*, pp. 1–16, 2019.

[3] M. Baza, M. Nabil, M. Ismail, M. Mahmoud, E. Serpedin, and M. Ashiqur Rahman, "Blockchain-based charging coordination mechanism for smart grid energy storage units," in *Proceedings - 2019 2nd IEEE International Conference on Blockchain, Blockchain 2019*. Atlanta, USA: IEEE, 2019, pp. 504–509.

[4] C. Brunner, A. Madhusudan, D. Engel, and B. Preneel, "Off-chain state channels in the energy domain," in *Power & Energy Society Innovative Smart Grid Technologies Conference (ISGT)*. Washington, DC, USA: IEEE, 2021.

[5] C. Decker and R. Wattenhofer, "A fast and scalable payment network with bitcoin duplex micropayment channels," in *Symposium on Stabilization, Safety, and Security of Distributed Systems*, vol. 9212. Edmonton, AB, Canada: Springer, Cham, 2015, pp. 3–18.

[6] A. Deshpande and M. Herlihy, "Privacy-Preserving Cross-Chain Atomic Swaps," in *4th Workshop on Trusted Smart Contracts (WTSC'20) in Association with Financial Cryptography 20 (FC 2020)*, C. Springer, Ed., Kota Kinabalu, Sabah, Malaysia, 2020.

[7] F. Gao, L. Zhu, M. Shen, K. Sharif, Z. Wan, and K. Ren, "A Blockchain-Based Privacy-Preserving Payment Mechanism for Vehicle-to-Grid Networks," *IEEE Network*, vol. 32, no. 6, pp. 184–192, nov 2018.

[8] L. Gudgeon, P. Moreno-sanchez, S. Roos, P. Mccorry, and A. Gervais, "SoK: Layer-Two Blockchain Protocols," in *Financial Cryptography and Data Security*. Kota Kinabalu, Sabah, Malaysia: Springer, 2020.

[9] International Standardization Organization, "Road vehicles — Vehicle to grid communication interface (ISO 15118)," 2019.

[10] B. Kirpes and C. Becker, "Processing electric vehicle charging transactions in a blockchain-based information system," in *Americas Conference on Information Systems 2018: Digital Disruption, AMCIS 2018*, 2018, pp. 1–5.

[11] F. Knirsch, A. Unterweger, and D. Engel, "Privacy-preserving Blockchain-based Electric Vehicle Charging with Dynamic Tariff Decisions," *Journal on Computer Science - Research and Development (CSRD)*, vol. 33, no. 1, pp. 71–79, 2018.

[12] L. Langer, F. Skopik, G. Kienesberger, and Q. Li, "Privacy Issues of Smart E-Mobility," in *39th Annual Conference of the IEEE Industrial Electronics Society, IECON 2013*. Vienna, Austria: IEEE, 2013, pp. 6682–6687.

[13] C. Liu, K. K. Chai, X. Zhang, E. T. Lau, and Y. Chen, "Adaptive Blockchain-Based Electric Vehicle Participation Scheme in Smart Grid Platform," *IEEE Access*, vol. 6, pp. 25 657–25 665, 2018.

[14] M. A. Mustafa, N. Zhang, G. Kalogridis, and Z. Fan, "Roaming electric vehicle charging and billing: An anonymous multi-user protocol," in *2014 IEEE International Conference on Smart Grid Communications, SmartGridComm 2014*. Venice, Italy: Institute of Electrical and Electronics Engineers Inc., jan 2015, pp. 939–945.

[15] F. Mwasilu, J. J. Justo, E. K. Kim, T. D. Do, and J. W. Jung, "Electric vehicles and smart grid interaction: A review on vehicle to grid and renewable energy sources integration," *Renewable and Sustainable Energy Reviews*, vol. 34, pp. 501–516, 2014.

[16] S. Nakamoto, "Bitcoin: A Peer-to-Peer Electronic Cash System," Tech. Rep., 2008. [Online]. Available: https://bitcoin.org/bitcoin.pdf

[17] Open Charge Alliance, "Open Charge Point Protocol (OCPP) 2.0.1," 2020.

[18] J. Poon and T. Dryja, "The Bitcoin Lightning Network: Scalable Off-Chain Instant Payments," Tech. Rep. 0, 2016. [Online]. Available: https://lightning.network/lightning-network-paper.pdf

[19] F. Reid and M. Harrigan, "An Analysis of Anonymity in the Bitcoin System," in *Security and Privacy in Social Networks*, Y. Altshuler, Y. Elovici, A. B. Cremers, N. Aharony, and A. Pentland, Eds. New York: Springer New York, 2013, pp. 197–223.

[20] Z. Su, Y. Wang, Q. Xu, M. Fei, Y. C. Tian, and N. Zhang, "A Secure Charging Scheme for Electric Vehicles with Smart Communities in Energy Blockchain," *IEEE Internet of Things Journal*, 2018.

[21] A. Unterweger, F. Knirsch, C. Leixnering, and D. Engel, "Lessons Learned from Implementing a Privacy-Preserving Smart Contract in Ethereum," in *9th IFIP International Conference on New Technologies, Mobility and Security (NTMS)*. Paris, France: IEEE, 2018, pp. 1–5.

[22] G. Wood, "Ethereum: A Secure Decentralised Generalised Transaction Ledger," Ethereum, Tech. Rep., 2017. [Online]. Available: https://ethereum.github.io/yellowpaper/paper.pdf

[23] F. Yucel, K. Akkaya, and E. Bulut, "Efficient and privacy preserving supplier matching for electric vehicle charging," *Ad Hoc Networks*, vol. 90, p. 101730, 2019. [Online]. Available: https://doi.org/10.1016/j.adhoc.2018.07.029

[24] D. Zelle, M. Springer, M. Zhdanova, and C. Krauß, "Anonymous charging and billing of electric vehicles," *ARES 2018*, 2018.

Trusted Verification of Over-the-Air (OTA) Secure Software Updates on COTS Embedded Systems

Anway Mukherjee, Ryan Gerdes and Tam Chantem
Department of Electrical and Computer Engineering, Virginia Tech, USA.
Email: {anwaym, rgerdes, tchantem} @vt.edu

Abstract—**Over-the-air (OTA) software updates are an important feature to remotely analyze and upgrade any section of currently running software on battery-operated electric vehicles and its supply equipment. Even though a secure OTA framework can verify and validate updates before installation, the integrity of the framework itself cannot be guaranteed, and can easily introduce system and software vulnerability with potential catastrophic consequences. In this paper, we show how a popular automotive OTA secure update framework (Uptane) can be deployed entirely inside a TEE-enabled commercial off-the-shelf (COTS) embedded device to extend its security considerations and improve its resilience against both internal and external security breaches. We also present a software analysis tool that leverages SAWScript to verify our proposed solution against any functional and logical inconsistency, while validating our approach on a real COTS hardware (Raspberry Pi 3B).**

I. Introduction

With the increase in popularity of smart infrastructure, the complex devices that interconnect them all to form the internet of things (IoTs) lacks a holistic framework that delivers visibility, segmentation, and protection throughout the entire network infrastructure (1) secured to prevent unauthorized access, and (2) support internal isolation to ensure execution correctness. For example, battery electric vehicles (BEVs) [1], operating on a battery management system (BMS), require periodic charging performed by specialized electric vehicle supply equipment (EVSE) deployed at designated BEV charging stations or residences [2]. The EVSEs are smart internet of thing (IoT) devices that can connect the BEVs to an available power source, with support for both grid-to-vehicles (G2V), and a reverse vehicle-to-grid (V2G) energy transactions. However, BEVs and EVSEs can be easily manipulated, individually or collectively, by adversaries to gain access and act as conduits to breach their internal security, leading to malicious attacks and life-threatening situations, for instance, traffic accidents [3] in BEVs, and disrupt or cause power systems failure through high or low voltages on feeder circuits in EVSEs [4].

Both BEVs and EVSEs are prone to external interference as well as internal software vulnerabilities. EVSEs are also limited by their size, weight and power (SWaP) constraints and network capacity, making them more vulnerable to attacks compared to other embedded and general purpose systems [3]. Over the air (OTA) updates is a popular interface to facilitate security and protection for said devices [5], [6]. OTA frameworks assist in remote diagnosis, and upgrades if required, for any reported security breach in compromised EVSEs and BEVs without having to deal with expensive in-person human attendance to fix the issue(s). While an OTA software update framework facilitates security updates, along with operational upgrades, it can also introduce unwanted security loopholes. For instance, in an autonomous BEV, nearly all driving operations (for e.g., where to turn, when to brake, controlling the speed of the car etc.) are automated, while specific manual cognitive decision-making control is left to the discretion of the driver. Thus, if a corrupt OTA update package which contains functional upgrades for the car is installed, an external agent can easily piggyback on the corrupt package to install malicious programs that will compromise the entire BEV thereby leading to catastrophic consequences. Note that even though we motivate our work with specific examples of BEVs and EVSEs for the rest of the paper, our approach can easily be applied to improve the security specifications of any existing system that utilizes secure OTA update framework running on TEE-compatible COTS embedded system.

OTA updates in EVSEs and BEVs, therefore, not only need to be (1) secure to prevent unauthorized access, but also (2) support internal software isolation to ensure functional correctness. Protecting and encrypting the communication channel and checking the authenticity of the new software are longstanding and vital security measures for any BEVs and EVSE devices. However, said security measures are inconsequential if the OTA update verification framework itself is compromised [7], [8]. Therefore, there is a need to tackle such a scenario, and design a framework that can detect and protect against such security breaches. Existing approaches to protect the OTA update verification framework include dedicated secure hardware-based solutions (e.g. trusted platform modules (TPMs), secure networking modules, secure grid etc.) [3], [9], [10]. They all require expensive, custom-built hardware with long time-to-market or time-to-deployment cycle. A readily available cheaper alternative is the use of trusted execution environment (TEE) [11] on commercial off-the-shelf (COTS) embedded processors. Examples of hardware support for TEE include the ARM TrustZone [12] which is popular in embedded devices. TEE leverages hardware security extensions to provide platform virtualization to run an application in secure isolation from the rest of the system. TEE can be quickly redeployed if an exploit is found since they are implemented using platform virtualization. Hence, TEE does not require

Workshop on Automotive and Autonomous Vehicle Security (AutoSec) 2021
25 February 2021, Virtual
https://dx.doi.org/10.14722/autosec.2021.23028
www.ndss-symposium.org

hardware redesign. In each platform-specific OS that supports TEE (for e.g., ARM TrustZone), an instance of TEE execution is initiated by a setup context, followed by the actual trusted execution inside an isolated environment, and exits through a destroy context. TEE is utilized by partitioning the code such that the portion that requires secure execution is run inside the TEE context and communicates with the rest of the partitioned code via a software-controlled exceptions called secure monitor calls (SMCs) [13].

This paper proposes a new secure software update framework that ensures that secure OTA updates, along with the entire OTA verification framework, can be deployed and serviced inside a trusted secure environment fully protected from any external or internal attacks. For proof of concept, we utilize the Uptane [6] framework to model a secure OTA update and verification framework in BEVs and EVSEs. Uptane is a secure open-source industrial software update standard for automobiles. The framework services protection against malicious attackers by signing and delivering software updates through a secure communication channel in EVSEs and BEVs. Our proposed solution isolates and deploys the entire OTA verification framework inside TEE to protect its integrity and avert any security breaches. We also formally verify our proposed solution framework by leveraging an open-source software analysis workbench (SAW) developed by Galois [14]. SAW is an essential tool to analyze semantic models of programs, and check for any software vulnerability that can potentially lead to security breaches. Our main contributions are as follows.

1) We leverage ARM TrustZone to present a novel design that aims to strengthen the security of OTA update and verification framework. Our approach proposes to migrate the entire OTA update and verification framework inside a TEE, and isolate all of its standard functionality within the scope of trusted execution for improved protection in BEVs and EVSEs.
2) We leverage SAW tool to propose a technique which can verify and validate our proposed framework to guarantee that our software implementation does not lead to any security vulnerability.
3) We validate our approach on a real hardware (Raspberry Pi 3B) using ARM TrustZone that runs OP-TEE, an open source trusted OS, side-by-side with real-time Linux `RT_PREEMPT`.

II. Preliminaries

A. Uptane

Uptane [6] is a popular open source secure software update framework that aims to protect software updates that are packaged by the OEM and delivered over-the-air to its recipients through secure wireless communication channels. This framework is the standard for secure updates in the automotive industry, and is designed to successfully prevent a variety of malicious state-of-the-art attacks. A standard open-source implementation of the Uptane framework can be divided into two broad categories; (1) the secure server representing the OEM, and (2) the client representing the recipient. A secure communication channel, for e.g., `https`, is used for data communication between the server and its client(s).

The secure server-side implementation consists of three sub-modules. First, the *images* repository stores the actual image package, along with related metadata which are securely signed by a private key. Second, the *director* sub-module validates vehicle manifests, and generates the vehicle-specific update images and metadata. Finally, the *timeserver* sub-module generates timestamp tokens to validate that the most recent update package is being delivered to the client. The client-side implementation similarly consists of multiple sub-modules. The *primary* client sub-module generates vehicle version manifest(s) with vehicle metadata and sends it back to the server-side director. A *manifest* consists of information pertaining to client-side system-wide status, which is analysed by the director, before generating any update package to redress detected vulnerabilities in the client. The primary client also maintains the update cycle by fetching and validating all signed images, and its metadata, from the director. It also queries the timeserver for signed attestation. The validated metadata in the client is stored in a *local* metadata staging sub-module. Finally, a *secondary* client fetches and validates all signed metadata from the primary before installing the update package(s) on to the system.

B. ARM TrustZone

The TrustZone [11] is ARM's open-source implementation of trusted execution environment for COTS embedded systems. It provides a secure virtualization platform where code that requires trusted execution can be executed in isolation from the entire system without loss of integrity. Mukherjee et. al. [13] details the architectural framework of a TrustZone consisting of side-by-side deployment of a normal execution environment (running the non-trusted OS), and secure execution environment (running the trusted OS). In non-trusted execution environment, the non-secure application(s) or code segments that do not require TEE execution, run on standard embedded hardware. In a trusted environment, all code and/or application(s) that require trusted execution have their data are stored in, and executed in isolation on specially augmented secure hardware components (e.g., CPU, memory, and peripherals). Signal and data communication between the two environments (TEE and non-TEE) is performed through a platform-specific secure message passing protocol. TEE delimits the code running in normal world from (1) changing the trusted OS system configurations, and (2) protect secure environment data/code from being accessed by the non-trusted software. This means that if the non-trusted execution environment and OS is compromised, the attack is confined to the access privileges of only the non-trusted OS.

C. SAW Verification Tool

The software analysis workbench (SAW) [14] provides the ability to formally verify any application code and identify

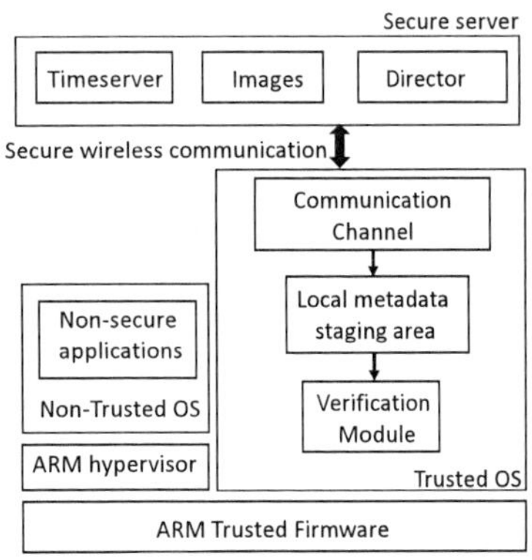

Fig. 1. An overview of our proposed update framework which is decoupled into (1) a secure Uptane server, and (2) a modified Uptane client-side implementation to run as trusted application(s) within the trusted OS inside TEE. The client consists of a communication channel and a metadata staging area, and services client-specific functionalities.

any software-level security vulnerabilities of said code. SAW provides a standard developmental kit (SDK) that can leverage a number of programming language-specific tools and solvers to automate the process of analysis and verification of complex software frameworks. Specifically, SAW utilizes symbolic execution to translate code into formal models, execute code on symbolic inputs, effectively unrolling loops, and translating the code into a circuit representation for cryptographic verification. As a verification tool, SAW provides a level of assurance beyond the capabilities of traditional frameworks since SAW is capable of performing an exhaustive testing of target applications against all combinations of input parameters. In this work, we leverage the SAW tool developed by Galois that uses Cryptol scripting language [15] for the high-level analysis and verification of target software.

III. Proposed Framework

A. Threat Model

While our proposed framework can be seamlessly integrated into any existing system that utilizes secure OTA update framework running on TEE-compatible COTS embedded system, we motivate our work by describing a setup where a standard secure update framework can lead to an internal security breach. For example, consider a BEV-EVSE collective IoT system. We now argue why it is not nearly enough to just have a secure OTA update framework in place inside an EVSE or a BEV. We consider the BEV with nearly all automated driving operations controlled by the on-board network of embedded devices. We also consider a setup where the BEV provides periodic V2G reverse grid charging through EVSE that forms a part of the broader IoT network. Therefore, the OTA update framework (1) acts as a client to acquire important updates from a server (or OEM) through a secure update process for the on-board embedded systems in the BEVs and EVSEs, and (2) directs the BEV/EVSE to download the update packages into its system for installation after in-situ rigorous verification and validation process. Here, we assume that the BEV or the EVSE has been compromised and an attacker has control over its internal software and data. The attacker can now easily manipulate the integrity of any of the following; (1) OTA verification framework, (2) the actual software update package, and (3) its signatures that were previously downloaded and stored in the BEV/EVSE from a secure server for verification and validation. A malicious update package, therefore, can easily be pushed into, and installed in the BEV/EVSE. The attacker can easily gain access to all the automotive features inside BEV leading to a range of catastrophic scenarios. Similarly, a corrupt EVSE can lead to charging termination (e.g., in smart grids), and impact the overall voltage and frequency limits of a system leading to energy-related vulnerabilities. Here we assume that the secure server (OEM) can maintain its own integrity. However, both the EVSE and the BEV, and its OTA update framework requires extended security to combat such threats.

B. Mitigation Strategy

We consider a TEE-enabled system for both EVSE and BEV which can (1) protect the integrity of an OTA update verification framework by running it within a TrustZone in isolation from the rest of the system, and (2) securely store update packages (both software and data) within a trusted storage. Implementing a verification and validation framework for OTA software updates within a secure execution environment has several advantages. A secure environment helps us isolate the update framework from the rest of the system without breaking the backward compatibility. It also gives us the flexibility to seamlessly deploy a trusted execution framework for any commercial off-the-shelf (COTS) embedded system, and use it for data protection over OTA channels without compromising the standard security requirements. Moreover, since the entire OTA update framework runs in seclusion inside a trusted OS, any internal or external attack on the rest of the software or system does not affect the integrity of the isolated OTA framework. In this work, we design (1) a trusted framework using TEE that provides an secure execution environment within which the standard Uptane verification framework operates, (2) instrument and re-factor the Uptane framework to integrate it within the TEE environment, and (3) create a communication gateway for secure data transfer between the Uptane OTA framework and a designated remote secure OEM server.

Figure 1 shows an example overview of our proposed system model inside BEV/EVSE. Since Uptane's software update process is based on a publish-subscribe model, we divide our work into three parts; (1) an Uptane-compliant secure server which complies with the Uptane standards, (2) a TEE-specific client-side implementation (inside BEV/EVSE) that includes all functional components that perform software and data exchange between the client sub-modules and the secure server, and (3) a secure standard communication protocol that services the client requests, and implements a co-ordinated data transfer between the server and the client. The client-side modifications ensure a seamless integration of the Uptane standard policies within the TEE framework. Since, it is the programmer's responsibility to ensure that the application

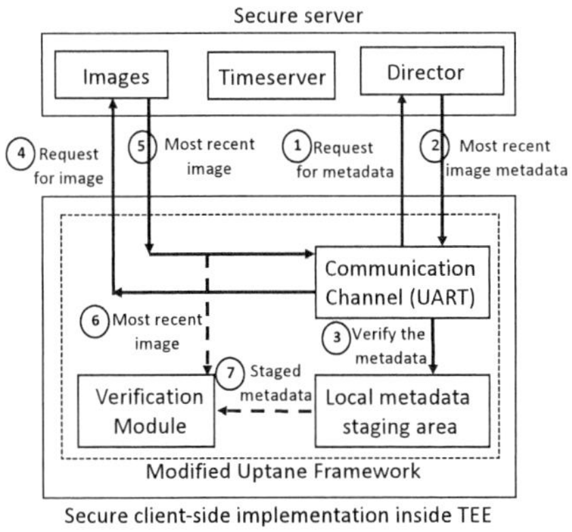

Fig. 2. An detailed overview of our proposed client-side implementation. The numbers associated with each arrow capture the chronological exchange of data between the secure server and the client-side sub-modules running within the TEE.

code running inside TEE do not inadvertently introduce any software-related security vulnerabilities, we formally verify our client-side implementation using the SAW tool to analyse and check for security vulnerabilities (Section V).

Our solution is based on the following preconditions which do not violate the Uptane standard verification policy. First, we assume that there is a secure server in place, which is compatible with the existing Uptane verification standards. Therefore, we keep Uptane's standard server design in tact. Second, we assign the client with the ability to establish connection to a verified server. We assume that the client is programmable, and can initiate an update cycle triggered periodically by a hardware interrupt subroutine. Finally, we attribute the client with the ability to perform a public key cryptography operation, as well as verification and validation of images supplied by a secure server within the guidelines supplied by the Uptane standards.

IV. TEE-ENABLED UPTANE CLIENT

A client, as part of the BEV/EVSE software module, services all the functionalities to verify and validate an Uptane-specifc OTA update framework. The client is deployed inside a TEE for isolated execution. An overview of our proposed solution is shown in Figure 2. We split our work into a two-step procedure; a client-side implementation within a TEE, and a secure server. The client-side implementation (1) issues request for most recent update for the secure server, along with (2) verification and validation of the its metadata before (3) securely installing the update(s) to the system. The secure server is responsible for servicing the update-specific images and all the relevant metadata when requested by the client-side. As previously mentioned, we maintain the functional and logical guidelines in our implementation as recommended by the Uptane standards. First, the client initiates an update cycle through a hardware interrupt. The client sends a request to a secure server to obtain the metadata for the most recent update available for downloading. Second, the secure server sends the requested update-specific metadata back to the client. The client stages the metadata for future validation. Next, the client sends another request to download the actual update image. Once the image has been downloaded from the secure server, the client matches the previously staged metadata with the metadata that is included in the actual update image. Finally, after successful verification, the client can (1) update the system with the downloaded image, and (2) update its local records with the most recently installed update. Next, we will describe in details the various sub-modules of our client-side implementation.

A. Communication Channel

This sub-module provides a communication channel between the server and client in the Uptane framework. In our implementation, we use a protocol similar to the unified diagnostic services (UDS) to service the communication layer. UDS is a diagnostic communication protocol popularly used in the automotive industry. Our communication channel inside the client mediates requests to and responses from the secure server, and services update-specific metadata for verification, download images for system update, and handles queries for a signed attestation of the timestamp for the downloaded images. Similar to the UDS protocol, each feature is associated with a service ID (SID) and the information and or data associated with the services are encapsulated in the payload of the communication message frame. A list of SIDs and their functionalities is described in Table I. For instance, a download metadata request message to secure server from the client is associated with an SID equal to 4, and the payload associated with the request contains various information including the the size of download, the location of the metadata in the server, and the type of metadata requested. In contrast, the SID associated with image download request message is 5. Each request is followed by a response message with a positive or negative validation. The associated payload with the response contains the requested metadata in case of successful message reception at the server, or a negative error code if the request message failed to comply with the SID-specific payload configuration. The SIDs distinguish the different message requests (and responses) between the server and the client.

For our physical medium of communication, we use a UART connection between the secure server and the client-side implementation. This sub-module, therefore, sets up a UART connection and establishes a communication channel to send and receive messages along with essential data between the server and the client. Our design also includes a UART-to-wifi proxy implementation that can support wireless communication for backward compatibility.

B. Local Metadata Staging Area

This sub-module contains a local list of Uptane-compliant files that constitutes the update-specific metadata of the images that have been downloaded from a secure server. Each metadata file can be categorized into four sub-classes based on their roles in the client-side update and verification framework. The following are the categories of metadata files; (1) Root

TABLE I
EXAMPLE SIDS FOR TARGET REQUESTS AND THEIR CORRESPONDING RESPONSES (YY = REQUEST PAYLOAD, ZZ = RESPONSE PAYLOAD)

SID	Request	Description	Positive Response
1	1 YY YY YY	Request to start update	11 ZZ ZZ ZZ
2	2 YY YY YY	Request to stop update	12 ZZ ZZ ZZ
3	3 YY YY YY	Request timestamp attestation	13 ZZ ZZ ZZ
4	4 YY YY YY	Request metadata download	14 ZZ ZZ ZZ
5	5 YY YY YY	Request image download	15 ZZ ZZ ZZ
6	6 YY YY YY	Request transfer data	16 ZZ ZZ ZZ
7	7 YY YY YY	Request transfer exit	17 ZZ ZZ ZZ

metadata is used to verify the metadata associated with all the other sub-classes, (2) Target metadata is used to verify an image. It also contains information on the server-specific metadata, including the current image version number, (3) Snapshot contains the signed metadata for all the other sub-classes, and (4) Timestamp metadata indicates whether the downloaded images and metadata are new and current.

C. Verification Module

If the client does not have latest image, it enters an update cycle through an interrupt procedure call. The local metadata staging area stores a local copy of the metadata of previously installed images in the client secure storage. This sub-module performs the step-by-step process of downloading the most recent image from the secure server to the client and verifying the image before it can be installed into the system.

Download Latest Image: The client first downloads the target metadata from the server. The information contains the filename used to identify the latest known image. If there is no target metadata about this image, we abort the update cycle. Additionally, in the case of failure, the client retains its previous target metadata instead of using the newly downloaded target metadata. Otherwise, we download the image, and verify (described in the section below) that it matches the target metadata. Finally, once the update cycle is completed, the client overwrites the latest image specific metadata to its local copy in the secure storage.

Verify Latest Image: The client verifies and validates that the latest image matches the latest metadata. The first step in the process is to download the latest image specific metadata from the server. The first step of validation includes checking that the client identifier in the metadata matches the actual client identifier, followed by a valid image filename. The next step is to check that the latest image version counter is greater than the previously installed image in the client-side. Then we decrypt the image metadata, followed by a hash checking between the downloaded image and the downloaded metadata in the staging area. If at any time this verification step fails to validate the image, the client aborts the update cycle, and waits for the next update trigger.

V. SOFTWARE ANALYSIS

Heretofore, we have successfully modified the Uptane client to run entirely in isolation inside a TEE to protect it from any external attacks. However, it does not guarantee that the client-side implementation of the trusted code running within TEE does not introduce any new vulnerabilities. Moreover, Uptane documentation provides a list of rules that must be followed to ensure that an Uptane client (and the update process) complies with its set standards. Therefore, we leverage the software analysis workbench (SAW), a popular software analysis tool developed at Galois, to formally verify properties of our implementation code. As an analysis tool, SAW is capable of testing a program against an exhaustive list of all input parameters, and can efficiently capture corner-cases when the application code will fail to comply with its functional and logical requirements. In this work, we have utilized SAW (1) to detect any logical and programming correctness with our Uptane-compliant trusted client application that runs within TEE, and (2) analyze client-specific functionalities that largely utilize cryptographic algorithms (e.g., SHA and ECDSA) to validate and verify downloaded update image(s) and their metadata.

We now demonstrate how we use SAW tool to prove the equivalence of the reference and implementation versions of the members of our image metadata, and detect any bug in an incorrect implementation. Our verification is structured as a sequence of commands, potentially along with definitions of functions that abstract over commonly used combinations of commands. Consider a part of the target client code, a `memcpy()` module that needs to be analyzed and verified against any logical or functional irregularities. SAW tool provides a library of reference implementation that can be used to compare with our target implementation of `memcpy()` to identify any existing bug in the code. Figure 3 shows the SAWScript that can automatically leverage symbolic execution to translate the target code into formal models to compare, analyze and verify its robustness against any security vulnerabilities. For instance, The `LLVM_extract` command instructs the SAW tool interpreter to perform symbolic simulation of our target function, and return the semantics of the function. The `let` statement then constructs a new term corresponding to the assertion of equality between two existing terms. The `prove` command verifies the validity of our assertion, or produce a counter-example that invalidates it. The parameter `thm` indicates the theorem solver that has been used in our target verification process.

Specifically, the SAW tool ensures that the software running inside the TEE complies with the standards outlined by the Uptane framework. Our implementation draws upon the standard `C` programming resources to realize the OTA framework inside TEE, primarily since TEE only supports a limited range of `C` headers and functions. Therefore, we utilize SAW tool to evaluate the memory safety assumptions (length of buffer, data integrity, data overflow etc.) for associated data schemas specific to our implementation. We also utilize the cryptographic algorithm analysis framework included with SAW tool to validate the Uptane client hashing and signature verification functions, including the compositional verification of said algorithmic functions. SAWScript leverages its embedded Cryptol programming tool to service any high-level cryptographic specifications.

```
#Extracting reference term: memcpy_ref
l <- llvm_load_module "memcpy.bc";
memcpy_ref <- llvm_extract l "memcpy_ref";

#Extracting implementation term: uptane_memcpy_imp
uptane_memcpy_imp <- llvm_extract l "uptane_memcpy_imp";


#Proving equivalence: memcpy_ref == uptane_memcpy_imp
let thm1 = {{ \x -> memcpy_ref x == uptane_memcpy_imp x }};
result <- prove abc thm1;
print result;
```

Fig. 3. An example SAWScript to analyze a target application code `uptane_memcpy_imp`, and prove its equivalence when compared against the SAW tool reference implementation `memcpy_ref`.

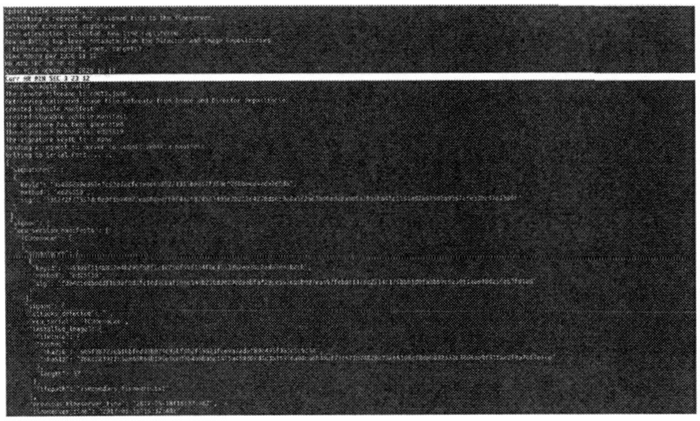

Fig. 4. Application log of Uptane client running on our experiment testbed. Results indicate that the OTA update requests are triggered periodically and the subsequent responses with image and metadata download from the server through a secure UART communication.

VI. Experiments

To validate our proposed approach in a realistic setting, we selected Uptane as the representative secure software update framework. We use the Raspberry Pi 3B (Rpi3B) as our example TEE-enabled embedded testbench that represents a TEE-enabled COTS-based automotive BEV and EVSE. Rpi3B is a small computer powered by Broadcom BCM2837 chipset consisting of quad-core ARM Cortex A53 processor, 1 GB LPDDR2 RAM, and numerous sensors (for eg., Barometer, IMU etc.). It can run Linux and other non-trusted operating systems. It also extends support for ARM TrustZone. We used the Linux `RT_PREEMPT` Kernel v4.6.3 as our non-trusted real-time OS, along with OP-TEE OS (as TEE) on the Rpi 3B that extends the support for ARM v8 embedded virtualization. Our modified Uptane client application is included as part of the trusted application suite and runs completely inside OP-TEE OS. An off-board Uptane-compliant secure server stores and services the update image and metadata to the client. The data transfer and communication between the server and the client is performed over a secure UART. Figure 4 shows an example update sequence at the Uptane client-side starting with (1) the client triggering a request to the secure server, followed by (2) timestamp attestation and verification, (3) metadata download request and validation by the client, and the subsequent (4) retrieval of update image downloaded from the secure server and ready for validation before installation.

VII. Conclusion

We present a secure design framework that leverages ARM TrustZone to isolate and execute the Uptane OTA update system within EVSEs/BEVs, thereby improving the security of such mission-critical systems against both external and internal system vulnerabilities. Our solution also includes a software analysis and verification tool that utilizes SAWScript to automatically validates our trusted application code against any programming, functional and logical defects that can gravely jeopardize the overall security of the system. The proposed approach was validated on an actual hardware testbed (Rpi3B) that runs the client code in isolation within TEE.

References

[1] A. M. Andwari, A. Pesiridis, S. Rajoo, R. Martinez-Botas, and V. Esfahanian, "A review of battery electric vehicle technology and readiness levels," *Renewable and Sustainable Energy Reviews*, vol. 78, pp. 414–430, 2017.

[2] Y. Huang and K. M. Kockelman, "Electric vehicle charging station locations: Elastic demand, station congestion, and network equilibrium," *Transportation Research Part D: Transport and Environment*, vol. 78, p. 102179, 2020.

[3] A. Fuchs, D. Kern, C. Krauß, and M. Zhdanova, "Securing electric vehicle charging systems through component binding," in *International Conference on Computer Safety, Reliability, and Security*. Springer, 2020, pp. 387–401.

[4] J. T. Johnson, "Securing vehicle charging infrastructure." Sandia National Lab.(SNL-NM), Albuquerque, NM (United States), Tech. Rep., 2019.

[5] D. K. Nilsson and U. E. Larson, "Secure firmware updates over the air in intelligent vehicles," in *ICC Workshops-2008 IEEE International Conference on Communications Workshops*. IEEE, 2008, pp. 380–384.

[6] T. K. Kuppusamy, L. A. DeLong, and J. Cappos, "Uptane: Security and customizability of software updates for vehicles," *ieee vehicular technology magazine*, vol. 13, no. 1, pp. 66–73, 2018.

[7] M. Tullsen, L. Pike, N. Collins, and A. Tomb, "Formal verification of a vehicle-to-vehicle (v2v) messaging system," in *International Conference on Computer Aided Verification*. Springer, 2018, pp. 413–429.

[8] K. Zandberg, K. Schleiser, F. Acosta, H. Tschofenig, and E. Baccelli, "Secure firmware updates for constrained iot devices using open standards: A reality check," *IEEE Access*, vol. 7, pp. 71 907–71 920, 2019.

[9] G. Macher, A. Höller, H. Sporer, E. Armengaud, and C. Kreiner, "A combined safety-hazards and security-threat analysis method for automotive systems," in *International Conference on Computer Safety, Reliability, and Security*. Springer, 2014, pp. 237–250.

[10] X. Wei, C. Du, and J. Zhao, "A network security situation awareness model for electric vehicle shared charging pile system," in *AIP Conference Proceedings*, vol. 2238, no. 1. AIP Publishing LLC, 2020, p. 020009.

[11] M. Sabt, M. Achemlal, and A. Bouabdallah, "Trusted execution environment: what it is, and what it is not," in *Trustcom/BigDataSE/ISPA, 2015 IEEE*, vol. 1. IEEE, 2015, pp. 57–64.

[12] S. Pinto and N. Santos, "Demystifying arm trustzone: A comprehensive survey," *ACM Computing Surveys (CSUR)*, vol. 51, no. 6, pp. 1–36, 2019.

[13] A. Mukherjee, T. Mishra, T. Chantem, N. Fisher, and R. Gerdes, "Optimized trusted execution for hard real-time applications on cots processors," in *Proceedings of the 27th International Conference on Real-Time Networks and Systems*, 2019, pp. 50–60.

[14] K. Carter, A. Foltzer, J. Hendrix, B. Huffman, and A. Tomb, "Saw: the software analysis workbench," in *Proceedings of the 2013 ACM SIGAda annual conference on High integrity language technology*, 2013, pp. 15–18.

[15] J. R. Lewis and B. Martin, "Cryptol: High assurance, retargetable crypto development and validation," in *IEEE Military Communications Conference, 2003. MILCOM 2003.*, vol. 2. IEEE, 2003, pp. 820–825.